# Mathematics Made Easy

## OTHER BOOKS BY THE AUTHOR

STORIES OF THE GREAT DRAMAS
THE COMPLETE BOOK OF ENGLISH
THE STORY OF THE HUMAN RACE
THE COLLEGE COURSE CULTURE BOOK
THE WONDER BOOK

# Mathematics
## MADE EASY

By HENRY THOMAS, Ph.D.

GARDEN CITY PUBLISHING CO., INC., NEW YORK

CL
COPYRIGHT, 1940
BY GARDEN CITY PUBLISHING CO., INC.

PRINTED IN THE UNITED STATES OF AMERICA

# Contents

INTRODUCTION . . . . . . . . . . . . vii

## PART I
## THE FUNDAMENTALS OF MATHEMATICS
### ARITHMETIC

| | | |
|---|---|---|
| I. | Reading and Writing Numbers . . . . . | 3 |
| II. | Addition . . . . . . . . . . . | 7 |
| III. | Subtraction . . . . . . . . . . | 11 |
| IV. | Multiplication . . . . . . . . . | 15 |
| V. | Division . . . . . . . . . . . | 22 |
| VI. | Fractions . . . . . . . . . . . | 26 |
| VII. | Decimals . . . . . . . . . . . | 35 |
| VIII. | Percentage . . . . . . . . . . | 42 |
| IX. | Measures and Weights . . . . . . . | 49 |
| X. | Short-Cuts . . . . . . . . . . | 60 |
| XI. | Graphs . . . . . . . . . . . | 70 |
| XII. | ALGEBRA . . . . . . . . . . . | 75 |
| XIII. | GEOMETRY . . . . . . . . . . | 123 |

## PART II
## THE PRACTICAL USES OF MATHEMATICS
### MATHEMATICS FOR BUSINESS

| | | |
|---|---|---|
| XIV. | Trade Discounts . . . . . . . . | 183 |
| XV. | Profit and Loss . . . . . . . . . | 189 |
| XVI. | Commission and Brokerage . . . . . | 201 |

## CONTENTS

| | | |
|---|---|---|
| XVII. | Transportation | 211 |
| XVIII. | Hours and Wages | 215 |
| XIX. | Interest | 224 |
| XX. | Payments and Collections | 238 |
| XXI. | Banking and Loans | 245 |
| XXII. | Investments | 259 |
| XXIII. | Property Taxes | 269 |
| XXIV. | Insurance | 278 |
| XXV. | Advertising | 295 |
| XXVI. | Problems of Manufacturers | 301 |
| XXVII. | Problems of Wholesalers and Retailers | 305 |

### MATHEMATICS FOR THE HOME

| | | |
|---|---|---|
| XXVIII. | Invoices and Payments | 313 |
| XXIX. | Budgets | 318 |
| XXX. | Income Taxes | 323 |
| XXXI. | Interior and Exterior Decorating | 328 |
| XXXII. | Ingredients for Cooking | 332 |

### Part III
### MATHEMATICS FOR ENTERTAINMENT

| | | |
|---|---|---|
| XXXIII. | Oddities and Curiosities | 339 |
| XXXIV. | Tricks, Stunts and Puzzles | 345 |
| | Mathematics of Chance (*Gambling*) | 361 |
| XXXV. | MATHEMATICAL SUPERSTITIONS | 363 |

# Introduction

THIS BOOK is designed to be a handy volume of practical mathematical information. Its purpose is to enable you to acquire the knack of quick and accurate computation in the problems of your everyday life—the problems that keep constantly arising in the shop, the store, the factory, the warehouse, the stock exchange, the bank, the office and the home.

No previous extensive knowledge of mathematics is necessary for the intelligent and effective use of this book, as the book is so arranged that you can teach yourself, step by step, all the necessary mathematical formulas and processes,—from the simplest problems in addition and subtraction to the most complicated calculations in taxation and compound interest.

With this object in view, the treatment of the book has been planned to be logical and gradual. The first part deals with the fundamentals of mathematics, including arithmetic, algebra, geometry, and various short cuts and helps to rapid calculation. Then comes the second part, dealing with practical uses of mathematics in the various industries, professions and occupations, as well as in private life. This is followed by the third part, which deals with the lighter side of mathematics— its oddities and curiosities, its tricks and stunts and puzzles, its strange combinations of figures and its peculiar superstitions. The aim of the book, in short, is to teach—or rather to enable you to teach yourself—and to amuse.

A word about the exercises in this book. They are all based upon specimen problems which are carefully designed and simply and adequately explained in every case. You will therefore find it easy to do the exercises. As a further practical aid in the use of this book, the answers to the exercises and to the problems in each chapter are in every instance placed at the end of each chapter. Thus you may check your own answers with those printed in the book.

PART I

The Fundamentals of Mathematics

# ARITHMETIC

## CHAPTER I
## Reading and Writing Numbers

### A. INTEGERS

OUR NUMERICAL SYSTEM is called the Arabic, because it was given to us by the Arabs. It consists of ten symbols, or digits: 0, 1, 2, 3, 4, 5, 6, 7, 8, 9. The value of a digit in a number depends upon its *position*. For example:

    2 is read as two
    02 is read as two
    002 is read as two
    20 is read as twenty
    200 is read as two hundred
    2000 is read as two thousand.

Ciphers placed *before* a digit do *not* change its value. But ciphers placed *after* a digit *do* change its value. One cipher placed after a digit multiplies it by ten; two ciphers multiply it by a hundred; three ciphers, by a thousand; and so on.

In order to facilitate the reading of numbers, we separate them by commas into groups of three. In thus separating them into groups of three, we count from *right to left*, and not from left to right. The Arabians, you must remember, do all their writing, like the Hebrews, from right to left. Take, for example, the number

    53, 675, 408, 569.

Reading this number, Arabian fashion, from right to left, we have nine units, six tens, five hundreds, eight thousands, no ten thousands, four hundred thousands, five millions, seven ten millions, six hundred millions, three billions, five ten billions. Translating this now into our left-to-right European and American way of reading numerals, we get: fifty-three billion, six hundred seventy-five million, four hundred eight thousand, five hundred sixty-nine.

# MATHEMATICS MADE EASY

When you read a figure, omit the word "and." It saves time and avoids complications. Translate your figures into the fewest possible words. Thus, 1208 should be read "twelve hundred eight," instead of "one thousand two hundred and eight."

### EXERCISE 1
Read the following figures:
- (a) 79,864,913
- (b) 902,837,756
- (c) 311,412,513
- (d) 620,732,843
- (e) 14,915,816,717
- (f) 96,884,765,651
- (g) 43,440,539,827
- (h) 19,999,215,416
- (i) 17,318,497,729,007
- (j) 90,804,000,762,401
- (k) 5,890,204,194,021
- (l) 72,109,983,840,439

### EXERCISE 2
Write the following figures:
- (a) Nine hundred sixty-seven thousand, eight hundred forty-three.
- (b) Three million, two thousand, forty-three.
- (c) Fifteen million, thirty-one thousand, seven hundred thirty-four.
- (d) Twenty-eight million, eight hundred eighty-three thousand, seven hundred forty-five.
- (e) Thirty-seven million, thirty-five thousand, two hundred sixty-two.
- (f) Twelve million, nine hundred eighty thousand, eight hundred thirty-nine.
- (g) Eleven million, seven hundred thirteen thousand.
- (h) One billion, six hundred fourteen million, three hundred fifty-two thousand, nine hundred twenty-one.
- (i) Ninety-one billion, forty-two million, one hundred twenty-three thousand, six hundred thirty.
- (j) Five hundred eighty-seven trillion, ninety-one.

## B. DECIMALS

The decimal point is used to express values less than one. In the Arabic system, as we have seen, the value of a digit is *multiplied by ten* as we move from *right to left*. In computing decimals, we find that the value of a digit is *divided by ten* as we move from *left to right*. For example:

.3 equals three tenths of one unit
.03 equals three hundredths of one unit
.003 equals three thousandths of one unit
.0003 equals three ten thousandths of one unit.

# READING AND WRITING NUMBERS 5

In integers, as we have noted, a cipher placed *before* a digit does *not* change its value, but a cipher placed *after* a digit *does* change its value. In decimals it is just the other way around. A cipher placed *before* a digit *does* change its value, but a cipher placed *after* a digit does *not* change its value. The following decimals are equal in value:

.3
.30
.300
.3000

When you read an integer together with a decimal, insert the word "and" between the integer and the decimal, as follows:

1507.032 is read "fifteen hundred seven and thirty-two thousandths."

69,040.02 is read "sixty-nine thousand forty and two hundredths."

### EXERCISE 3

Read the following figures:

(a) 63.109
(b) 49.07
(c) 6,005.8941
(d) 869.0006
(e) 13,694.7743
(f) 31,000.9
(g) 115.659
(h) 2,975.1461
(i) 8,961.8961

### EXERCISE 4

Write the following as decimals:
(a) Fifty-five thousand and six hundred ninety-seven thousandths.
(b) Nine thousand and nine thousandths.
(c) Thirty-six hundred thirteen and eighty-four hundred thirteen ten thousandths.
(d) Fifty-four million, eight hundred twenty-two thousand, four hundred fourteen, and five tenths.
(e) Three hundred twenty-one thousand, four hundred sixty-four, and one hundred twenty-three ten thousandths.
(f) Nine million ninety-six and ninety-six ten thousandths.

## ANSWERS
### EXERCISE 1

(a) Seventy-nine million, eight hundred sixty-four thousand, nine hundred thirteen.
(b) Nine hundred two million, eight hundred thirty-seven thousand, seven hundred fifty-six.
(c) Three hundred eleven million, four hundred twelve thousand, five hundred thirteen.
(d) Six hundred twenty million, seven hundred thirty-two thousand, eight hundred forty-three.

# MATHEMATICS MADE EASY

(e) Fourteen billion, nine hundred fifteen million, eight hundred sixteen thousand, seven hundred seventeen.
(f) Ninety-six billion, eight hundred eighty-four million, seven hundred sixty-five thousand, six hundred fifty-one.
(g) Forty-three billion, four hundred forty million, five hundred thirty-nine thousand, eight hundred twenty-seven.
(h) Nineteen billion, nine hundred ninety-nine million, two hundred fifteen thousand, four hundred sixteen.
(i) Seventeen trillion, three hundred eighteen billion, four hundred ninety-seven million, seven hundred twenty-nine thousand, seven.
(j) Ninety trillion, eight hundred four billion, seven hundred sixty-two thousand, four hundred one.
(k) Five trillion, eight hundred ninety billion, two hundred four million, one hundred ninety-four thousand, twenty-one.
(l) Seventy-two trillion, one hundred nine billion, nine hundred eighty-three million, eight hundred forty thousand, four hundred thirty-nine.

## EXERCISE 2

(a) 967,843
(b) 3,002,043
(c) 15,031,734
(d) 28,883,745
(e) 37,035,262
(f) 12,980,839
(g) 11,713,000
(h) 1,614,352,921
(i) 91,042,123,630
(j) 587,000,000,000,091

## EXERCISE 3

(a) Sixty-three and one hundred nine thousandths.
(b) Forty-nine and seven hundredths.
(c) Six thousand five and eighty-nine hundred forty-one ten thousandths.
(d) Eight hundred sixty-nine and six ten thousandths.
(e) Thirteen thousand six hundred ninety-four and seventy-seven hundred forty-three ten thousandths.
(f) Thirty-one thousand and nine tenths.
(g) One hundred fifteen and six hundred fifty-nine thousandths.
(h) Twenty-nine hundred seventy-five and fourteen hundred sixty-one ten thousandths.
(i) Eighty-nine hundred sixty-one and eighty-nine hundred sixty-one ten thousandths.

## EXERCISE 4

(a) 55,000.697
(b) 9,000.009
(c) 3613.8413
(d) 54,822,414.5
(e) 321,464.0123
(f) 9,000,096.0096

## CHAPTER II
# Addition

ALL OF US, whether we are engaged in business, in occupations, or in the professions, are daily confronted with the necessity of adding figures. In order to save time, learn to add swiftly and accurately. When you add a column of figures, get into the habit of *grouping* the figures instead of adding them singly. Add the *short* way instead of the long way. Note, for example, the following column:

$$\begin{array}{c}5\\3\\4\\9\\2\\3\\7\\2\\4\\8\end{array}$$

The long way to add this column is to take up each figure separately—5+3 are 8, +4 are 12, +9 are 21, and so on. Total, 47. The *short* way, however, is to arrange the figures, at least in your mind, if not on paper, as follows:

$$\left.\begin{array}{c}5\\3\\4\end{array}\right\} \text{group one} = 12$$

plus

$$\left.\begin{array}{c}9\\2\\3\end{array}\right\} \text{group two} = 26$$

plus

$$\left.\begin{array}{c}7\\2\end{array}\right\} \text{group three} = 35$$

plus

$$\left.\begin{array}{c}4\\8\end{array}\right\} \text{group four} = 47$$

# MATHEMATICS MADE EASY

## EXERCISE 5

Practice the following examples, first by the individual figure method, and then by the group method. When you have gained facility in the group method, you will note a considerable saving of time.

If you find that you are a little bit shaky either in speed or in accuracy, make up a number of similar examples and practice on them until you have acquired the necessary skill. In mathematics, as in music, *skill depends upon practice*.

It should take you *not more than a minute and a quarter* to add the following ten sums:

| (a) 8 | (b) 1 | (c) 8 | (d) 9 | (e) 11 | (f) 23 |
|---|---|---|---|---|---|
| 4 | 7 | 5 | 8 | 15 | 34 |
| 6 | 9 | 4 | 7 | 16 | 89 |
| 3 | 6 | 3 | 9 | 19 | 76 |

| (g) 59 | (h) 124 | (i) 172 | (j) 821 |
|---|---|---|---|
| 80 | 268 | 283 | 372 |
| 77 | 579 | 934 | 694 |
| 35 | 234 | 514 | 453 |
| 49 | 576 | 689 | 575 |
| 93 | 895 | 756 | 696 |

## HOW TO PROVE AN ADDITION

There are two simple ways of proving an addition:

1. Add the columns in the opposite direction. That is, if you have added from the top to the bottom, now reverse your process and add from the bottom to the top—and vice versa.

2. Add each column separately, arrange the totals as in the illustration that follows, and then add the totals:

```
4,573  The first (right hand) column totals    22
6,924  The second column totals                16
7,348  The third column totals                 19
9,237  The fourth (left hand) column totals    26
28,082                                      28082
```

## EXERCISE 6

The following exercise is designed to develop speed and accuracy in horizontal as well as in vertical addition. Add across in each hori-

# ADDITION

zontal column, and down in each vertical column. The grand total, at the lower right-hand corner, should be the same for the sum of the horizontal additions as for the sum of the vertical additions.

```
2  4  6  8  3  5  1  7  9  ....
1  3  5  7  9  4  6  2  8  ....
8  9  7  9  7  5  6  8  4  ....
4  6  2  8  3  5  9  5  7  ....
7  5  4  8  3  9  4  2  8  ....
9  7  4  3  5  4  6  7  4  ....
9  7  7  6  4  5  7  9  4  ....
2  5  7  9  6  4  3  7  9  ....
8  6  5  7  4  3  8  6  5  ....
9  8  6  4  5  3  6  8  4  ....

.. .. .. .. .. .. .. .. .. ....
```

## EXERCISE 7

Try to add the following nine sums in eight minutes. If you can do it in *less* than eight minutes, you may call yourself fairly expert in the art of addition:

(a)  19
     28
     36
     40
     51
     98
    107

(b)    112
       150
       856
       665
     1,291
        64
       671

(c) 527,101
    198,620
    412,680
    210,863
    768,510
    169,087
    307,627

(d) 10,471,998
       250,469
       984,323
    14,110,652
     3,081,467
     6,843,147
     3,856,205
       253,884
     4,952,324
     4,025,451

(e) 1,421,682
    2,186,925
    1,010,586
       17,030
      224,983
      671,270
    1,930,352
        2,673
          864
    1,083,146

(f)     2,068
       21,184
      527,534
       94,985
      412,512
      246,582
      255,700
      251,285
      366,076
      207,682
    1,309,255

|  |  |  |
|---|---|---|
| (g) 726,703.008 | (h) 7.0885 | (i) 6,037.0771 |
| 256,323.68 | 9.1548 | 9,180.5564 |
| 415.9 | 4.8118 | 3,100.0012 |
| 641,468.291 | 9.0519 | 99,192.9702 |
| 286,702.439 | 4.0383 | 91,829.08 |
| 75 | 38.4197 | 1,006.732 |
| 368,012.184 | 93.6851 | 2,505.8543 |
| 140,000.005 | 7,006.0032 | 6,269.1744 |
| 247,853.169 | 49.5928 | 780,878.5544 |

## ANSWERS
### EXERCISE 5
(a) 21  (b) 23  (c) 20  (d) 33  (e) 61  (f) 222  (g) 393  (h) 2,676  (i) 3,348  (j) 3,611

### EXERCISE 6
The horizontal totals (beginning with the top row) are: 45, 45, 63, 49, 50, 49, 58, 52, 52, and 53, with a grand total of 516. The vertical totals (beginning with the column at the left) are: 59, 60, 53, 69, 49, 47, 56, 61, and 62, with a grand total of 516.

### EXERCISE 7
(a) 379
(b) 3,809
(c) 2,594,488
(d) 48,829,920
(e) 8,549,511
(f) 3,694,863
(g) 2,667,553.676
(h) 7,221.8461
(i) 1,000,000

## CHAPTER III
## Subtraction

OUR DAILY LIFE is a constant succession of additions and subtractions. Every minute subtracted from the twenty-four hours means so much less time left for our work and our play and our sleep. How much time are we going to devote to this or that conference, to our meals, to the reading of such and such a report, to shaving, to dressing for the theater? How much time will that leave us for the writing of that report, the preparation of that speech, the consideration of that territory for the new store, the finishing of that job, the romp around the block with Jimmy, the discussion of Mary's engagement with the rest of the family? All our time is so preciously weighed out to us, so many minutes per hour, so many days per month, and so many years per life, that we must learn to add and to subtract our moments with the utmost care in order to get the greatest value out of each and every one of them. We've got to learn to budget our time.

And our money! How much can we spend on our rent, our meals, our amusements, in order that we may have such and such a sum left for the dentist's and the doctor's bill, Freddie's tuition at college, Mary's piano lessons, mother's new hat, the week-end trip to Cousin Betty's? How can we subtract our pennies from our dollars on each of these items, in order to leave as much as possible for all the other items? Whether we like it or not, our daily life compels us to become expert subtractors.

The following exercises will help you along that highly desirable road:

### EXERCISE 8

Practice these twenty-six examples in subtraction until you can do them all in *less than two minutes*. If you need further practice in speed and in accuracy, you can make up your own examples.

(a) 98  (b) 87  (c) 86  (d) 95  (e) 74  (f) 53
    84      62      53      23      64      41

12                MATHEMATICS MADE EASY

(g) 71      (h) 82       (i) 93        (j) 64       (k) 45       (l) 54
    23          69           57            38           39           47

(m) 151     (n) 296      (o) 385       (p) 73.4     (q) 6.29
    46          107          168           31.9         4.03

(r) 132     (s) 345      (t) 873       (u) 764.1    (v) 93.203
    56          289          594           387.9        30.866

(w) 7749    (x) 37,451   (y) 975,312,468   (z) 1607.5362
    4152        35,689       286,987,539       1098.7496

### THE AUSTRIAN METHOD

In giving change to a customer, we use the so-called "Austrian method" of subtraction. That is, instead of *subtracting* the amount of the purchase from the amount of the coin or bill given in payment, we *add* from the amount of the purchase up to the next higher money unit, then to the next, and so on until we come to the amount of the coin or bill given in payment. For example, if the amount of the purchase is $3.23, and the bill given in payment is $10.00, we give the customer the following money units for his change: 2 cents, to make the sum $3.25; then 25 cents, to make the sum $3.50; then 50 cents, to make the sum $4.00; then a dollar, to make the sum $5.00; and finally $5.00, to bring the sum up to $10.00.

### EXERCISE 9

Using the "Austrian method," subtract the following amounts from $10.00:

(a) $1.67   (b) $2.17   (c) $7.29   (d) $8.16   (e) $6.78   (f) $3.62
(g) $3.55   (h) $6.80   (i) $6.92   (j) $5.77   (k) $4.06   (l) $8.88
(m) $8.11   (n) $2.63   (o) $1.31   (p) $3.49   (q) $7.21   (r) $5.14
(s) $6.92   (t) $6.45   (u) $7.15   (v) $4.37   (w) $5.42   (x) $7.01
(y) $9.38   (z) $5.64

### COMPLEMENTS

The *complement* of a number is the difference between that number and the next higher unit of ten or a power of ten. For example:

# SUBTRACTION

| Number | Next higher unit of ten |
|--------|-------------------------|
| 3      | 10                      |
| 57     | 100                     |
| 469    | 1000                    |

Hence the complement of 3—that is, the difference between 3 and 10—is 7; the complement of 57—the difference between 57 and 100—is 43; the complement of 469—the difference between 469 and 1000—is 531.

In subtracting by the "complement" method, we add the complement of the *subtrahend* (the quantity to be subtracted) to the *minuend* (the quantity from which the subtraction is made), and then we subtract 10. For example:

(1) Subtract 6 from 8.

Add the complement of the subtrahend 6, which is 4, to the minuend 8, which equals 12; and subtract from this sum the unit of 10, which leaves you 2.

(2) Subtract 34 from 79.

$$\begin{array}{r} 79 \\ -34 \\ \hline ? \end{array}$$

6 (the complement of 4) $+9-10=5$
7 (the complement of 3) $+7-10=4$
Answer, 45

When we have a problem in which several numbers are to be added and subtracted, we sometimes find it advisable to use the "complement method." This method is convenient in computing your bank balances, your deposits, and your disbursed checks. Take, for example, the following problem:

| Old Balance | Deposit  | Checks   | New Balance |
|-------------|----------|----------|-------------|
| $753.87    | $124.32 | $321.24 | ?           |

Let us translate this into a problem of addition and subtraction, as follows:

$$\$753.87 + \$124.32 - \$321.24 = ?$$

And now let us compute it by the "arithmetical complement" method. Let us start with the right-hand digit of the subtrahend:

The complement of 4 is 6. Add this complement to the

14  MATHEMATICS MADE EASY

right-hand digits of the deposit and the old balance, 2 and 7. This gives you a sum of 15. Now subtract 10 from this sum, and you get a remainder of 5.

Going through the same process with all the other digits, you get the following results:

8 (the complement of 2)+3+8−10=9
9 (the complement of 1)+4+3−10=6
8 (the complement of 2)+2+5−10=5
7 (the complement of 3)+1+7−10=5

Answer (reading from the bottom to the top), $556.95

## EXERCISE 10

In the following examples use the "arithmetical complement" method to perform the additions and subtractions indicated by the plus and minus signs.

(a) $655.39+$146.70−$271.35
(b) $429.36+$385.63−$547.60
(c) $830.09+$238.27−$173.38
(d) $1270.35+$2236.29−$1422.25
(e) $7534.42+$3147.29−$3432.28
(f) $29456.42+$31325.47−$17422.79
(g) $33265.63+$45671.28−$43244.22
(h) $127,342.56+$231,437.21−$125,225.75
(i) $255,461.59+$332,749.31−$187,987.87
(j) $324,532.22+$225,332.47−$548,864.69

## ANSWERS
### EXERCISE 8

(a) 14      (b) 25      (c) 33      (d) 72      (e) 10      (f) 12
(g) 48      (h) 13      (i) 36      (j) 26      (k) 6       (l) 7
(m) 105     (n) 189     (o) 217     (p) 41.5    (q) 2.26
(r) 76      (s) 56      (t) 279     (u) 376.2   (v) 62.337
(w) 3597    (x) 1762    (y) 688,324,929         (z) 508.7866

### EXERCISE 9

(a) $8.33   (b) $7.83   (c) $2.71   (d) $1.84   (e) $3.22   (f) $6.38
(g) $6.45   (h) $3.20   (i) $3.08   (j) $4.23   (k) $5.94   (l) $1.12
(m) $1.89   (n) $7.37   (o) $8.69   (p) $6.51   (q) $2.79   (r) $4.86
(s) $3.08   (t) $3.55   (u) $2.85   (v) $5.63   (w) $4.58   (x) $2.99
(y) $ .62   (z) $4.36

### EXERCISE 10

(a) $530.74         (b) $267.39         (c) $894.98
(d) $2084.39        (e) $7249.43        (f) $43,359.10
(g) $35,692.69      (h) $233,554.02     (i) $400,223.03
                    (j) $1000.

CHAPTER IV
# Multiplication

*Multiplication* may be defined as *wholesale addition*. It is the abbreviated process of adding any given quantity a certain number of times. Thus, 4×5=4+4+4+4+4 (4 added 5 times).

The following terms are commonly used in multiplication:
The *multiplicand* is the number which is to be multiplied.
The *multiplier* is the number which does the multiplying.
The *product* is the result of the multiplication.

In the example, 20 feet × 3 = 60 feet, the term *20 feet* is the multiplicand, *3* is the multiplier, and *60 feet* is the product.

When you speak of 20 feet, 10 quarts, 15 automobiles, $300, you are using *concrete* numbers. But when you speak of 20, 10, 15, and 300, you are using *abstract* numbers. The multiplicand may be a concrete number, but the multiplier must always be an abstract number. That is, you can multiply 10 quarts by 4, but you cannot multiply 10 quarts by 4 apples. When the multiplicand is a concrete number,—that is, when it represents a certain object, the product is expressed in terms of that object. For example, 10 quarts × 4 = 40 quarts.

The following exercises are designed to give you practice in oral and written multiplication:

### EXERCISE 11

Multiply at sight:

(a) 431 ×2     (b) 321 ×3     (c) 410 ×4     (d) 497 ×5     (e) 753 ×6     (f) 194 ×7

(g) 795 ×8     (h) 276 ×9     (i) 137 ×10     (j) 278 ×11     (k) 384 ×12     (l) 479 ×13

15

## EXERCISE 12

Make a multiplication table by filling in the boxes in the diagram below. The figure in each box should be the product of the number at the *left margin* and the number at the *top margin*. (Three boxes are filled in to start you off. Thus, 5×6=30; 7×9=63; 9×12=108.)

| 1 | 2 | 3 | 4 | 5 | 6 | 7 | 8 | 9 | 10 | 11 | 12 | 13 | 14 | 15 | 16 |
|---|---|---|---|---|---|---|---|---|----|----|----|----|----|----|----|
| 2 |   |   |   |   |   |   |   |   |    |    |    |    |    |    |    |
| 3 |   |   |   |   |   |   |   |   |    |    |    |    |    |    |    |
| 4 |   |   |   |   |   |   |   |   |    |    |    |    |    |    |    |
| 5 |   |   |   |   | 30|   |   |   |    |    |    |    |    |    |    |
| 6 |   |   |   |   |   |   |   |   |    |    |    |    |    |    |    |
| 7 |   |   |   |   |   |   |   | 63|    |    |    |    |    |    |    |
| 8 |   |   |   |   |   |   |   |   |    |    |    |    |    |    |    |
| 9 |   |   |   |   |   |   |   |   |    |    | 108|    |    |    |    |
| 10|   |   |   |   |   |   |   |   |    |    |    |    |    |    |    |
| 11|   |   |   |   |   |   |   |   |    |    |    |    |    |    |    |
| 12|   |   |   |   |   |   |   |   |    |    |    |    |    |    |    |
| 13|   |   |   |   |   |   |   |   |    |    |    |    |    |    |    |
| 14|   |   |   |   |   |   |   |   |    |    |    |    |    |    |    |
| 15|   |   |   |   |   |   |   |   |    |    |    |    |    |    |    |
| 16|   |   |   |   |   |   |   |   |    |    |    |    |    |    |    |

## EXERCISE 13

Multiply the following examples, and try to do them all in *three* minutes:

(a) 931
    856

(b) 962
    943

(c) 974
    878

(d) 884
    763

(e) 889
    778

(f) 667
    556

(g) 9284
    8759

(h) 8638
    6387

(i) 7596
    7518

(j) 9986
    8638

## HOW TO PROVE A MULTIPLICATION

There are two simple ways of proving a multiplication:

1. Interchange the multiplicand and the multiplier, as in the following example:

```
    2346              357
     357             2346
   16422             2142
   11730             1428
    7038             1071
  837,522             714
                  837,522
```

# MULTIPLICATION

2. Divide the product either by the multiplicand or by the multiplier, as follows:

$$
\begin{array}{r}
2{,}346\phantom{)} \\
357{\overline{\smash{)}837{,}522}} \\
714\phantom{,522} \\
\hline
1235\phantom{,22} \\
1071\phantom{,22} \\
\hline
1642\phantom{,2} \\
1428\phantom{,2} \\
\hline
2142 \\
2142 \\
\end{array}
$$

## TIME-SAVERS IN MULTIPLICATION

The following practical methods will save you considerable time in your everyday calculations. They will also help you to eliminate errors:

1. To multiply a number by 5, add one zero to the number and divide by 2; to multiply by 25, add two zeros and divide by 4; by 125, add three zeros and divide by 8.

2. To multiply an integer by 10, 100, 1000, etc.

Add to the number as many zeros as there are in the multiplier.

$$347 \times 10 = 3{,}470$$
$$347 \times 100 = 34{,}700$$
$$347 \times 1000 = 347{,}000$$

3. To multiply a number containing a decimal by 10, 100, 1000, etc.

Move the decimal point to the right, as many places as there are zeros in the multiplier.

$$53.072 \times 10 = 530.72$$
$$53.072 \times 100 = 5{,}307.2$$
$$53.072 \times 1000 = 53{,}072$$

4. To multiply a number of two digits by 11, add the digits and place the sum between them.

$$54 \times 11 = 594$$

If the sum of the two digits is more than 10, you must also add 1 to the digit on the left.

$$69 \times 11 = 759.$$ You get the 7 by adding 1 to the 6.

5. To multiply numbers of more than two digits by 11.
Multiply the number by 10, and add the multiplicand to the product.

$$347 \times 11 = 3,470 + 347 = 3817$$

6. To multiply a number by 101, 1001, etc.
Multiply the number by 100, 1000, etc., and add the multiplicand to the product.

$$347 \times 101 = 34,700 + 347 = 35,047$$
$$347 \times 1001 = 347,000 + 347 = 347,347$$

7. To multiply a number by 9, 99, 999, etc.
Multiply the number by 10, 100, 1000, etc., and subtract the multiplicand from the product.

$$256 \times 9 = 2,560 - 256 = 2,304$$
$$256 \times 99 = 25,600 - 256 = 25,344$$
$$256 \times 999 = 256,000 - 256 = 255,744$$

## EXERCISE 14

Do the following examples by the time-saving methods as outlined above:
(a) $68 \times 5$; $168 \times 25$; $325 \times 25$; $64 \times 125$; $282 \times 25$.
(b) $257 \times 10$; $3456 \times 100$; $45.345 \times 100$; $6.535 \times 1000$.
(c) $35 \times 11$; $78 \times 11$; $425 \times 11$; $346 \times 11$; $568 \times 11$.
(d) $252 \times 101$; $56 \times 1001$; $127 \times 1001$; $127 \times 101$.
(e) $593 \times 9$; $417 \times 9$; $1253 \times 9$; $2564 \times 9$.
(f) $47 \times 99$; $552 \times 99$; $1236 \times 99$; $34 \times 999$; $426 \times 999$.

## ALIQUOT PARTS

An *aliquot* part of a unit is a *fractional* part that will exactly divide that unit. Thus, 5, 10, 20, 25, and 50 are aliquot parts of 100.

A knowledge of the more commonly used fractional parts of

# MULTIPLICATION

10, 100, and 1000 will prove to be a great time-saver in multiplication. Familiarize yourself with the following table of fractional parts:

$\frac{1}{2}$ of 10 = 5;   of 100 = 50;   of 1000 = 500
$\frac{1}{3}$ " " = $3\frac{1}{3}$;   " " = $33\frac{1}{3}$;   " " = $333\frac{1}{3}$
$\frac{2}{3}$ " " = $6\frac{2}{3}$;   " " = $66\frac{2}{3}$;   " " = $666\frac{2}{3}$
$\frac{1}{4}$ " " = 2.5;   " " = 25;   " " = 250
$\frac{3}{4}$ " " = 7.5;   " " = 75;   " " = 750
$\frac{1}{6}$ " " = $1\frac{2}{3}$;   " " = $16\frac{2}{3}$;   " " = $166\frac{2}{3}$
$\frac{5}{6}$ " " = $8\frac{1}{3}$;   " " = $83\frac{1}{3}$;   " " = $833\frac{1}{3}$
$\frac{1}{8}$ " " = $1\frac{1}{4}$;   " " = $12\frac{1}{2}$;   " " = 125
$\frac{3}{8}$ " " = $3\frac{3}{4}$;   " " = $37\frac{1}{2}$;   " " = 375
$\frac{5}{8}$ " " = $6\frac{1}{4}$;   " " = $62\frac{1}{2}$;   " " = 625
$\frac{7}{8}$ " " = $8\frac{3}{4}$;   " " = $87\frac{1}{2}$;   " " = 875
$\frac{1}{12}$ " " = $\frac{5}{6}$;   " " = $8\frac{1}{3}$;   " " = $83\frac{1}{3}$
$\frac{5}{12}$ " " = $4\frac{1}{6}$;   " " = $41\frac{2}{3}$;   " " = $416\frac{2}{3}$
$\frac{7}{12}$ " " = $5\frac{5}{6}$;   " " = $58\frac{1}{3}$;   " " = $583\frac{1}{3}$

## DRILL ON ALIQUOT PARTS

(a) 50 is what part of 100?
(b) $16\frac{2}{3}$ is what part of 100?
(c) $33\frac{1}{3}$ is what part of 100?
(d) 1.25 is what part of 10?
(e) .25 is what part of 1?
(f) $8\frac{1}{3}$ is what part of 100?
(g) $41\frac{2}{3}$ is what part of 100?
(h) $3\frac{3}{4}$ is what part of 10?
(i) $62\frac{1}{2}$ is what part of 100?
(j) $8\frac{1}{3}$ is what part of 10?
(k) $6\frac{2}{3}$ is what part of 10?
(l) 875 is what part of 1000?
(m) $58\frac{1}{3}$ is what part of 100?
(n) $37\frac{1}{2}$ is what part of 100?
(o) .375 is what part of 1?
(p) 7.5 is what part of 10?
(q) $12\frac{1}{2}$ is what part of 100?
(r) $3\frac{1}{3}$ is what part of 10?
(s) $8\frac{3}{4}$ is what part of 10?
(t) $6\frac{1}{4}$ is what part of 10?

## HOW TO MULTIPLY BY FRACTIONAL PARTS OF 100

You can save yourself a great deal of time and effort if you use the aliquot or the fractional part method in multiplication, whenever the multiplicand or the multiplier is a fractional part of 100.

For example, suppose you want to figure out the cost of 4 dozen shirts at 75 cents a shirt. All you need to do by the fractional method is to multiply 48 by 100 and to take $\frac{3}{4}$ of the product. For 75 is $\frac{3}{4}$ of 100.

$$48 \times 100 = 4800$$
$$\tfrac{3}{4} \text{ of } 4800 = 3600$$

Answer, 3600 cents, or $36.

In like manner, you can use the following short methods in multiplication by the fractional parts of 100:

1. To multiply by $12\frac{1}{2}$, multiply by 100 and divide by 8. For $12\frac{1}{2} = \frac{1}{8}$ of 100.
2. To multiply by $33\frac{1}{3}$, multiply by 100 and divide by 3. For $33\frac{1}{3} = \frac{1}{3}$ of 100.
3. To multiply by $16\frac{2}{3}$, multiply by 100 and divide by 6. For $16\frac{2}{3} = \frac{1}{6}$ of 100.
4. To multiply by 75, multiply by 100 and take $\frac{3}{4}$ of the product. For $75 = \frac{3}{4}$ of 100.
5. To multiply by $37\frac{1}{2}$, multiply by 100 and take $\frac{3}{8}$ of the product. For $37\frac{1}{2} = \frac{3}{8}$ of 100.
6. To multiply by $62\frac{1}{2}$, multiply by 100 and take $\frac{5}{8}$ of the product. For $62\frac{1}{2} = \frac{5}{8}$ of 100.
7. To multiply by $87\frac{1}{2}$, multiply by 100 and take $\frac{7}{8}$ of the product. For $87\frac{1}{2} = \frac{7}{8}$ of 100.
8. To multiply by $66\frac{2}{3}$, multiply by 100 and take $\frac{2}{3}$ of the product. For $66\frac{2}{3} = \frac{2}{3}$ of 100.
9. To multiply by $8\frac{1}{3}$, multiply by 100 and take $\frac{1}{12}$ of the product. For $8\frac{1}{3} = \frac{1}{12}$ of 100.
10. To multiply by $41\frac{2}{3}$, multiply by 100 and take $\frac{5}{12}$ of the product. For $41\frac{2}{3} = \frac{5}{12}$ of 100.

## EXERCISE 15

Multiply the following examples by the aliquot method:
(a) $87\frac{1}{2} \times 64$    (b) $16\frac{2}{3} \times 96$    (c) $37\frac{1}{2} \times 128$    (d) $83\frac{1}{3} \times 72$
(e) $62\frac{1}{2} \times 88$    (f) $75 \times 64$    (g) $66\frac{2}{3} \times 939$    (h) $25 \times 468$
(i) $33\frac{1}{3} \times 2793$    (j) $12\frac{1}{2} \times 144$    (k) $8\frac{1}{3} \times 360$    (l) $41\frac{2}{3} \times 72$

## ANSWERS
### EXERCISE 11

(a) 862    (b) 963    (c) 1640    (d) 2485    (e) 4518    (f) 1358
(g) 6360    (h) 2484    (i) 1370    (j) 3058    (k) 4608    (l) 6227

# MULTIPLICATION

### EXERCISE 12

| 1 | 2 | 3 | 4 | 5 | 6 | 7 | 8 | 9 | 10 | 11 | 12 | 13 | 14 | 15 | 16 |
|---|---|---|---|---|---|---|---|---|----|----|----|----|----|----|----|
| 2 | 4 | 6 | 8 | 10 | 12 | 14 | 16 | 18 | 20 | 22 | 24 | 26 | 28 | 30 | 32 |
| 3 | 6 | 9 | 12 | 15 | 18 | 21 | 24 | 27 | 30 | 33 | 36 | 39 | 42 | 45 | 48 |
| 4 | 8 | 12 | 16 | 20 | 24 | 28 | 32 | 36 | 40 | 44 | 48 | 52 | 56 | 60 | 64 |
| 5 | 10 | 15 | 20 | 25 | 30 | 35 | 40 | 45 | 50 | 55 | 60 | 65 | 70 | 75 | 80 |
| 6 | 12 | 18 | 24 | 30 | 36 | 42 | 48 | 54 | 60 | 66 | 72 | 78 | 84 | 90 | 96 |
| 7 | 14 | 21 | 28 | 35 | 42 | 49 | 56 | 63 | 70 | 77 | 84 | 91 | 98 | 105 | 112 |
| 8 | 16 | 24 | 32 | 40 | 48 | 56 | 64 | 72 | 80 | 88 | 96 | 104 | 112 | 120 | 128 |
| 9 | 18 | 27 | 36 | 45 | 54 | 63 | 72 | 81 | 90 | 99 | 108 | 117 | 126 | 135 | 144 |
| 10 | 20 | 30 | 40 | 50 | 60 | 70 | 80 | 90 | 100 | 110 | 120 | 130 | 140 | 150 | 160 |
| 11 | 22 | 33 | 44 | 55 | 66 | 77 | 88 | 99 | 110 | 121 | 132 | 143 | 154 | 165 | 176 |
| 12 | 24 | 36 | 48 | 60 | 72 | 84 | 96 | 108 | 120 | 132 | 144 | 156 | 168 | 180 | 192 |
| 13 | 26 | 39 | 52 | 65 | 78 | 91 | 104 | 117 | 130 | 143 | 156 | 169 | 182 | 195 | 208 |
| 14 | 28 | 42 | 56 | 70 | 84 | 98 | 112 | 126 | 140 | 154 | 168 | 182 | 196 | 210 | 224 |
| 15 | 30 | 45 | 60 | 75 | 90 | 105 | 120 | 135 | 150 | 165 | 180 | 195 | 210 | 225 | 240 |
| 16 | 32 | 48 | 64 | 80 | 96 | 112 | 128 | 144 | 160 | 176 | 192 | 208 | 224 | 240 | 256 |

### EXERCISE 13

(a) 796,936   (b) 907,166   (c) 855,172   (d) 674,492   (e) 691,642
(f) 370,852   (g) 81,318,556   (h) 55,170,906   (i) 57,106,728   (j) 86,259,068

### EXERCISE 14

(a) 340;   4200;   8125;   8000;   7050.
(b) 2570;   345,600;   4534.5;   6535.
(c) 385;   858;   4675;   3806;   6248.
(d) 25,452;   56,056;   127,127;   12,827.
(e) 5337;   3753;   11,277;   23,076.
(f) 4653;   54,648;   122,364;   33,966;   425,574.

### ANSWERS FOR DRILL ON ALIQUOT PARTS

(a) $\frac{1}{2}$   (b) $\frac{1}{6}$   (c) $\frac{1}{3}$   (d) $\frac{1}{8}$   (e) $\frac{1}{4}$
(f) $\frac{1}{12}$   (g) $\frac{5}{12}$   (h) $\frac{3}{8}$   (i) $\frac{5}{8}$   (j) $\frac{4}{5}$
(k) $\frac{2}{3}$   (l) $\frac{7}{8}$   (m) $\frac{7}{12}$   (n) $\frac{3}{8}$   (o) $\frac{3}{8}$
(p) $\frac{3}{4}$   (q) $\frac{1}{8}$   (r) $\frac{1}{3}$   (s) $\frac{7}{8}$   (t) $\frac{5}{8}$

### EXERCISE 15

(a) 5600   (b) 1600   (c) 4800   (d) 6000
(e) 5500   (f) 4800   (g) 62,600   (h) 11,700
(i) 93,100   (j) 1800   (k) 3000   (l) 3000

## CHAPTER V
## Division

THE FOLLOWING TERMS are commonly used in division:
The *dividend* is the number which is to be divided.
The *divisor* is the number by which the dividend is divided.
The *quotient* is the result of the division.
The *remainder* is the number that is left over at the end of the division when the divisor does not evenly divide the dividend.

Thus, $16 \div 3 = 5$ with a remainder of 1. The remainder is written at the end of the quotient, thus: $5\frac{1}{3}$.

### HOW TO PROVE A DIVISION

To prove a division, multiply the quotient by the divisor, and add the remainder, if any.

Example:

$$\begin{array}{r} 342 \\ 67\overline{)22929} \\ 201\phantom{00} \\ \overline{\phantom{0}282\phantom{0}} \\ 268\phantom{0} \\ \overline{\phantom{00}149} \\ 134 \\ \overline{\phantom{00}15} \end{array}$$

Answer, $342\frac{15}{67}$

Proof:

$$\begin{array}{r} 342 \\ \times 67 \\ \hline 2394 \\ 2052\phantom{0} \\ \hline 22914 \\ 15 \\ \hline 22929 \end{array}$$

# DIVISION

## TIME-SAVERS IN DIVISION

1. To divide by 10, 100, 1000, etc., point off as many figures in the dividend, counting from right to left, as there are zeros in the divisor.

$$436 \div 10 = 43.6$$
$$436 \div 100 = 4.36$$
$$436 \div 1000 = .436$$

2. To divide by 20, divide by 10, and then by 2; by 30, divide by 10, and then by 3. And so on, up to 90.
3. To divide by 200, divide by 100, and then by 2. And so on, up to 900.
4. To divide by 2000, divide by 1000, and then by 2. And so on.
5. To divide by 5, multiply by 2, and then divide by 10.

$$33,545 \div 5$$
$$33,545 \times 2 = 67,090$$
$$67,090 \div 10 = 6709$$

6. To divide by 25, multiply by 4, and then divide by 100.
7. To divide by 125, multiply by 8, and then divide by 1000.
8. To divide by $33\frac{1}{3}$, multiply by 3, and then divide by 100.
9. To divide by any aliquot part of 100, divide by 100, and multiply the result by the *inverted* fraction represented by the aliquot. In other words, *invert* or *reverse* the process of multiplication by aliquot. For example:

(a) Divide 8000 by $66\frac{2}{3}$

$$8000 \div 100 = 8$$
$$8 \times \tfrac{3}{2} = 12$$

(You will recall, from your table of aliquots, that $66\frac{2}{3}$ is $\frac{2}{3}$ of 100. And the fraction $\frac{2}{3}$, when inverted, becomes $\frac{3}{2}$.)

(b) Divide 13,224 by $16\frac{2}{3}$

$$13,224 \div 100 = 132.24$$
$$132.24 \times 6 = 793.44$$

($16\frac{2}{3}$ is $\frac{1}{6}$ of 100. And the fraction $\frac{1}{6}$, when inverted, becomes 6.)

The following exercises will give you practice in oral and in

MATHEMATICS MADE EASY

written division. Try to do the examples in these exercises as rapidly and as accurately as possible:

### EXERCISE 16
Find the quotients:
(a) 8624÷2;   2738÷2;   357,912÷2.
(b) 6930÷3;   2781÷3;   268,452÷3.
(c) 8848÷4;   6696÷4;   391,076÷4.
(d) 5105÷5;   3915÷5;   134,265÷5.
(e) 1866÷6;   4134÷6;   223,722÷6.
(f) 1477÷7;   2422÷7;   353,199÷7.
(g) 3288÷8;   5128÷8;   321,272÷8.
(h) 4599÷9;   3231÷9;   226,332÷9.

### EXERCISE 17
Find the quotients:
(a) 6116÷11            (f) 642,544÷16
(b) 2304÷12            (g) 355,299÷21
(c) 12,454÷13          (h) 324,432÷24
(d) 706,398÷14         (i) 679,023÷27
(e) 844,335÷15         (j) 242,576÷72

### EXERCISE 18
Find the quotients:
(a) 796,936÷428        (f) 370,852÷114
(b) 907,166÷481        (g) 81,318,556÷2321
(c) 85,172÷487         (h) 55,170,906÷2129
(d) 674,492÷221        (i) 57,106,728÷3798
(e) 691,642÷389        (j) 86,259,068÷4319

### EXERCISE 19
Perform the following divisions and put the remainders at the end of the quotient. For example: 665÷6=110 $\frac{5}{6}$.
(a) 234,519÷4          (f) 348,409÷24
(b) 963,731÷5          (g) 760,025÷81
(c) 842,631÷11         (h) 1,357,845÷778
(d) 1,285,091÷16       (i) 110,341,815÷8516
(e) 710,603÷21         (j) 258,660,596÷12,957

### EXERCISE 20
Divide mentally:
(a) 1927÷10;   213,709÷10;   1968÷10;   4018÷10.
(b) 312,907÷100;   7205÷100;   2482÷100;   22,819÷100.

# DIVISION

(c) 586÷1000;   2699÷1000;   83÷1000;   975,863,603÷1000.
(d) 2148÷20;   8109÷30;   4816÷40;   6515÷50;   9618÷60;
    7714÷70;   8248÷80;   2754÷90.
(e) 8428÷200;   2715÷300;   6448÷400;   7550÷500;   3642÷600;
    14,721÷700;   16,480÷800;   814,500÷900.

## EXERCISE 21
Divide the following by the use of aliquot parts of 100:
(a) 28,000÷87$\frac{1}{2}$    (b) 3500÷62$\frac{1}{2}$    (c) 2100÷33$\frac{1}{3}$
(d) 960÷37$\frac{1}{2}$    (e) 6500÷83$\frac{1}{3}$    (f) 6612÷16$\frac{2}{3}$
(g) 45,670÷5    (h) 4575÷25    (i) 1500÷125
(j) 2800÷87$\frac{1}{2}$    (k) 2400÷75    (l) 800÷16$\frac{2}{3}$

## ANSWERS
### EXERCISE 16
(a) 4312;  1369;  178,956.   (b) 2310;  927;  89,484.   (c) 2212;  1674;  97,769.
(d) 1021;  783;  26,853.   (e) 311;  689;  37,287.   (f) 211;  346;  50,457.
(g) 411;  641;  40,159.   (h) 511;  359;  25,148.

### EXERCISE 17
(a) 556    (b) 192    (c) 958    (d) 50,457    (e) 56,289
(f) 40,159    (g) 16,919    (h) 13,518    (i) 25,149    (j) 3,508

### EXERCISE 18
(a) 1862    (b) 1886    (c) 1756    (d) 3052    (e) 1778
(f) 2668    (g) 35,036    (h) 25,914    (i) 15,036    (j) 19,972

### EXERCISE 19
(a) 58,629$\frac{3}{4}$    (b) 192,746$\frac{1}{5}$    (c) 76,602$\frac{9}{11}$    (d) 80,318$\frac{3}{16}$
(e) 33,838$\frac{5}{21}$    (f) 14,517$\frac{1}{24}$    (g) 9,383$\frac{2}{81}$    (h) 1745$\frac{235}{778}$
(i) 12,957$\frac{8}{8516}$    (j) 19,963$\frac{5}{12957}$

### EXERCISE 20
(a) 192.7;   21,370.9;   196.8;   401.8
(b) 3,129.07;   72.05;   24.82;   228.19
(c) .586;   2.699;   .083;   975,863.603
(d) 107.4;   270.3;   120.4;   130.3;   160.3;   110.2;   103.1;   30.6
(e) 42.14;   9.05;   16.12;   15.1;   6.07;   21.03;   20.6;   905.

### EXERCISE 21
(a) 320    (b) 56    (c) 63    (d) 25.6    (e) 78
(f) 396.72    (g) 9134    (h) 183    (i) 12    (j) 32
(k) 32    (l) 48

## CHAPTER VI
# Fractions

THE WORD *fraction* comes from the Latin *fractus*, which means *broken*. A *fraction* is a *broken unit*, or *part* of a unit.

The *terms* of a fraction are the *numerator*, which is written *above* the line, and the *denominator*, which is written *below* the line. In the fraction, $\frac{7}{16}$, 7 is the numerator and 16 is the denominator.

A *proper fraction* is a fraction whose numerator is *less* than the denominator.

An *improper fraction* is a fraction whose numerator is *more* than the denominator.

### REDUCTION OF FRACTIONS TO HIGHER TERMS

You may reduce a fraction to higher terms by multiplying both the numerator and the denominator by the same number.

For example, reduce $\frac{5}{6}$ to sixtieths.

In order to do this, you multiply both the 5 and the 6 by 10, and you get $\frac{50}{60}$.

Now, how do you get the 10? By *dividing* the higher denominator, 60, by the lower denominator, 6.

In like manner, reduce $\frac{7}{9}$ to hundred-seventeenths.

$$\frac{7}{9} = \frac{?}{117}$$
$$117 \div 9 = 13$$
$$7 \times 13 = 91$$

Answer, $\frac{7}{9} = \frac{91}{117}$

### EXERCISE 22

Find the missing numerators. In other words, reduce the fractions to higher terms, as indicated:

(a) $\frac{1}{8} = \frac{}{72}$
(b) $\frac{5}{6} = \frac{}{36}$
(c) $\frac{4}{9} = \frac{}{27}$
(d) $\frac{3}{5} = \frac{}{25}$
(e) $\frac{3}{14} = \frac{}{56}$
(f) $\frac{7}{12} = \frac{}{60}$
(g) $\frac{3}{7} = \frac{}{28}$
(h) $\frac{9}{10} = \frac{}{40}$
(i) $\frac{3}{4} = \frac{}{16}$
(j) $\frac{4}{5} = \frac{}{75}$
(k) $\frac{1}{2} = \frac{}{72}$
(l) $\frac{5}{8} = \frac{}{32}$
(m) $\frac{15}{28} = \frac{}{84}$
(n) $\frac{24}{45} = \frac{}{180}$
(o) $\frac{21}{34} = \frac{}{374}$

# FRACTIONS

## REDUCTION OF FRACTIONS TO LOWER TERMS

You may reduce a fraction to lower terms by dividing both the numerator and the denominator by the same number.

Reduce $\frac{48}{128}$ to sixty-fourths.

Divide both sides by 2, and you get $\frac{24}{64}$.

This fraction, you will note, can be reduced to still lower terms. To reduce a fraction to the *lowest* terms, keep on dividing both the numerator and the denominator, each time by the same number, until you can no longer divide them in this way.

Let us take the fraction, $\frac{72}{120}$, and reduce it to the lowest terms:

Dividing the numerator and the denominator by 2, we get $\frac{36}{60}$.

Dividing them again by 2, we get $\frac{18}{30}$.

Dividing them again by 2, we get $\frac{9}{15}$.

Dividing them by 3, we get $\frac{3}{5}$.

$$\frac{72}{120} = \frac{3}{5}$$

This process of reducing fractions to their lowest terms is called *cancellation*.

### EXERCISE 23

Reduce to the lowest terms:
(a) $\frac{16}{18}$  (b) $\frac{24}{30}$  (c) $\frac{81}{162}$  (d) $\frac{39}{52}$  (e) $\frac{68}{85}$
(f) $\frac{144}{216}$  (g) $\frac{288}{384}$  (h) $\frac{693}{1089}$  (i) $\frac{128}{208}$  (j) $\frac{234}{416}$
(k) $\frac{195}{210}$  (l) $\frac{108}{312}$  (m) $\frac{162}{513}$  (n) $\frac{204}{459}$  (o) $\frac{426}{1207}$

## REDUCTION OF IMPROPER FRACTIONS TO MIXED NUMBERS

To reduce an improper fraction to a mixed number, divide the numerator by the denominator.

(a) $\frac{9}{2} = 9 \div 2 = 4\frac{1}{2}$
(b) $\frac{22}{6} = 22 \div 6 = 3\frac{4}{6} = 3\frac{2}{3}$

### EXERCISE 24

Change the following improper fractions to mixed numbers:
(a) $\frac{5}{2}$  (b) $\frac{25}{6}$  (c) $\frac{21}{8}$  (d) $\frac{3}{1}$  (e) $\frac{47}{3}$
(f) $\frac{54}{7}$  (g) $\frac{17}{4}$  (h) $\frac{16}{3}$  (i) $\frac{19}{10}$  (j) $\frac{52}{5}$
(k) $\frac{68}{9}$  (l) $\frac{72}{3}$  (m) $\frac{16}{13}$  (n) $\frac{29}{15}$  (o) $\frac{16}{5}$
(p) $\frac{73}{2}$  (q) $\frac{41}{3}$  (r) $\frac{18}{10}$  (s) $\frac{92}{8}$  (t) $\frac{49}{2}$

## REDUCTION OF MIXED NUMBERS TO IMPROPER FRACTIONS

To reduce a mixed number to an improper fraction, multiply the whole number by the denominator, add the numerator to the product, and write the denominator under this sum.

$$6\tfrac{2}{3} = \frac{6 \times 3 + 2}{3} = \tfrac{20}{3}$$

### EXERCISE 25

Change the following mixed numbers to improper fractions:
(a) $5\tfrac{1}{2}$ (b) $8\tfrac{3}{7}$ (c) $4\tfrac{5}{9}$ (d) $23\tfrac{1}{2}$ (e) $8\tfrac{1}{6}$
(f) $7\tfrac{1}{4}$ (g) $22\tfrac{1}{9}$ (h) $7\tfrac{2}{3}$ (i) $3\tfrac{1}{7}$ (j) $3\tfrac{7}{10}$
(k) $5\tfrac{3}{8}$ (l) $7\tfrac{2}{3}$ (m) $4\tfrac{2}{11}$ (n) $3\tfrac{9}{20}$ (o) $5\tfrac{7}{15}$
(p) $11\tfrac{3}{16}$ (q) $17\tfrac{3}{14}$ (r) $9\tfrac{3}{5}$ (s) $4\tfrac{7}{19}$ (t) $8\tfrac{5}{12}$

## THE LEAST COMMON DENOMINATOR

When two or more fractions have the same denominator, they are said to have a *common denominator*.

Fractions that have a common denominator are called *similar fractions*.

To reduce two or more fractions to *similar fractions*, reduce them to fractions that have the *least common denominator*,—that is, the *lowest possible figure* that can serve as a denominator for all the fractions.

(a) Reduce $\tfrac{1}{2}$, $\tfrac{2}{3}$, and $\tfrac{3}{4}$ to similar fractions.

The least common denominator of 2, 3, and 4—that is, the lowest possible figure that can divide 2, 3, and 4—is 12. Hence

$$\tfrac{1}{2} = \tfrac{6}{12}; \quad \tfrac{2}{3} = \tfrac{8}{12}; \quad \tfrac{3}{4} = \tfrac{9}{12}.$$

(b) Reduce $\tfrac{5}{8}$, $\tfrac{11}{24}$, $\tfrac{1}{6}$, and $\tfrac{4}{9}$ to similar fractions.

The least common denominator of 8, 24, 6, and 9 is 72. Hence

$$\tfrac{5}{8} = \tfrac{45}{72}; \quad \tfrac{11}{24} = \tfrac{33}{72}; \quad \tfrac{1}{6} = \tfrac{12}{72}; \quad \tfrac{4}{9} = \tfrac{32}{72}.$$

### EXERCISE 26

Find the least common denominator in each of the following groups of fractions:

(a) $\tfrac{3}{8}$  $\tfrac{5}{9}$  $\tfrac{2}{3}$ (c) $\tfrac{1}{6}$  $\tfrac{3}{14}$  $\tfrac{2}{3}$  $\tfrac{5}{21}$
(b) $\tfrac{4}{5}$  $\tfrac{5}{9}$  $\tfrac{7}{30}$ (d) $\tfrac{5}{12}$  $\tfrac{3}{10}$  $\tfrac{5}{6}$  $\tfrac{9}{28}$

# FRACTIONS

(e) $\frac{4}{15}$  $\frac{11}{18}$  $\frac{29}{30}$
(f) $\frac{3}{22}$  $\frac{5}{14}$  $\frac{16}{33}$  $\frac{8}{21}$
(g) $\frac{5}{6}$  $\frac{9}{10}$  $\frac{19}{22}$

(h) $\frac{1}{6}$  $\frac{7}{10}$  $\frac{23}{30}$  $\frac{7}{12}$
(i) $\frac{11}{12}$  $\frac{19}{20}$  $\frac{43}{45}$
(j) $\frac{5}{6}$  $\frac{17}{21}$  $\frac{23}{28}$  $\frac{11}{12}$

## ADDITION OF FRACTIONS

To add fractions, proceed as follows:

1. Reduce the fractions to similar fractions having the least common denominator.
2. Write the sum of the numerators over the least common denominator.
3. Reduce the result to the lowest terms.

Add:

$\frac{1}{3}, \frac{1}{2}, \frac{5}{6}$
$\frac{1}{3} = \frac{4}{12}$
$\frac{1}{2} = \frac{6}{12}$
$\frac{5}{6} = \frac{10}{12}$
$\frac{4}{12} + \frac{6}{12} + \frac{10}{12} = \frac{20}{12} = 1\frac{8}{12} = 1\frac{2}{3}$

To add mixed numbers, reduce the mixed numbers to fractions, and then proceed with the three steps as outlined above.

Add:

$5\frac{1}{2}, 1\frac{1}{3}, 4\frac{1}{4}$
$\frac{11}{2}, \frac{4}{3}, \frac{17}{4}$
$\frac{11}{2} = \frac{66}{12}$
$\frac{4}{3} = \frac{16}{12}$
$\frac{17}{4} = \frac{51}{12}$
$\frac{66}{12} + \frac{16}{12} + \frac{51}{12} = \frac{133}{12} = 11\frac{1}{12}$

Another way to add mixed numbers is to add the whole numbers and the fractions separately, and then to add the results.

Add:

$5\frac{1}{2}, 1\frac{1}{3}, 4\frac{1}{4}$
$5\frac{1}{2}$
$1\frac{1}{3}$
$4\frac{1}{4}$
$\overline{10\frac{13}{12}} = 10 + 1\frac{1}{12} = 11\frac{1}{12}$

## MATHEMATICS MADE EASY

### EXERCISE 27

Add the following groups of fractions and reduce the answer to lowest terms:

(a) $\frac{1}{2}$  $\frac{2}{3}$  $\frac{1}{6}$
(b) $\frac{2}{3}$  $\frac{3}{4}$  $\frac{4}{5}$
(c) $\frac{5}{8}$  $\frac{1}{6}$  $\frac{2}{9}$
(d) $\frac{3}{4}$  $\frac{2}{5}$  $\frac{1}{12}$
(e) $\frac{1}{4}$  $\frac{2}{3}$  $\frac{7}{9}$
(f) $\frac{3}{5}$  $\frac{4}{9}$  $\frac{7}{30}$
(g) $\frac{5}{6}$  $\frac{3}{14}$  $\frac{1}{9}$  $\frac{5}{21}$
(h) $\frac{7}{12}$  $\frac{7}{10}$  $\frac{1}{6}$  $\frac{5}{28}$
(i) $\frac{7}{15}$  $\frac{11}{18}$  $\frac{7}{30}$
(j) $\frac{3}{22}$  $\frac{1}{14}$  $\frac{14}{33}$  $\frac{11}{21}$
(k) $\frac{5}{6}$  $\frac{7}{10}$  $\frac{17}{22}$
(l) $\frac{1}{6}$  $\frac{1}{10}$  $\frac{23}{30}$  $\frac{5}{12}$
(m) $\frac{5}{12}$  $\frac{19}{20}$  $\frac{41}{45}$
(n) $\frac{1}{6}$  $\frac{4}{21}$  $\frac{17}{28}$  $\frac{11}{12}$

### SUBTRACTION OF FRACTIONS

To subtract one fraction from another, reduce them both to simple fractions having the least common denominator, write the difference over the common denominator, and reduce the result to the lowest terms.

(a) Subtract $\frac{1}{3}$ from $\frac{3}{8}$.

$$\frac{3}{8} = \frac{9}{24}$$
$$\frac{1}{3} = \frac{8}{24}$$
$$\frac{9}{24} - \frac{8}{24} = \frac{1}{24}$$

(b) Subtract $5\frac{2}{3}$ from $9\frac{7}{8}$.

$$9\frac{7}{8} = 9\frac{21}{24}$$
$$5\frac{2}{3} = 5\frac{16}{24}$$
$$9\frac{21}{24} - 5\frac{16}{24} = 4\frac{5}{24}$$

### EXERCISE 28

Subtract and reduce the remainder to lowest terms:

(a) $\frac{3}{4} - \frac{2}{3}$
(b) $\frac{4}{9} - \frac{2}{7}$
(c) $\frac{37}{45} - \frac{1}{3}$
(d) $2\frac{1}{10} - \frac{1}{5}$
(e) $\frac{3}{8} - \frac{2}{9}$
(f) $\frac{2}{3} - \frac{1}{6}$
(g) $\frac{5}{6} - \frac{1}{4}$
(h) $\frac{11}{21} - \frac{14}{33}$
(i) $\frac{11}{18} - \frac{7}{30}$
(j) $\frac{7}{10} - \frac{5}{28}$
(k) $\frac{5}{6} - \frac{5}{21}$
(l) $\frac{11}{12} - \frac{17}{28}$
(m) $\frac{41}{45} - \frac{5}{12}$
(n) $1\frac{5}{12} - \frac{23}{30}$
(o) $1\frac{7}{12} - \frac{9}{10}$
(p) $1\frac{1}{12} - \frac{5}{6}$
(q) $\frac{19}{30} - \frac{2}{7}$
(r) $2\frac{2}{3} - 1\frac{3}{4}$
(s) $\frac{41}{45} - \frac{5}{9}$
(t) $1\frac{5}{12} - \frac{3}{4}$
(u) $\frac{11}{18} - \frac{7}{15}$

### MULTIPLICATION OF FRACTIONS

To multiply fractions, proceed as follows:

1. Change all the numbers to fractions. Whole numbers are to be regarded as having 1 for the denominator. Thus, $6 = \frac{6}{1}$.

FRACTIONS 31

2. Cancel as much as you can.
3. Find the product of the cancelled numerators and the cancelled denominators.

(a) Multiply $6 \times \frac{3}{4}$.
Reduce to fractions: $\frac{6}{1} \times \frac{3}{4}$

Cancel: $\dfrac{\overset{3}{\cancel{6}} \times 3}{1 \times \cancel{4}}$
$\phantom{Cancel:\ }\phantom{\dfrac{a}{a}}_{2}$

Multiply: $\frac{9}{2} = 4\frac{1}{2}$.

(b) Multiply $\frac{11}{12}$ by $\frac{4}{5}$ by $6\frac{1}{4}$
Reduce to fractions: $\frac{11}{12} \times \frac{4}{5} \times \frac{25}{4}$

Cancel: $\dfrac{11}{12} \times \dfrac{\cancel{4}}{\cancel{5}} \times \dfrac{\overset{5}{\cancel{25}}}{\cancel{4}}$

Multiply: $\frac{55}{12} = 4\frac{7}{12}$

## EXERCISE 29

### A

Multiply mentally, cancelling to reduce the work:

(a) $\frac{4}{5} \times \frac{5}{4}$
(b) $\frac{2}{3} \times \frac{6}{7}$
(c) $\frac{4}{9} \times \frac{3}{16}$
(d) $\frac{2}{3} \times \frac{9}{16} \times \frac{4}{9}$
(e) $\frac{2}{3} \times \frac{3}{4} \times \frac{2}{5}$

(f) $\frac{5}{8} \times \frac{3}{7} \times \frac{7}{15}$
(g) $\frac{3}{4} \times \frac{5}{6} \times \frac{1}{10}$
(h) $\frac{7}{8} \times \frac{7}{10} \times \frac{8}{49}$
(i) $\frac{2}{3} \times \frac{3}{7} \times \frac{1}{2}$
(j) $\frac{7}{12} \times \frac{7}{16} \times \frac{48}{49}$

### B

Multiply, making use of cancellation wherever possible:

(a) $32 \times \frac{3}{8}$
(b) $36 \times \frac{5}{6}$
(c) $378 \times \frac{2}{9}$
(d) $4 \times 2\frac{2}{5}$
(e) $18 \times 7\frac{2}{9}$

(f) $16 \times 4\frac{1}{8}$
(g) $8\frac{1}{8} \times 2\frac{2}{13}$
(h) $2\frac{3}{16} \times 2\frac{2}{7}$
(i) $8\frac{1}{10} \times 1\frac{1}{9}$
(j) $6\frac{6}{11} \times 7\frac{1}{3}$

### C

Multiply, making use of cancellation wherever possible:

(a) $\frac{11}{39} \times \frac{6}{7} \times \frac{13}{22}$
(b) $\frac{42}{55} \times \frac{11}{12} \times \frac{5}{7}$

## MATHEMATICS MADE EASY

(c) $4\frac{8}{11} \times 3\frac{2}{3} \times \frac{6}{13}$
(d) $1\frac{1}{3} \times 9\frac{2}{5} \times \frac{15}{16}$
(e) $1\frac{4}{5} \times 7\frac{7}{9} \times 1\frac{1}{13}$
(f) $1\frac{7}{8} \times 12\frac{2}{3} \times 1\frac{3}{5} \times 1\frac{5}{19}$
(g) $2\frac{3}{16} \times 2\frac{1}{7} \times 1\frac{3}{25} \times \frac{4}{21}$
(h) $9\frac{3}{5} \times 6\frac{6}{11} \times 1\frac{11}{24} \times 3\frac{13}{14} \times \frac{1}{86}$
(i) $1\frac{15}{17} \times 3\frac{3}{14} \times 6\frac{3}{8} \times 3\frac{1}{9} \times \frac{9}{40}$
(j) $1\frac{29}{35} \times 2\frac{5}{22} \times 1\frac{1}{35} \times 1\frac{11}{21} \times 2\frac{1}{16} \times 2\frac{5}{8} \times \frac{5}{8} \times \frac{5}{12}$

### DIVISION OF FRACTIONS

To divide fractions, *invert* the numerator and the denominator of the *divisor*, and then multiply the fractions. Note: To *invert* a fraction means to put the denominator *above* the line and the numerator *below* the line.

(a) Divide $3\frac{3}{4} \div 9$

$\frac{15}{4} \div \frac{9}{1}$

$\frac{15}{4} \times \frac{1}{9}$

$$\frac{\overset{5}{\cancel{15}} \times 1}{4 \times \cancel{9}} = \frac{5}{12}$$
$\phantom{xxxx}3$

(b) Divide $9 \div 3\frac{3}{4}$

$\frac{9}{1} \div \frac{15}{4}$

$\frac{9}{1} \times \frac{4}{15}$

$$\frac{\overset{3}{\cancel{9}}}{1} \times \frac{4}{\underset{5}{\cancel{15}}} = \frac{12}{5} = 2\frac{2}{5}$$

(c) Divide $6\frac{3}{4} \div 1\frac{7}{8}$

$\frac{27}{4} \div \frac{15}{8}$

$\frac{27}{4} \times \frac{8}{15}$

$$\frac{\overset{9}{\cancel{27}} \times \overset{2}{\cancel{8}}}{\underset{1}{\cancel{4}} \times \underset{5}{\cancel{15}}} = \frac{18}{5} = 3\frac{3}{5}$$

# FRACTIONS

## EXERCISE 30

### A

Divide mentally, using cancellation:

(a) $10 \div \frac{2}{3}$
(b) $8 \div \frac{4}{5}$
(c) $7 \div \frac{14}{25}$
(d) $6 \div \frac{3}{7}$
(e) $11 \div \frac{11}{15}$
(f) $\frac{4}{5} \div \frac{4}{5}$
(g) $\frac{2}{3} \div \frac{5}{6}$
(h) $\frac{11}{12} \div \frac{5}{6}$
(i) $\frac{2}{3} \div \frac{2}{9}$
(j) $\frac{6}{7} \div \frac{3}{14}$

### B

Divide, using cancellation wherever possible:

(a) $4\frac{1}{8} \div \frac{3}{4}$
(b) $2\frac{2}{3} \div \frac{7}{16} \div 1\frac{1}{7}$
(c) $\frac{4}{9} \div 5\frac{1}{3} \div 1\frac{1}{3}$
(d) $4\frac{1}{2} \div \frac{9}{16} \div 8$
(e) $16\frac{4}{5} \div 2\frac{2}{11} \div 15\frac{2}{5}$
(f) $1\frac{1}{3} \div 6\frac{2}{3} \div 1\frac{7}{8} \div \frac{2}{25}$
(g) $9\frac{1}{7} \div 4\frac{2}{3} \div 8\frac{1}{4} \div \frac{8}{10}$
(h) $8\frac{1}{3} \div 1\frac{2}{5} \div 6\frac{1}{4} \div 4\frac{1}{6}$
(i) $3\frac{1}{7} \div 8\frac{7}{16} \div 1\frac{7}{15} \div 2\frac{2}{7}$
(j) $9\frac{9}{10} \div 6\frac{7}{8} \div 5\frac{2}{5} \div 1\frac{1}{15}$

## ANSWERS

### EXERCISE 22

(a) 9  (b) 30  (c) 12  (d) 15  (e) 12  (f) 35
(g) 12  (h) 36  (i) 12  (j) 100  (k) 36  (l) 20
(m) 45  (n) 96  (o) 231

### EXERCISE 23

(a) $\frac{8}{9}$  (b) $\frac{4}{5}$  (c) $\frac{1}{2}$  (d) $\frac{3}{4}$  (e) $\frac{4}{5}$  (f) $\frac{2}{3}$
(g) $\frac{3}{4}$  (h) $\frac{7}{11}$  (i) $\frac{8}{15}$  (j) $\frac{9}{16}$  (k) $\frac{13}{14}$  (l) $\frac{9}{26}$
(m) $\frac{6}{19}$  (n) $\frac{4}{9}$  (o) $\frac{4}{17}$

### EXERCISE 24

(a) $2\frac{1}{2}$  (b) $4\frac{1}{6}$  (c) $2\frac{5}{8}$  (d) 3  (e) $15\frac{2}{3}$
(f) $7\frac{5}{7}$  (g) $4\frac{1}{4}$  (h) $5\frac{1}{3}$  (i) $1\frac{9}{10}$  (j) $10\frac{2}{3}$
(k) $7\frac{5}{8}$  (l) 24  (m) $2\frac{2}{7}$  (n) $1\frac{4}{15}$  (o) $3\frac{1}{5}$
(p) $36\frac{1}{2}$  (q) $13\frac{2}{3}$  (r) $1\frac{4}{5}$  (s) $11\frac{1}{2}$  (t) $24\frac{1}{2}$

### EXERCISE 25

(a) $\frac{11}{2}$  (b) $\frac{59}{7}$  (c) $\frac{41}{9}$  (d) $\frac{47}{2}$  (e) $\frac{49}{6}$
(f) $\frac{29}{4}$  (g) $\frac{109}{9}$  (h) $\frac{23}{3}$  (i) $\frac{22}{7}$  (j) $\frac{27}{10}$
(k) $\frac{43}{8}$  (l) $\frac{23}{5}$  (m) $\frac{46}{11}$  (n) $\frac{69}{20}$  (o) $\frac{82}{15}$
(p) $\frac{179}{16}$  (q) $\frac{241}{14}$  (r) $\frac{43}{5}$  (s) $\frac{83}{10}$  (t) $\frac{101}{12}$

# MATHEMATICS MADE EASY

### EXERCISE 26
(a) 72  (b) 90  (c) 126  (d) 420  (e) 90
(f) 462  (g) 330  (h) 60  (i) 180  (j) 84

### EXERCISE 27
(a) $1\frac{1}{3}$  (b) $2\frac{13}{60}$  (c) $1\frac{1}{72}$  (d) $1\frac{7}{30}$
(e) $1\frac{25}{36}$  (f) $1\frac{5}{18}$  (g) $1\frac{25}{68}$  (h) $1\frac{22}{35}$
(i) $1\frac{14}{45}$  (j) $1\frac{2}{7}$  (k) $2\frac{101}{330}$  (l) $1\frac{9}{20}$
(m) $2\frac{5}{18}$  (n) $1\frac{37}{42}$

### EXERCISE 28
(a) $\frac{1}{12}$  (b) $\frac{10}{63}$  (c) $\frac{22}{45}$  (d) $1\frac{9}{10}$  (e) $1\frac{1}{72}$  (f) $\frac{1}{2}$
(g) $\frac{7}{12}$  (h) $\frac{23}{231}$  (i) $\frac{17}{45}$  (j) $\frac{73}{140}$  (k) $\frac{25}{42}$  (l) $\frac{13}{42}$
(m) $\frac{89}{180}$  (n) $\frac{13}{20}$  (o) $\frac{41}{60}$  (p) $\frac{1}{4}$  (q) $\frac{73}{210}$  (r) $\frac{11}{12}$
(s) $\frac{16}{45}$  (t) $\frac{2}{3}$  (u) $\frac{13}{90}$

### EXERCISE 29A
(a) 1  (b) $\frac{4}{7}$  (c) $\frac{1}{12}$  (d) $\frac{1}{6}$  (e) $\frac{1}{5}$
(f) $\frac{1}{6}$  (g) $\frac{1}{18}$  (h) $\frac{1}{10}$  (i) $\frac{1}{7}$  (j) $\frac{1}{4}$

### EXERCISE 29B
(a) 12  (b) 30  (c) 84  (d) $9\frac{3}{8}$  (e) 130
(f) 66  (g) $17\frac{1}{2}$  (h) 5  (i) 9  (j) 48

### EXERCISE 29C
(a) $\frac{1}{7}$  (b) $\frac{1}{2}$  (c) 8  (d) 12  (e) 14
(f) 48  (g) 1  (h) 10  (i) 27  (j) 9

### EXERCISE 30A
(a) 15  (b) 10  (c) $12\frac{1}{2}$  (d) 14  (e) 15
(f) 1  (g) $\frac{4}{5}$  (h) $1\frac{1}{10}$  (i) 3  (j) 4

### EXERCISE 30B
(a) $5\frac{1}{2}$  (b) $5\frac{1}{3}$  (c) $\frac{1}{16}$  (d) 1  (e) $\frac{1}{2}$
(f) $1\frac{1}{3}$  (g) $\frac{320}{399}$  (h) $\frac{8}{35}$  (i) $\frac{1}{9}$  (j) $\frac{1}{4}$

## CHAPTER VII
# Decimals

A *decimal* is a fraction whose denominator is 10, 100, 1000, or any other power of 10. The denominator is not written, but is indicated by the position of the decimal point.

$$2.5 = 2\tfrac{5}{10}$$
$$2.53 = 2\tfrac{53}{100}$$
$$2.536 = 2\tfrac{536}{1000}$$

Sometimes an arithmetical calculation may be shortened if you change a common fraction into a decimal fraction. For example, if you want to compute the cost of $56\tfrac{1}{4}$ yards of muslin at $17\tfrac{1}{2}$ cents a yard, it is best to change $\tfrac{1}{4}$ yard and $\tfrac{1}{2}$ cent to their equivalent decimal fractions:

```
      56.25
      $.175
      -----
      28125
      39375
      5625
      -------
      $9.84375        Answer, $9.84
```

On the other hand, it is sometimes better to change a decimal fraction into a common fraction. For example, if you want to compute the cost of 64 pounds of meat at $12\tfrac{1}{2}$ cents a pound, change $12\tfrac{1}{2}$ cents to $\tfrac{1}{8}$ of a dollar:

$$64 \times \tfrac{1}{8} = \$8$$

To change a common fraction into a decimal fraction, place a decimal point after the numerator, and divide by the denominator.

Reduce $\tfrac{2}{5}$ to a decimal fraction.

```
        .4
      5)2.0              Answer, .4
```

Sometimes a common fraction cannot be reduced to an exact decimal fraction. In that case, carry the division to four decimal points,—that is, to ten-thousandths.

Reduce $\frac{17}{21}$ to a decimal fraction.

$$\begin{array}{r} .8095 \\ 21\overline{)17.0000} \\ 168\phantom{0000} \\ \hline 200\phantom{000} \\ 189\phantom{000} \\ \hline 110\phantom{00} \\ 105\phantom{00} \\ \hline 5\phantom{00} \end{array}$$ Answer, .8095

To change a decimal fraction to a common fraction, omit the decimal point, and divide the fraction by 10, 100, 1000, etc., depending on whether it represents tenths, hundredths, thousandths, etc.

Reduce .44 to a common fraction.

$$44 \div 100 = \tfrac{44}{100} = \tfrac{22}{50} = \tfrac{11}{25}$$

Note: Every example in division may be expressed by a common fraction. Thus, $234 \div 1000 = \tfrac{234}{1000}$; $39 \div 476 = \tfrac{39}{476}$.

The following exercises will give you practice in the interchanging of decimal and common fractions:

## EXERCISE 31

Express these common fractions as decimals:

(a) $\frac{1}{2}$    (b) $\frac{1}{3}$    (c) $\frac{1}{4}$    (d) $\frac{1}{5}$    (e) $\frac{2}{5}$
(f) $\frac{3}{5}$    (g) $\frac{3}{4}$    (h) $\frac{5}{6}$    (i) $\frac{1}{6}$    (j) $\frac{2}{3}$
(k) $\frac{1}{8}$    (l) $\frac{1}{9}$    (m) $\frac{3}{8}$    (n) $\frac{5}{8}$    (o) $\frac{7}{8}$

## EXERCISE 32

Match up the fractions in the left-hand column with the correct decimals in the right-hand column. For example, if you think the first fraction corresponds to the top decimal, your answer should be (a); if you think it corresponds to the second fraction, your answer should be (b). And so on.

1. $\frac{7}{8}$        (a) .1429
2. $\frac{2}{9}$        (b) .8333
3. $\frac{1}{6}$        (c) .0625

# DECIMALS

4. $\frac{1}{12}$            (d) .25
5. $\frac{5}{6}$            (e) .0833
6. $\frac{1}{16}$           (f) .625
7. $\frac{5}{8}$            (g) .375
8. $\frac{1}{7}$            (h) .1667
9. $\frac{3}{8}$            (i) .875
10. $\frac{1}{4}$           (j) .2222

## EXERCISE 33

Express these fractions as decimals to the nearest ten-thousandth. That is, if the fifth figure after the decimal point (hundred-thousandths) is five or more, add one to the fourth figure after the decimal point. For example, $\frac{1}{3}$ is .33333; since the fifth figure is only 3, nothing is added to the fourth figure and it is properly expressed as .3333. But the fraction $\frac{2}{3}$ is .66666; since the fifth figure is 6, it is dropped and one is added to the fourth figure. It then reads .6667.

(a) $\frac{2}{11}$    (b) $\frac{5}{12}$    (c) $\frac{7}{13}$    (d) $\frac{9}{14}$    (e) $\frac{8}{15}$
(f) $\frac{11}{16}$    (g) $\frac{13}{17}$    (h) $\frac{19}{68}$    (i) $\frac{25}{72}$    (j) $\frac{47}{84}$
(k) $\frac{41}{108}$    (l) $\frac{61}{110}$    (m) $\frac{71}{126}$    (n) $\frac{47}{144}$    (o) $\frac{107}{156}$
(p) $\frac{53}{168}$    (q) $\frac{151}{216}$    (r) $\frac{181}{264}$    (s) $\frac{217}{312}$

## EXERCISE 34

Express these decimals as common fractions:

(a) .5          (b) .75         (c) .625        (d) .875
(e) .735       (f) .1875       (g) .375        (h) .05
(i) .005       (j) .08         (k) .008

## ADDITION AND SUBTRACTION OF DECIMALS

To add or to subtract decimals, write the numbers so that the decimal points line up directly one under the other.

         Add:   34.5,   5.25,   6.034
         34.5
          5.25
          6.034
         ―――――
         45.784

      Subtract 4.534 from 35.2
         35.2
          4.534
         ―――――
         30.666

## MULTIPLICATION OF DECIMALS

To multiply by a decimal, multiply as if by a whole number, and count off (from the right to the left) as many decimal places as there are in the multiplicand and the multiplier together.

(a) 52×.67

$$\begin{array}{r} .67 \\ 52 \\ \hline 134 \\ 335 \\ \hline 34.84 \end{array}$$

Answer, 34.84

(b) .042×2.57

$$\begin{array}{r} 2.57 \\ .042 \\ \hline 514 \\ 1028 \\ \hline .10794 \end{array}$$

Answer, .10794

(c) .122×.02

$$\begin{array}{r} .122 \\ .02 \\ \hline .00244 \end{array}$$

Answer, .00244

### EXERCISE 35

Multiply mentally:

(a) 4×.25
(b) 8×.375
(c) 24×.2
(d) 49×.3
(e) 9×.08
(f) 18×.003
(g) 16×.012
(h) 12×.12
(i) 11×.11
(j) 26×.05

### EXERCISE 36

Multiply:

(a) 1.46×2.3
(b) .043×.74
(c) 7.31×12
(d) 5.8×.068
(e) .834×3.1
(f) 24.5×.87

# DECIMALS

(g) .74×2.9
(h) 47.5×6.58
(i) 2.96×6.36
(j) .0986×4.08
(k) 2.793×25.68
(l) .2886×2.829
(m) 31.22×263.4
(n) 26.52×2.289
(o) 26.67×233.4
(p) .002001×.1668
(q) .27852×26.277
(r) 259.14×19.161
(s) .22788×22.554
(t) .29958×2.5914

## DIVISION OF DECIMALS

1. To divide a decimal by a whole number, divide as if both the dividend and the divisor were whole numbers, and write the decimal point in the quotient as soon as the decimal point in the dividend is reached.

$$23.8 \div 17$$

```
      1.4
17)23.8
   17
   ‾‾
    68
    68
```
Answer, 1.4

2. To divide by a decimal, multiply both the dividend and the divisor by such a power of 10 as shall make the divisor a whole number. Then divide as if both the dividend and the divisor were whole numbers, and write the decimal point in the quotient as soon as the decimal point in the dividend is reached.

This is much simpler than it sounds, as you will see from the following examples:

(a) Divide 2.88÷2.4
   2.88×10=28.8
   2.4×10=24

```
      1.2
24)28.8
   24
   ‾‾
    48
    48
```
Answer, 1.2

## MATHEMATICS MADE EASY

(b) Divide 115.6 ÷ .34
$$115.6 \times 100 = 11560$$
$$.34 \times 100 = 34$$

$$\begin{array}{r} 340 \\ 34\overline{)11560} \\ \underline{102}\phantom{00} \\ 136\phantom{0} \\ \underline{136}\phantom{0} \end{array}$$

Answer, 340

(c) Divide 8.12 ÷ .029
$$8.12 \times 1000 = 8120$$
$$.029 \times 1000 = 029 = 29$$

$$\begin{array}{r} 280 \\ 29\overline{)8120} \\ \underline{58}\phantom{00} \\ 232\phantom{0} \\ \underline{232}\phantom{0} \end{array}$$

Answer, 280

## EXERCISE 37

Divide:

(a) 30.222 by 20.7
(b) .28692 by 6.66
(c) 789.48 by .0108
(d) 354.96 by 52.2
(e) 2.32686 by .279
(f) 19.1835 by 2.205
(g) 19.314 by 26.1
(h) 2812.95 by 427.5
(i) 169.4304 by 26.64
(j) 3.620592 by 367.2

### ANSWERS
### EXERCISE 31

| | | | | |
|---|---|---|---|---|
| (a) .5 | (b) .3333 | (c) .25 | (d) .2 | (e) .4 |
| (f) .6 | (g) .75 | (h) .8333 | (i) .1667 | (j) .6667 |
| (k) .125 | (l) .1111 | (m) .375 | (n) .625 | (o) .875 |

### EXERCISE 32

| | | | | |
|---|---|---|---|---|
| 1. (i) | 2. (j) | 3. (h) | 4. (e) | 5. (b) |
| 6. (c) | 7. (f) | 8. (a) | 9. (g) | 10. (d) |

### EXERCISE 33

| | | | | |
|---|---|---|---|---|
| (a) .1818 | (b) .4176 | (c) .5385 | (d) .6429 | (e) .5333 |
| (f) .6875 | (g) .7059 | (h) .3016 | (i) .3472 | (j) .5595 |
| (k) .3796 | (l) .5546 | (m) .5635 | (n) .3264 | (o) .6859 |
| (p) .3155 | (q) .6991 | (r) .6856 | (s) .6955 | |

# DECIMALS

## EXERCISE 34
(a) $\frac{1}{2}$  (b) $\frac{3}{4}$  (c) $\frac{5}{8}$  (d) $\frac{7}{8}$
(e) $\frac{147}{200}$  (f) $\frac{3}{16}$  (g) $\frac{3}{8}$  (h) $\frac{1}{20}$
(i) $\frac{1}{200}$  (j) $\frac{2}{25}$  (k) $\frac{1}{125}$

## EXERCISE 35
(a) 1  (b) 3  (c) 4.8  (d) 14.7  (e) .72
(f) .054  (g) .192  (h) 1.44  (i) 1.21  (j) 1.3

## EXERCISE 36
(a) 3.358  (b) .03182  (c) 87.72  (d) .3944
(e) 2.5854  (f) 21.315  (g) 2.146  (h) 312.55
(i) 18.8256  (j) .402288  (k) 71.72424  (l) .8164494
(m) 8223.348  (n) 60.70428  (o) 6224.778  (p) .0003337668
(q) 7.31867004  (r) 4965.38154  (s) 5.13960552  (t) .776331612

## EXERCISE 37
(a) 1.46  (b) .043  (c) 73,100  (d) 6.8  (e) 8.34
(f) 8.7  (g) .74  (h) 6.58  (i) 6.36  (j) .00986

## CHAPTER VIII
## Percentage

*Per cent* means *by the hundred*. In dealing with percentage, therefore, we are dealing with decimals whose denominator is 100.

Thus, 25 percent (written 25%) = $\frac{25}{100}$ or .25.

As you will readily see, percentage can be reduced to common fractions or to decimals, and vice versa.

(a) Reduce 6% to a common fraction.
   6% = $\frac{6}{100}$ = $\frac{3}{50}$

(b) Reduce 6% to a decimal.
   6% = .06

To reduce a number written with the percent sign to a decimal, omit the percent sign and move the decimal point two places to the left.

$$2\tfrac{1}{2}\% = .02\tfrac{1}{2}, \text{ or } .025$$
$$125\% = 1.25$$

To reduce a common fraction to a percentage, reduce it to a decimal (by dividing the numerator by the denominator), and then write it in the percent form.

Reduce $\tfrac{1}{8}$ to a percentage.
$\tfrac{1}{8} = 1 \div 8 = .125$ or $.12\tfrac{1}{2} = 12\tfrac{1}{2}\%$

The following exercises are designed to give you practice in the simple computation of percentage:

### EXERCISE 38

Change to percentage:

(a) $\frac{18}{100}$  (b) .93  (c) .8  (d) .0625  (e) $\frac{3}{6}$
(f) $\frac{6}{1000}$  (g) $\frac{2}{3}$  (h) .83$\tfrac{1}{3}$  (i) $\frac{5}{8}$  (j) $\frac{1}{2}$
(k) $\frac{1}{8}$  (l) .75  (m) .08  (n) .16$\tfrac{2}{3}$  (o) $\frac{1}{10}$
(p) $\frac{7}{8}$  (q) $\frac{4}{5}$  (r) .7  (s) $\frac{1}{4}$  (t) $\frac{1}{20}$

## PERCENTAGE

### EXERCISE 39
Change to decimals:
(a) 71%   (b) 4%   (c) $37\frac{1}{2}$%   (d) $66\frac{2}{3}$%   (e) $\frac{1}{10}$%
(f) .70%   (g) $\frac{1}{2}$%   (h) .09%   (i) $1\frac{1}{2}$%   (j) $\frac{1}{8}$%
(k) $\frac{1}{16}$%   (l) $\frac{2}{3}$%   (m) $1\frac{1}{4}$%   (n) 250%   (o) 80%
(p) 125%   (q) .36%   (r) 35%   (s) $\frac{1}{4}$%   (t) 110%

### EXERCISE 40
Match the fractions in the left-hand column with the corresponding percent in the right-hand column.

1. $\frac{1}{2}$
2. $\frac{1}{3}$
3. $\frac{2}{3}$
4. $\frac{1}{4}$
5. $\frac{3}{4}$
6. $\frac{1}{5}$
7. $\frac{2}{5}$
8. $\frac{3}{5}$
9. $\frac{4}{5}$
10. $\frac{1}{6}$
11. $\frac{5}{6}$
12. $\frac{1}{8}$
13. $\frac{3}{8}$
14. $\frac{5}{8}$
15. $\frac{7}{8}$
16. $\frac{1}{10}$
17. $\frac{3}{10}$
18. $\frac{7}{10}$
19. $\frac{9}{10}$
20. $\frac{1}{20}$

(a) 20%
(b) 80%
(c) $83\frac{1}{3}$%
(d) $87\frac{1}{2}$%
(e) $37\frac{1}{2}$%
(f) 50%
(g) 10%
(h) 70%
(i) $33\frac{1}{3}$%
(j) 5%
(k) $66\frac{2}{3}$%
(l) 25%
(m) $16\frac{2}{3}$%
(n) 30%
(o) 75%
(p) 90%
(q) 60%
(r) $62\frac{1}{2}$%
(s) 40%
(t) $12\frac{1}{2}$%

Some of the percents are used so frequently that it is well to remember their equivalent common fractions. Familiarize yourself with the following table:

$50\% = \frac{1}{2}$      $80\% = \frac{4}{5}$          $87\frac{1}{2}\% = \frac{7}{8}$
$25\% = \frac{1}{4}$      $12\frac{1}{2}\% = \frac{1}{8}$   $3\frac{1}{8}\% = \frac{1}{32}$
$20\% = \frac{1}{5}$      $6\frac{1}{4}\% = \frac{1}{16}$   $16\frac{2}{3}\% = \frac{1}{6}$
$40\% = \frac{2}{5}$      $37\frac{1}{2}\% = \frac{3}{8}$   $33\frac{1}{3}\% = \frac{1}{3}$
$60\% = \frac{3}{5}$      $62\frac{1}{2}\% = \frac{5}{8}$   $66\frac{2}{3}\% = \frac{2}{3}$
                $83\frac{1}{3}\% = \frac{5}{6}$

Example: Take $83\frac{1}{3}$% of $666.
$\frac{5}{6}$ of $666 = $555.

## MATHEMATICS MADE EASY

The following terms are commonly used in percentage:

The *base* (B) is the number of which the percent is taken. In the example, 33 is 50% of 66, the number 66 is the *base*.

The *rate* (R) is the number of hundredths of the base. In the example, 33 is .50 of 66, the decimal .50 is the *rate*.

The *percentage* (P) *is the product of the base and the rate.* P = B × R

For example:

(a) Find 25% of $75.
Multiply 25%, or .25 (R) by $75 (B)

```
    75
   .25
   ───
   375
  150
  ─────
  18.75
```
Answer, $18.75

(b) Find ½% of $270.
½% = .005

```
    270
   .005
   ─────
   1.350
```
Answer, $1.35

*The rate equals the percentage divided by the base.* R = P ÷ B

What percent of $97 is $6.79?
Divide $6.79 (P) by $97 (B)

```
      .07
   97)6.79
      6 79
```
Answer, .07, or 7%

## EXERCISE 41

Find the rate. What percent of

(a) 135 is 54?
(b) 384 is 64?
(c) 8640 is 1080?
(d) .125 is .05?
(e) .02 is .0075?
(f) 13½ is 2 7/10?
(g) 36720 is 73.44?
(h) 162.5 is 48.75?
(i) 82 is 143.5?
(j) 279 is 139.5?
(k) 63 is 28?
(l) 567 is 378?
(m) 648 is 243?
(n) 756 is 441?
(o) 972 is 405?
(p) .108 is 675?

# PERCENTAGE

(q) 1134 is 252?
(r) 1296 is 810?
(s) 3456 is 1512?
(t) .1215 is .04374?

*The base equals the percentage divided by the rate.*  $B = P \div R.$

$135 is 15% of what number?
Divide $135 (P) ÷ .15 (R)

```
         9 00
   .15)135.00
       135
```
Answer, $900

## EXERCISE 42

Find the base. Find the number of which

(a) 270 is 15%.
(b) 348 is 60%.
(c) 44 is $66\frac{2}{3}$%.
(d) 40 is $12\frac{1}{2}$%.
(e) 60 is 75%.
(f) 320 is 125%.
(g) 48 is $133\frac{1}{3}$%.
(h) 5.84 is $87\frac{1}{2}$%.
(i) 108 is $6\frac{1}{4}$%.
(j) 360 is 40%.
(k) 195 is $62\frac{1}{2}$%.
(l) 208 is $57\frac{1}{4}$%.
(m) 96 is $44\frac{4}{9}$%.
(n) 40 is $\frac{1}{6}$%.
(o) 97.2 is 12%.
(p) 235.647 is 9%.
(q) 1842.61 is 11%.
(r) 82,404 is 108%.
(s) .98742 is 6%.
(t) .18 is $\frac{1}{2}$%.

## FIGURING THE PERCENTAGE OF YOUR BANK BALANCE

Suppose, at the beginning of the year you have a bank balance of $5000, and at the end of the year you have a bank balance of $4500. By what percent has your balance decreased?

$5000—$4500 = $500
$500 is what percent of $5000?

Using our formula, we divide the percentage by the base to get the rate $(P \div B = R)$:

500 ÷ 5000 = .10, or 10%     Answer, decrease of 10%.

Suppose, at the beginning of the year you have $5000, and at the end of the year you have $5600. By what percent has your balance increased?

$5600—$5000 = $600
$600 is what percent of $5000?
600 ÷ 5000 = .12, or 12%     Answer, increase of 12%.

## EXERCISE 43

Each of twenty men started the year with a bank balance of $4500. At the end of the year they had the amounts listed below. Name the percent of $4500 by which the balance was increased or decreased.

For example: One man's balance at the end of the year is $2250. Answer: Decrease of 50%.

(a) $5400
(b) $4000
(c) $4200
(d) $4725
(e) $4320
(f) $1125
(g) $1500
(h) $4218.75
(i) $750
(j) $5062.50
(k) $4365
(l) $4515
(m) $0.90
(n) $30
(o) $13,725
(p) $9900
(q) $4140
(r) $1687.50
(s) $562.50
(t) $375

### GENERAL PROBLEMS IN PERCENTAGE

Let us now look at the following three types of problems:

1. A store keeper buys a dozen pairs of shoes for $32 and sells them at a $12\frac{1}{2}\%$ profit. How much does he get for them?

In other words, what is 32 increased by $12\frac{1}{2}\%$ of itself?

$$B \times R = P$$
$$\$32 \times .12\frac{1}{2} = \$4$$
$$\$32 + \$4 = \$36 \qquad \text{Answer, } \$36$$

2. A store keeper sells a radio for $253, and makes a profit of 10% on the transaction. What did he pay for the radio?

In other words, what number increased by 10% of itself is $253?

The missing number is the base, or 100%. When we increase it by 10%, we get 100%+10%, or 110% of the missing number. The rate, therefore, is 110%.

$$? \times 110\% = \$253$$
$$? \times 1.10 = \$253$$

To get the missing number, you divide 253 by 1.10, or 1.1 (just as in proving a multiplication, you divide the product by the multiplier to get the multiplicand).

$$\$253 \div 1.1 = \$230 \qquad \text{Answer, } \$230.$$

## PERCENTAGE

3. A man sells his automobile for $840. He loses 25% on the transaction. How much did he pay for his automobile originally?

In other words, what number decreased by 25% is $840?

The missing number is the base, or 100%. When we decrease it by 25%, we get 75% of the missing number. The rate, therefore, is 75%.

$$? \times 75\% = \$840$$
$$? \times \tfrac{3}{4} = \$840$$
$$\$840 \div \tfrac{3}{4} = \$1120 \qquad \text{Answer, } \$1120.$$

### EXERCISE 44

What is

(a) 48 increased by $12\tfrac{1}{2}\%$ of itself?
(b) 42 increased by $33\tfrac{1}{3}\%$ of itself?
(c) 99 increased by $11\tfrac{1}{9}\%$ of itself?
(d) 31 increased by 7% of itself?
(e) .043 increased by 26% of itself?
(f) 35 decreased by $42\tfrac{6}{7}\%$ of itself?
(g) 88 decreased by $72\tfrac{8}{11}\%$ of itself?
(h) .24 decreased by $66\tfrac{2}{3}\%$ of itself?
(i) 4.7 decreased by 13% of itself?
(j) 532 decreased by 19% of itself?

### EXERCISE 45

What number increased by

(a) 10% of itself is 352?
(b) 25% of itself is 800?
(c) $33\tfrac{1}{3}\%$ of itself is 120?
(d) $62\tfrac{1}{2}\%$ of itself is 169?
(e) $87\tfrac{1}{2}\%$ of itself is 120?
(f) 6% of itself is 477?
(g) 8% of itself is 1.944?
(h) $3\tfrac{1}{2}\%$ of itself is 16.767?
(i) 17% of itself is .2106?
(j) 23% of itself is 296.43?

### EXERCISE 46

What number decreased by

(a) $12\tfrac{1}{2}\%$ of itself is 196?
(b) $37\tfrac{1}{2}\%$ of itself is 400?
(c) $83\tfrac{1}{3}\%$ of itself is 35?
(d) $6\tfrac{1}{4}\%$ of itself is 480?
(e) $11\tfrac{1}{9}\%$ of itself is 720?
(f) $14\tfrac{2}{7}\%$ of itself is 42?
(g) 7% of itself is 16.74?
(h) 9% of itself is 245.7?
(i) $4\tfrac{1}{2}\%$ of itself is 9550?
(j) 18% of itself is 2.46?

# MATHEMATICS MADE EASY

## ANSWERS
### EXERCISE 38

(a) 18%  (b) 93%  (c) 80%  (d) $6\frac{1}{4}$%  (e) 60%
(f) $\frac{6}{10}$%  (g) $66\frac{2}{3}$%  (h) $83\frac{1}{3}$%  (i) $62\frac{1}{2}$%  (j) 50%
(k) $12\frac{1}{2}$%  (l) 75%  (m) 8%  (n) $16\frac{2}{3}$%  (o) 10%
(p) $87\frac{1}{2}$%  (q) 80%  (r) 70%  (s) 25%  (t) 5%

### EXERCISE 39

(a) .71  (b) .04  (c) .375  (d) $.66\frac{2}{3}$  (e) .10
(f) .007  (g) .005  (h) .0009  (i) .015  (j) .00125
(k) .000625  (l) $.006\frac{2}{3}$  (m) .0125  (n) 2.5  (o) .8
(p) 1.25  (q) .0036  (r) .35  (r) .25  (t) 1.1

### EXERCISE 40

1. (f)   2. (i)   3. (k)   4. (l)   5. (o)   6. (a)   7. (s)
8. (q)   9. (b)   10. (m)  11. (c)  12. (t)  13. (e)  14. (r)
15. (d)  16. (g)  17. (n)  18. (h)  19. (p)  20. (j)

### EXERCISE 41

(a) 40%  (b) $16\frac{2}{3}$%  (c) $12\frac{1}{2}$%  (d) 40%  (e) $37\frac{1}{2}$%
(f) 20%  (g) 2%  (h) 30%  (i) 175%  (j) 50%
(k) $44\frac{4}{9}$%  (l) $66\frac{2}{3}$%  (m) $37\frac{1}{2}$%  (n) $58\frac{1}{3}$%  (o) $41\frac{2}{3}$%
(p) 6250%  (q) $22\frac{2}{9}$%  (r) $62\frac{1}{2}$%  (s) $43\frac{3}{4}$%  (t) 36%

### EXERCISE 42

(a) 1800  (b) 580  (c) 66  (d) 320  (e) 80
(f) 256  (g) 36  (h) $6.64  (i) 1728  (j) 900
(k) 312  (l) 364  (m) 216  (n) 24,000  (o) 810
(p) 2618.3  (q) 16,751  (r) 76,300  (s) 16.457  (t) 36

### EXERCISE 43

(a) Increase of 20%.
(b) Decrease of $11\frac{1}{9}$%.
(c) Decrease of $6\frac{2}{3}$%.
(d) Increase of 5%.
(e) Decrease of 4%.
(f) Decrease of 75%.
(g) Decrease of $66\frac{2}{3}$%.
(h) Decrease of $6\frac{1}{4}$%.
(i) Decrease of $83\frac{1}{3}$%.
(j) Increase of $12\frac{1}{2}$%.
(k) Decrease of 3%.
(l) Increase of $\frac{1}{3}$%.
(m) Decrease of 99.98%.
(n) Decrease of $99\frac{1}{3}$%.
(o) Increase of 205%.
(p) Increase of 120%.
(q) Decrease of 8%.
(r) Decrease of $62\frac{1}{2}$%.
(s) Decrease of $87\frac{1}{2}$%.
(t) Decrease of $91\frac{2}{3}$%.

### EXERCISE 44

(a) 54  (b) 56  (c) 110  (d) 33.17  (e) .05418
(f) 20  (g) 24  (h) .08  (i) 4.089  (j) 430.92

### EXERCISE 45

(a) 320  (b) 640  (c) 90  (d) 104  (e) 64
(f) 450  (g) 1.8  (h) 16.2  (i) .18  (j) 241

### EXERCISE 46

(a) 224  (b) 640  (c) 210  (d) 512  (e) 810
(f) 49  (g) 18  (h) 270  (i) 10,000  (j) 3

## CHAPTER IX
# Measures and Weights

### A. MEASURES

IN OUR EVERYDAY EXPERIENCES, we frequently find it necessary to refer to various measures of space, time and material. The following tables will be found helpful in the rapid calculation of the more common measurements:

*Linear Measure*

| | |
|---|---|
| 12 inches (in.) | = 1 foot (ft.) |
| 3 feet | = 1 yard (yd.) |
| $5\frac{1}{2}$ yards | = 1 rod (rd.) |
| 320 rods } | |
| 1760 yards } | = 1 mile (mi.) |
| 5280 feet } | |

A *hand* (4 in.) is used in measuring the height of a horse; a *fathom* (6 ft.) is used in measuring the depth of water; and a *knot* (nautical mile, 6080.27 ft.) is used in measuring distances at sea.

*Square Measure*

| | |
|---|---|
| 144 square inches (sq. in.) | = 1 square foot (sq. ft.) |
| 9 square feet | = 1 square yard (sq. yd.) |
| $30\frac{1}{4}$ square yards | = 1 square rod (sq. rd.) |
| 160 square rods | = 1 acre (A) |
| 640 acres | = 1 square mile (sq. mi.) |

*Cubic Measure*

| | |
|---|---|
| 1728 cubic inches (cu. in.) | = 1 cubic foot (cu. ft.) |
| 27 cubic feet | = 1 cubic yard (cu. yd.) |
| 128 cubic feet | = 1 cord (cd.) |

A cord of wood is 8 ft. long, 4 ft. wide, and 4 ft. high.

*Liquid Measure*

| | |
|---|---|
| 4 gills (gi.) | = 1 pint (pt.) |
| 2 pints | = 1 quart (qt.) |
| 4 quarts | = 1 gallon (gal.) |

*Apothecaries' Liquid Measure*
(used by druggists and physicians)

60 minims (m.) = 1 fluid drachm (f ʒ)
8 fluid drachms = 1 fluid ounce (f ℥)
16 fluid ounces = 1 pint (O)
8 pints = 1 gallon (Cong.)

*Dry Measure*

2 pints = 1 quart
8 quarts = 1 peck (pk.)
4 pecks = 1 bushel (bu.)

## B. WEIGHTS

There are three kinds of weights used in business, in occupational, in professional and in private life. Jewelers use *Troy* weight; druggists and physicians use *Apothecaries'* weight; others use *Avoirdupois* weight.

*Troy Weight*

24 grains (gr.) = 1 pennyweight (pwt.)
20 pennyweights = 1 ounce (oz.)
12 ounces = 1 pound (lb.)
1 carat (K) = 3.168 grains

The carat is used to measure diamonds and gold. 1 K (1 carat) of gold means $\frac{1}{24}$ part. Thus, gold marked 14 K means that $\frac{14}{24}$ of the weight is pure gold and $\frac{10}{24}$ is an alloy, or baser metal.

*Apothecaries' Weight*
(used by druggists and physicians)

20 grains = 1 scruple (sc.)
3 scruples = 1 dram (dr.)
8 drams = 1 ounce
12 ounces = 1 pound

*Avoirdupois Weight*

16 ounces = 1 pound
100 pounds = 1 hundredweight (cwt.)
2000 pounds = 1 ton (T)
2240 pounds = 1 long ton

# MEASURES AND WEIGHTS

Coal is weighed at the mines by the long ton. The government uses the long ton system in computing the duty on goods taxable by the ton.

## REDUCTION OF WEIGHTS AND MEASURES

Suppose you want to add 5 pounds and 6 ounces, or 4 hours and 20 minutes, or 6 bushels and 2 quarts. Before you can do this, you must be able to reduce the units to *common lower denominations*, as follows:

5 lb. 6 oz. = (5×16 oz.)+6 oz. = 80 oz.+6 oz. = 86 oz.
4 hr. 20 min. = (4×60 min.)+20 min. = 240 min.+20 min. = 260 min.
6 bu. 2 qt. = (6×32 qt.)+2 qt. = 192 qt.+2 qt. = 194 qt.

Or else, you must be able to reduce the units to *common higher denominations*, as follows:

5 lb. 6 oz. = $5\frac{6}{16}$ lb. = $5\frac{3}{8}$ lb.
4 hr. 20 min. = $4\frac{20}{60}$ hr. = $4\frac{1}{3}$ hr.
6 bu. 2 qt. = $6\frac{2}{32}$ qt. = $6\frac{1}{16}$ qt.

Reduce 4 hours to seconds:

4 hr. = 4×60 min. = 240 min.
240 min. = 240×60 sec. = 14400 seconds.

Reduce 65 pints to higher denominations:

2)65 pt.
4)32 qt.....1 pt.
   8 gal...1 pt.                 Answer, 8 gal. 1 pt.

Reduce 106 inches to yards:

12)106 in.
  3)8 ft.....10 in.
     2 yd..2 ft.....10 in.        Answer, 2 yd. 2 ft. 10 in.

From the above examples, we note the following:

To reduce to *lower* units, from pounds to ounces, from hours to minutes, from yards to feet, etc., you *multiply*.

To reduce to *higher* units, from ounces to pounds, from minutes to hours, from feet to yards, etc., you *divide*.

## EXERCISE 47

Reduce:

(a) 45 ft. 9 in. to inches
(b) 62 rods to yards
(c) 48 rods to feet
(d) 25 miles to feet
(e) $62\frac{1}{2}$ miles to yards
(f) $6\frac{1}{4}$ miles to inches
(g) $6\frac{1}{2}$ hours to minutes
(h) $2\frac{1}{2}$ hours to seconds
(i) 30 days to hours
(j) 4 cu. yds. to cubic inches
(k) 20 cu. ft. to cu. inches
(l) 43 acres to square rods
(m) 32 sq. miles to acres
(n) 56 sq. rods to sq. yds.
(o) 19 sq. yds. to sq. inches
(p) 19 sq. miles to sq. rods
(q) 1 sq. mi. to sq. inches

## EXERCISE 48

Reduce to higher units:

(a) 108 inches to feet
(b) 972 inches to yards
(c) 35 feet to yards and feet
(d) 99 feet to rods
(e) 1000 inches to rods and inches
(f) 720 rods to miles and rods
(g) 10,000 cubic inches to cu. ft. and cu. in.
(h) 10,000 seconds to hours, minutes, and seconds
(i) 10,000 days to years and days
(j) 1,000,000 square yards to acres, sq. rods, and sq. yds.

## EXERCISE 49

Reduce:

(a) 17 lb. to oz.   (b) 18 T. to lb.   (c) 12 oz. (Troy) to pennyweights
(d) 8 lb. (Troy) to grains   (e) 3 T. to oz.   (f) 19 gal. to pts.
(g) 6 bbl. to qts.   (h) 9 bu. to pts.   (i) 17 pecks to pts.
(j) 7 qts. to pts.

## EXERCISE 50

Reduce to higher denominations:

(a) 196 oz. (av.)
(b) 3600 lb.
(c) 291 pwt.
(d) 10,000 gr.
(e) 196 oz. (Troy)
(f) 164 pts. (liquid)
(g) 164 pts. (dry)
(h) 19 pecks
(i) 27 qts. (liquid)
(j) 27 qts. (dry)

# MEASURES AND WEIGHTS

## ADDITION OF WEIGHTS AND MEASURES

Add:

3 hr. 54 min. 30 sec., 2 hr. 34 min. 23 sec., 6 hr. 36 min. 45 sec.

| hr. | min. | sec. |
|---|---|---|
| 3 | 54 | 30 |
| 2 | 34 | 23 |
| 6 | 36 | 45 |
| 13 | 5 | 38 |

First you add the seconds in the right hand column. The sum of the seconds is 98. This equals 1 minute, 38 seconds. You put down the 38 seconds and you carry the 1 minute over to the next column. Adding 1, 54, 34, and 36 minutes, you get 125 minutes. This equals 2 hours, 5 minutes. You put down the 5 minutes and you carry the 2 hours over to the next column. And now adding 2, 3, 2, and 6 hours, you get 13 hours. Your answer, therefore, is 13 hr. 5 min. 38 sec.

### EXERCISE 51

Add:

(a) 60 yds. 1 ft. 9 in.; 14 yds. 2 ft. 4 in.; 89 yds. 1 ft. 7 in.
(b) 16 mi. 159 rds. 3 yds.; 18 mi. 211 rds. 4 yds.; 8 mi. 3 yds.
(c) 41 A. 121 sq. rods. 20 sq. yds.; 612 A. 19 sq. yds.; 18 sq. rods. 27 sq. yds.
(d) 16 cu. ft. 1522 cu. in.; 19 cu. ft. 103 cu. in.; 21. cu. ft. 495 cu. in.
(e) 21 hrs. 48 min. 53 sec.; 18 hrs. 35 min. 54 sec.; 9 hrs. 34 min. 42 sec.

### EXERCISE 52

Add:

(a) 2 T. 5 cwt. 16 lb.; 1 T. 9 cwt. 93 lb.; 5 T. 13 cwt. 75 lb.
(b) 19 lb. 14 oz.; 18 lb. 13 oz.; 21 lb. 15 oz.; 12 lb. 11 oz.
(c) 3 T. 6 cwt. 17 lb. 5 oz.; 2 T. 19 lb. 15 oz.; 9 T. 14 oz.
(d) 3 lb. (Troy) 9 oz. 18 pwt.; 4 lb. 11 oz. 5 pwt.; 2 lb. 3 oz. 17 pwt.
(e) 17 pwt. 19 gr.; 10 oz. 18 pwt. 21 gr.; 11 oz. 16 pwt. 23 gr.
(f) 3 lb. (Troy) 8 oz. 17 pwt.; 5 lb. 5 pwt.; 8 pwt. 19 gr.; 3 lb. 9 gr.
(g) 3 bbl. 18 gal. 3 qt.; 1 bbl. 9 gal. 1 qt.; 2 bbl. 19 gal. 2 qt.
(h) 3 qts. 1 pt. 3 gi.; 2 qt. 1 pt. 2 gi.; 1 qt. 1 gi.
(i) 19 bu. 3 pk. 7 qt.; 17 bu. 2 pk. 5 qt.; 3 bu. 1 qt.
(j) 3 pk. 6 qt. 1 pt.; 1 pk. 1 pt.; 2 pk. 5 qt. 1 pt.

## SUBTRACTION OF WEIGHTS AND MEASURES
From 10 bu. 2 pk. 6 qt. subtract 3 bu. 3 pk. 7 qt.

| bu. | pk. | qt. |
|---|---|---|
| 10 | 2 | 6 |
| 3 | 3 | 7 |
| 6 | 2 | 7 |

You begin your subtraction with the right hand column. Since you cannot subtract 7 quarts from 6 quarts, you borrow 1 peck from the next column (leaving one peck), and you change the borrowed peck into 8 quarts. You now add the 8 quarts to the 6 quarts, and you get 14 quarts. 14 quarts—7 quarts = 7 quarts. Since you cannot subtract 3 pecks from 1 peck, you borrow 1 bushel from the next column (leaving 9 bushels), and you change the bushel into 4 pecks. Adding the 4 pecks to the 1 peck, you get 5 pecks. 5 pecks—3 pecks = 2 pecks. Finally, 9 bushels—3 bushels = 6 bushels. Your answer, therefore, is 6 bu. 2 pk. 7 qt.

### EXERCISE 53
Subtract:

(a) 39 yds. 1 ft. 3 in. — 26 yds. 2 ft. 9 in.
(b) 8 cu. yds. 16 cu. ft. 311 cu. in. — 6 cu. yds. 21 cu. ft. 951 cu. in.
(c) 13 mi. 412 A. 15 sq. rds. — 10 mi. 511 A. 122 sq. rds.
(d) 19 sq. yds. 4 sq. ft. 67 sq. in. — 16 sq. yds. 7 sq. ft. 112 sq. in.
(e) 19 hrs. 31 min. 42 sec. — 17 hrs. 58 min. 53 sec.

### EXERCISE 54
Subtract:

(a) 5 T. 3 cwt. 19 lb. 14 oz. — 2 T. 5 cwt. 27 lb. 15 oz.
(b) 9 lb. (Troy) 10 oz. 17 pwt. — 3 lb. 11 oz. 18 pwt. 17 gr.
(c) 3 bbl. 19 gal. 2 qt. 1 pt. — 1 bbl. 23 gal. 3 qt. 3 gi.
(d) 19 bu. 2 pk. 5 qt. 1 pt. — 16 bu. 3 pk. 7 qt.

## MULTIPLICATION OF WEIGHTS AND MEASURES
Multiply 4 ft. 6 in. by 7

| ft. | | in. |
|---|---|---|
| 4 | | 6 |
| | × | 7 |
| 31 | | 6 |

# MEASURES AND WEIGHTS

7×6 inches = 42 inches, or 3 feet 6 inches. Write down 6 inches, and carry over the 3 feet. Then 7×4 feet = 28 feet, +3 feet = 31 feet.

Answer, 31 ft. 6 in.

## EXERCISE 55

Multiply:

(a) 2 yds. 1 ft. 9 in. by 9
(b) 41 rd. 3 yds. 1 ft. 7 in. by 12
(c) 10 mi. 211 rd. 4 yd. by 7
(d) 5 sq. yds. 8 sq. ft. 56 sq. in. by 5
(e) 93 A. 43 sq. rds. 19 sq. yds. by 8
(f) 4 cu. yds. 17 cu. ft. 543 cu. in. by 7
(g) 19 cu. ft. 823 cu. in. by 11
(h) 8 sq. mi. 345 A. 93 sq. rds. by 7
(i) 2 days 13 hrs. 54 min. 12 sec. by 8
(j) 10 years 4 da. 19 hr. by 7

## EXERCISE 56

Multiply:

(a) 5 T. 3 cwt. 19 lb. 11 oz. by 9
(b) 2 lb. (Troy) 8 oz. 17 pwt. 18 gr. by 3
(c) 2 bbl. 19 gal. 3 qt. 1 pt. 3 gi. by 9
(d) 4 bu. 3 pk. 7 qt. 1 pt. by 5

## DIVISION OF WEIGHTS AND MEASURES

### A

*Division of a Weight or a Measure by an Abstract Number*

Divide 2 hr. 6 min. 30 sec. by 5

```
      hr.    min.    sec.
   5)2       6       30
            25       18
```

You begin with the left hand column. Since you cannot divide 2 hours by 5, you change the 2 hours to 120 minutes, and add them to the second column. 120 minutes + 6 minutes = 126 minutes. Divide 126 minutes by 5, and you get 25 minutes, with a remainder of 1 minute. Change this 1 minute to 60 seconds and add them to the third column. 60 seconds + 30 seconds = 90 seconds. Divide this by 5, and you have 18 seconds.

Answer, 25 min. 18 sec.

## B
*Division of One Weight or Measure by Another Weight or Measure*

Divide 21 ft. 4 in. by 5 ft. 4 in.

Reduce both numbers to the same denomination, either to feet or to inches.

(a) Reduce to feet:

21 ft. 4 in. = $21\frac{1}{3}$ ft.
5 ft. 4 in. = $5\frac{1}{3}$ ft.

$21\frac{1}{3}$ ft. $\div 5\frac{1}{3}$ ft. $= \dfrac{\cancel{64}^{4}}{\cancel{3}} \times \dfrac{\cancel{3}}{\cancel{16}} = 4$

(b) Reduce to inches:

21 ft. 4 in. = 256 in.
5 ft. 4 in. = 64 in.
256 in. ÷ 64 in. = 4

### EXERCISE 57

Divide:

(a) 10 ft. 8 in. by 4
(b) 10 mi. 16 rds. 5 yds. by 3
(c) 10 A. 19 sq. rds. 18 sq. yds. by 4
(d) 4 cu. yds. 5 cu. ft. 128 cu. in. by 8
(e) 15 hrs. 33 min. 53 sec. by 7
(f) 32 ft. 9 in. by 6 in.
(g) 8 mi. 100 rds. by 10 rds.
(h) 15 A. 16 sq. rds. by 8 sq. rds.
(i) 10 cu. yds. by 12 cu. ft.

### EXERCISE 58

Divide:

(a) 9 T. 7 cwt. 17 lb. 13 oz. by 7
(b) 17 T. 19 cwt. 18 lb. 8 oz. by 12 oz.
(c) 3 lb. 10 oz. 18 pwt. 11 gr. by 3
(d) 5 lb. 11 oz. 17 pwt. 10 gr. by 20 gr.
(e) 2 bbl. 20 gal. 3 qt. 1 pt. 3 gi. by 4
(f) 4 bbl. 18 gal. 2 qt. 1 pt. 3 gi. by 5 gi.
(g) 5 bu. 2 pk. 6 qt. 1 pt. by 7
(h) 4 bu. 3 pk. 7 qt. 1 pt. by 2 qt.

## MEASURES AND WEIGHTS

### EXERCISE 59
*Problems*

1. A fence is to be $\frac{5}{8}$ of a mile long. How many boards 10 ft. long will be needed if the fence is 5 boards high?
2. A field is to be fenced with barbed wire. If the field is 13 rd. 1 yd. 1 ft. long and 6 rd. 2 yd. 2 ft. wide, how much barbed wire will be needed for a fence which is two wires high?
3. A field containing 10 A. 32 sq. rds. is to be divided into lots of 16 sq. rds. How many lots can be obtained?
4. How many hours were there in the month of March, 1939?
5. A man received $5 per day for every week day during February, 1939. What was his total pay for the month?
6. If an automobile travels 18 miles in 30 minutes, how long does it take for it to travel a mile?
7. If a man walks at the rate of a mile in 16 minutes, how far will he walk in 2 hours?
8. If a man takes 80 steps of $2\frac{1}{2}$ feet in a minute, how long will it take him to walk 3 miles?
9. A floor space of 286 sq. ft. is to be covered with tiles of 16 sq. in. How many tiles will be needed?
10. How many packages of 9 cu. in. can you make from a cubic foot of ice cream?

### EXERCISE 60
*Problems*

1. The avoirdupois pound is how many times as heavy as the troy pound?
2. Express 10 lb. avoirdupois in terms of troy pounds.
3. If a cubic foot of jack pine wood weighs 50 lb., how many cubic feet will there be in a ton?
4. If ivory weighs $.0694\frac{4}{9}$ lb. per cu. in., how much will a cu. ft. weigh?
5. A cubic foot of water weighs $62\frac{1}{2}$ lb. How many ounces does a cubic inch of water weigh?
6. Which is heavier, a pound of iron or a pound of gold?

## ANSWERS

### EXERCISE 47

(a) 549 inches  (b) 341 yards  (c) 792 feet  (d) 132,000 feet  (e) 110,000 yards
(f) 398,000 in.  (g) 390 min.  (h) 9000 sec.  (i) 720 hours  (j) 186,624 cu. in.
(k) 34,560 cu. in.  (l) 6880 square rods  (m) 20,480 acres  (n) 1694 sq. yards
(o) 11,664 sq. inches  (p) 1,945,600 square rods  (q) 4,014,489,600 square inches

### EXERCISE 48

(a) 9 feet  (b) 27 yards  (c) 11 yards 2 feet  (d) 6 rods
(e) 5 rods, 10 in.  (f) 2 mi. 80 rods  (g) 5 cu. ft. 1360 cu. inches
(h) 2 hours, 46 min., 4 seconds  (i) 27 years, 145 days
(j) 206 acres, 97 square rods, 103 square yards.

### EXERCISE 49

(a) 282 oz.  (b) 36,000 lb.  (c) 240 pwt.  (d) 46,080 gr.
(e) 96,000 oz.  (f) 152 pts.  (g) 756 qts.  (h) 576 pts.
(i) 282 pts.  (j) 14 pts.

### EXERCISE 50

(a) 12 lb. 4 oz.  (b) 1 T. 16 cwt.  (c) 1 lb. 2 oz. 11 pwt.
(d) 1 lb. 8 oz. 16 pwt. 16 gr.  (e) 16 lb. 4 oz.
(f) 20 gal. 2 qts.  (g) 2 bu. 2 pks. 2 qts.  (h) 4 bu. 3 pks.
(i) 6 gal. 3 qts.  (j) 3 pks. 3 qts.

### EXERCISE 51

(a) 165 yds. (or 30 rods) 1 ft. 8 in.  (b) 43 mi. 51 rds. $4\frac{1}{2}$ yds.
(c) 1 sq. mi. 140 sq. rds. $25\frac{3}{4}$ sq. yds.  (d) 2 cu. yds. 3 cu. ft. 392 cu. in.
(e) 2 days, 1 hr. 59 min. 29 sec.

### EXERCISE 52

(a) 9 T. 8 cwt. 84 lb.  (f) 11 lb. 9 oz. 11 pwt. 4 gr.
(b) 73 lb. 5 oz.  (g) 7 bbl. 16 qt.
(c) 14 T. 6 cwt. 38 lb. 2 oz.  (h) 1 gal. 2 qt. 1 pt. 2 gi.
(d) 11 lb. 1 oz.  (i) 40 bu. 2 pk. 5 qt.
(e) 1 lb. 11 oz. 13 pwt. 15 gr.  (j) 1 bu. 3 pk. 4 qt. 1 pt.

### EXERCISE 53

(a) 12 yds. 1 ft. 6 in.  (b) 1 cu. yd. 21 cu. ft. 1088 cu. in.
(c) 2 mi. 540 A. 53 sq. rds.  (d) 2 sq. yds. 5 sq. ft. 99 sq. in.
(e) 1 hr. 32 min. 49 sec.

### EXERCISE 54

(a) 2 T. 17 cwt. 91 lb. 15 oz.  (c) 1 bbl. 27 gal. 1 qt. 2 gi.
(b) 5 lb. 10 oz. 18 pwt. 7 gr.  (d) 2 bu. 2 pk. 6 qt. 1 pt.

### EXERCISE 55

(a) 4 rds. 1 yd. 9 in.  (b) 1 mi. 179 rds. 3 yds. 2 ft. 6 in.
(c) 74 mi. 282 rds. 1 ft. 6 in.  (d) 29 sq. yds. 5 sq. ft. 136 sq. in.
(e) 1 sq. mi. 106 A. 29 sq. rds. 6 sq. ft. 108 sq. in.
(f) 32 cu. yds. 13 cu. ft. 345 cu. in.  (g) 7 cu. yds. 25 cu. ft. 413 cu. in.
(h) 59 mi. 499 A. 11 sq. rds.  (i) 2 weeks 6 da. 15 hrs. 13 min. 36 sec.
(j) 70 yrs. 4 wks. 5 da. 13 hrs.

# MEASURES AND WEIGHTS

### EXERCISE 56

(a) 46 T. 8 cwt. 77 lb. 3 oz.
(b) 8 lb. 2 oz. 13 pwt. 6 gr.
(c) 23 bbl. 22 gal. 1 pt. 3 gi.
(d) 24 bu. 3 pk. 5 qt. 1 pt.

### EXERCISE 57

(a) 2 ft. 8 in.
(b) 3 mi. 112 rds. $1\frac{2}{3}$ yds.
(c) 2 A. 44 sq. rds. 27 sq. yds. 1 sq. ft. 99 sq. in.
(d) 14 cu. ft. 232 cu. in.
(e) 2 hrs. 13 min. $24\frac{5}{7}$ sec.
(f) $65\frac{1}{2}$  (g) 42  (h) 22  (i) $22\frac{1}{2}$

### EXERCISE 58

(a) 1 T. 6 cwt. 73 lb. $15\frac{4}{9}$ oz.
(b) $7091\frac{1}{3}$
(c) 1 lb. 3 oz. 12 pwt. $19\frac{2}{3}$ gr.
(d) 1724.9
(e) 20 gal. 3 qt. 1 pt. $3\frac{3}{4}$ gi.
(f) 926.2
(g) 3 pk. 2 qt. $\frac{1}{2}$ pt.
(h) 79.25

### EXERCISE 59

#### SOLUTION TO PROBLEM 1

$\frac{5}{8}$ of 5280 ft. = 3300 ft., length of space to be covered by fence.
Since fence is to be 5 boards high, total space to be covered by fence = 3300×5, or 16,500 ft.
Since each board is 10 ft. long, the number of boards needed for fence is 16,500 ft. ÷ 10 ft., or 1650.

2. 39 rd. 2 yd. 1 ft. 6 in.  3. 102  4. 744  5. $120  6. 1 min. 40 sec.
7. $7\frac{1}{2}$ miles  8. 79 min. 12 sec.  9. 2574  10. 192

### EXERCISE 60

1. $1.2152\frac{7}{8}$  2. $12.152\frac{7}{8}$ lb.  3. 40 cubic feet.
4. 120 lb.  5. $.5786\frac{11}{24}$ oz.  6. A pound of iron. Iron is weighed in avoirdupois pounds; gold, in troy pounds.

## CHAPTER X
## Short-Cuts

WE HAVE already considered, in our earlier chapters, some of the practical time-savers in calculation. This chapter contains a number of other short-cuts that will insure greater speed and accuracy in your everyday computations. Remember, time is money. A short-cut to computation is a short-cut to success.

### SHORT-CUTS IN ADDITION

(a) When four columns are to be added, proceed as follows:

```
  1452
  2748
  9345
  3246
  4753
 ────
   21
  544
 ────
21544
```

Start adding with the left hand column from the bottom to the top, 4+3+9+2+1=19. Take the 19 and *annex* it (don't add it) to the top figure in the next column. This will give you 194. Now add this column from the top to the bottom, 194+7+3+2+7=213. Write down at the bottom the first two figures of this sum, 21, and annex the 3 to the bottom of the next column. This will give you 35. Now add this column up to the top, 35+4+4+4+5=52. Annex this 52 to the top figure of the next column. This will give you 522. Now add this column down to the bottom, 522+8+5+6+3=544. Write this down at the bottom, *one figure to the right of the 21.* Then add the two figures,

```
   21
  544
 ────
21544
```

## SHORT-CUTS

(b) When five columns are to be added, proceed as follows:

```
  25623
  37498
  42356
  17694
  53672
  ─────
  17
    68
      43
  ──────
  176843
```

Start, as in example a, with the left hand column, adding from the bottom to the top, $5+1+4+3+2=15$. Annex this to the top figure in the next column, and add down from the top to the bottom, $155+7+2+7+3=174$. Write down 17 at the bottom, annex the 4 to the bottom figure of the next column, and add up, $46+6+3+4+6=65$. Annex this to the top figure of the next column and add down, $652+9+5+9+7=682$. Write down the 68 at the bottom, one figure to the right of 17. Now annex the 2 to the bottom of the last column and add up, $22+4+6+8+3=43$. Write down the 43 at the bottom, one figure to the right of 68, add the three figures, and you have the answer, 176,843.

### EXERCISE 61

Add by left hand addition:

| 1. 7838 | 2. 9798 | 3. 2838 | 4. 8777 |
|---|---|---|---|
| 9927 | 8988 | 6495 | 3474 |
| 4126 | 7867 | 7372 | 5578 |
| 6819 | 1799 | 3996 | 3194 |
|  |  | 4547 | 5944 |
|  |  | 3888 | 7888 |
|  |  | 9667 | 5528 |
|  |  | 5264 | 9268 |

| 5. 9328 | 6. 8177 | 7. 4924 | 8. 1668 |
|---|---|---|---|
| 6422 | 6383 | 3868 | 4611 |
| 5388 | 5244 | 5583 | 8316 |
| 9638 | 6833 | 9977 | 9994 |
| 5563 | 6558 | 4844 | 5073 |
| 5937 | 8786 | 5866 | 2777 |
| 9286 | 9888 | 8863 | 3033 |
| 4270 | 9236 | 4236 | 8677 |
|  |  | 4661 | 2775 |
|  |  | 5693 | 4432 |

## MATHEMATICS MADE EASY

|  | 9. 47859 |  | 10. 44970 |
|---|---|---|---|
|  | 36980 |  | 58468 |
|  | 58538 |  | 93556 |
|  | 86937 |  | 64294 |
|  | 51295 |  | 92852 |
|  | 88726 |  | 86261 |
|  | 96674 |  | 46883 |
|  | 74622 |  | 27465 |
|  | 59453 |  | 15667 |
|  | 77881 |  | 50889 |

## SHORT-CUTS IN SUBTRACTION
### A
### Subtraction by Ciphers

|  (a) | (b) |
|---|---|
| 65672 | 65672+16=65688 |
| —49984 | —49984+16=50000 |
| 15688 | 15688 |

Add to the minuend and to the subtrahend a number which, by such addition, will make the subtrahend end in ciphers. It is then an easy matter to do your subtraction.

### EXERCISE 62

Subtract by adding enough to the subtrahend to make it end in ciphers—and the same amount to the minuend:

1. 7264
  —6498

2. 8727
  —3469

3. 7872
  —4596

4. 34567
  —19968

5. 72864
  —69984

6. 93664
  —59997

7. 88888
  —44429*

8. 64322
  —49898

9. 729,684
  —399,846

10. 978,531
  —899,946

### B
### Subtraction in Couples

|  (a) | (b) |
|---|---|
| 928476 | 96 86 77 |
| —367859 | —40 80 60 |
| 560617 | 56 06 17 |

*In this case, 15 is added to the subtrahend, leaving an easy remainder. When this is written down, 15 is added to it, thus making up for the other addition.

Add such numbers to the couples as will make the subtrahends end in ciphers. In the above example, you add 4 to the left hand couple, 2 to the middle couple, and 1 to the right hand couple.

## EXERCISE 63
### Subtract in Couples

1.  645866
    —482957

2.  825140
    —674637

3.  978675
    —385769

4.  96734538
    —48783619

5.  10,000,000
    — 8,060,409

## SHORT-CUTS IN MULTIPLICATION
### A
#### Multiplying in the "Teens"

When you multiply in the "teens"—that is, by any number between 12 and 20—proceed as follows:

(A) Multiply the figures of the multiplicand, from right to left, by the right hand figure of the multiplier. (B) If there is anything to carry, add it to the next product, and (C) add also to each product the figure of the multiplicand on the right of the figure multiplied. (D) Put down the right hand figure of the product in each case, and (E) carry the left hand figure if there is one. (F) When you have multiplied the last figure and put down the right hand figure of the product, add this last figure to the last figure carried. This will give you the final figure of the product.

Note the two following examples:

1. Multiply 19 by 18

    19
    ×18
    ―――
    342

   A. $8 \times 9 = 72$.
   B. Put down 2 and carry 7 to be added to the next product.
   C. $8 \times 1 = 8$; $8 + 7 + 9 = 24$.
   D. Put down 4.
   E. Carry 2.
   F. $1 + 2 = 3$.                Answer, 342.

2. Multiply 245 by 17

```
  245
 ×17
 ————
 4165
```

7×5=35.   Put down 5 and carry 3.
7×4=28; 28+3+5=36.   Put down 6 and carry 3.
7×2=14; 14+3+4=21.   Put down 1 and carry 2.
2+2=4.                         Answer, 4165.

## EXERCISE 64

Multiply the following, using the special method for numbers in the "teens":

| | | | |
|---|---|---|---|
| 1. 19 by 19 | 2. 18 by 18 | 3. 19 by 17 | 4. 17 by 16 |
| 5. 18 by 17 | 6. 19 by 14 | 7. 18 by 13 | 8. 19 by 12 |
| 9. 18 by 16 | 10. 17 by 15 | 11. 16 by 14 | 12. 18 by 15 |
| 13. 19 by 13 | 14. 17 by 14 | 15. 16 by 13 | 16. 18 by 14 |
| 17. 19 by 16 | 18. 17 by 13 | 19. 19 by 15 | 20. 19 by 18 |

### B

### Multiplying Numbers with Similar Digits

Numbers of two digits, with the same figure in the tens places, such as 35 and 38, 42 and 47, 63 and 69, can be multiplied as follows:

A. Multiply the units together.
B. Add the units, multiply the sum by one of the tens digits, and annex a zero.
C. Multiply the tens digits together, and annex two zeros.
D. Add the three products together.

For example, multiply 62 by 68:

A. 2×8=16
B. 2+8=10; 10×6=60; annex a zero, and you get 600
C. 6×6=36; annex two zeros, and you get 3600
D. 16+600+3600=4216.

## EXERCISE 65

Multiply the following, using the special method for numbers with similar digits:

SHORT-CUTS

1. 39 by 37   2. 48 by 46   3. 59 by 54   4. 67 by 63
5. 74 by 76   6. 83 by 89   7. 92 by 97   8. 96 by 56
9. 84 by 74   10. 73 by 53  11. 92 by 42  12. 87 by 47
13. 66 by 46  14. 53 by 43  15. 89 by 79

C

### Multiplication by Factoring

1. Multiply 2345 by 18

    $2345 \times 18 = 2345 \times 2 \times 9$

    $2345 \times 2 = 4690$

    $4690 \times 9 = 42210$        Answer, 42,210

2. Multiply $652 \times 84$

    $652 \times 84 = 652 \times 2 \times 6 \times 7$

    $652 \times 2 = 1304$

    $1304 \times 6 = 7824$

    $7824 \times 7 = 54768$        Answer, 54,768

### EXERCISE 66

Multiply the following numbers by the factoring method:

1. 293 by 14   2. 384 by 27   3. 576 by 35   4. 667 by 28
5. 788 by 16   6. 394 by 36   7. 677 by 45   8. 485 by 18
9. 768 by 42   10. 879 by 32  11. 723 by 63  12. 495 by 22
13. 778 by 84  14. 586 by 49  15. 869 by 24  16. 687 by 56
17. 596 by 48  18. 192 by 64  19. 182 by 72  20. 476 by 54

D

### Complement Multiplication

The complement of a number, as we have seen, is the difference between that number and the next higher unit of 10 or of a power of 10. Thus, the complement of 94 is 6 (the difference between 94 and 100), the complement of 964 is 36 (the difference between 964 and 1000), and so on.

In the complement multiplication of two digit numbers, you proceed as follows:

1. You multiply the complements together.
2. You subtract the complement of one number from the other number, and you multiply the result by 100.
3. You add products 1 and 2.

Examples:

(a) 94×92

   1. 6×8=48
   2. 94—8=86; 86×100=8600
   3. 48+8600=8648.

(b) 88×89

   1. 12×11=132
   2. 88—11=77; 77×100=7700
   3. 132+7700=7832

In the complement multiplication of three digit numbers, you get the difference between the numbers and 1000, and you multiply the difference between the complement of one of the numbers and the other number by 1000. With four digits, you use 10,000 as your basic number; with five digits, 100,000; and so on.

Example:

938×984

   1. 62×16=992
   2. 938—16=922; 922×1000=922000
   3. 992+922000=922,992

## EXERCISE 67

Multiply the following, using the arithmetical complement method:

1. 92 by 94
2. 93 by 97
3. 996 by 987
4. 973 by 994
5. 977 by 993
6. 981 by 997
7. 9973 by 9986
8. 9977 by 9993
9. 9979 by 9986
10. 9981 by 9997
11. 9983 by 9985
12. 9821 by 9912
13. 9764 by 9873
14. 9791 by 9912
15. 9643 by 9872
16. 99,872 by 98,983
17. 99,734 by 99,887
18. 99,814 by 99,923
19. 999,896 by 999,523
20. 999,720 by 999,894

## SHORT-CUTS IN DIVISION
### A
#### Division by Factoring

(a) Divide 23652 by 108

$108 = 9 \times 12$
Hence $23652 \div 108 = 23652 \div 9 \div 12$

9)23652
12)2628
    219                          Answer, 219

(b) Divide 59400 by 198

$198 = 2 \times 9 \times 11$
Hence $59400 \div 198 = 59400 \div 2 \div 9 \div 11$

2)59400
9)29700
11)3300
    300                          Answer, 300

### EXERCISE 68
Divide by the factoring method:

1. 22561 by 77
2. 36540 by 84
3. 33102 by 63
4. 39600 by 99
5. 34692 by 147

### B
#### Divisibility of Numbers

Any number is divisible by 1.

Any even number is divisible by 2.

Any number is divisible by 3, if the sum of its digits is divisible by 3. Thus, 74529 is divisible by 3 because the sum of its digits, 27, is divisible by 3.

Any number is divisible by 4, if its last two digits are divisible by 4. Thus, 459236 is divisible by 4 because 36 is divisible by 4.

Any number is divisible by 5 if it ends in 5 or in 0.

Any even number divisible by 3 is divisible by 6.

Any number is divisible by 8, if its last 3 digits are divisible by 8. Thus, 379432 is divisible by 8 because 432 is divisible by 8.

Any number is divisible by 9, if the sum of its digits is divisible by 9. Thus, 4,356,738 is divisible by 9 because the sum of its digits, 36, is divisible by 9.

Any number ending in zero is divisible by 10.

Any number is divisible by 11 if the sum of its digits in the even places equals the sum of its digits in the odd places. Thus, 267,894 is divisible by 11, because the sum of its digits in the even places, 6+8+4, is equal to the sum of its digits in the odd places, 2+7+9.

A number is also divisible by 11 when the difference between the sum of the odd and the even digits is divisible by 11. Thus, 9,382,626 is divisible by 11 because 29 (9+8+6+6)−7 (3+2+2)=22, which is divisible by 11.

## ANSWERS
### EXERCISE 61

| | | | |
|---|---|---|---|
| 1. 28,710 | 2. 28,452 | 3. 43,967 | 4. 49,651 |
| 5. 55,832 | 6. 61,105 | 7. 58,515 | 8. 51,356 |
| 9. 678,965 | 10. 581,305 | | |

### EXERCISE 62

| | | | |
|---|---|---|---|
| 1. 766 | 2. 5258 | 3. 3276 | 4. 14,599 |
| 5. 2880 | 6. 33,667 | 7. 44,459 | 8. 14,424 |
| 9. 329,838 | 10. 78,585 | | |

### EXERCISE 63

| | | |
|---|---|---|
| 1. 162,909 | 2. 150,503 | 3. 592,906 |
| 4. 47,950,919 | 5. 1,939,591 | |

### EXERCISE 64

| | | | |
|---|---|---|---|
| 1. 361 | 2. 324 | 3. 323 | 4. 272 |
| 5. 306 | 6. 266 | 7. 234 | 8. 228 |
| 9. 288 | 10. 255 | 11. 224 | 12. 270 |
| 13. 247 | 14. 238 | 15. 208 | 16. 252 |
| 17. 304 | 18. 221 | 19. 285 | 20. 342 |

### EXERCISE 65

| | | | |
|---|---|---|---|
| 1. 1443 | 2. 2208 | 3. 3186 | 4. 4221 |
| 5. 5624 | 6. 7387 | 7. 8924 | 8. 5376 |
| 9. 6216 | 10. 3869 | 11. 3864 | 12. 4089 |
| 13. 3036 | 14. 2279 | 15. 7031 | |

## SHORT-CUTS

### EXERCISE 66

1. 4102
2. 10,368
3. 20,160
4. 18,676
5. 12,608
6. 14,184
7. 30,465
8. 8730
9. 32,256
10. 28,128
11. 45,549
12. 10,890
13. 65,352
14. 28,714
15. 20,856
16. 38,472
17. 28,608
18. 12,288
19. 13,104
20. 25,704

### EXERCISE 67

1. 8648
2. 9021
3. 903,052
4. 967,162
5. 970,161
6. 978,057
7. 99,590,378
8. 99,700,161
9. 99,650,294
10. 99,780,057
11. 99,680,255
12. 97,345,752
13. 96,399,972
14. 97,058,392
15. 95,195,696
16. 9,885,630,176
17. 9,962,130,058
18. 9,973,714,322
19. 999,419,049,608
20. 999,614,029,680

### EXERCISE 68

1. 293
2. 435
3. 524
4. 400
5. 236

# CHAPTER XI
# Graphs

A *graph* is a pictorial, or *graphical*, representation of statistics.

Thus, a pictorial way to show the comparative rainfall in a certain district from month to month is to draw a graph depicting a row of vertical glass tubes, one for each month, each of them "filled," or shaded, to a depth which represents the number of inches of rainfall for that month.

A similar graph can be drawn to depict a row of thermometers, each representing the average temperature for each month of the year.

For example, suppose the record shows the following monthly rainfall and average temperature for Massachusetts in a certain year:

| Month | Total Rainfall | Average Temperature |
|---|---|---|
| January | 4.5 inches | 22 degrees |
| February | 5.3 " | 21 " |
| March | 3.7 " | 29 " |
| April | 5.6 " | 36 " |
| May | 3.9 " | 44 " |
| June | 3.1 " | 62 " |
| July | 2.0 " | 74 " |
| August | 3.2 " | 80 " |
| September | 4.5 " | 75 " |
| October | 4.0 " | 60 " |
| November | 6.1 " | 40 " |
| December | 4.2 " | 25 " |

# GRAPHS

Graphically these statistics may be depicted as follows:

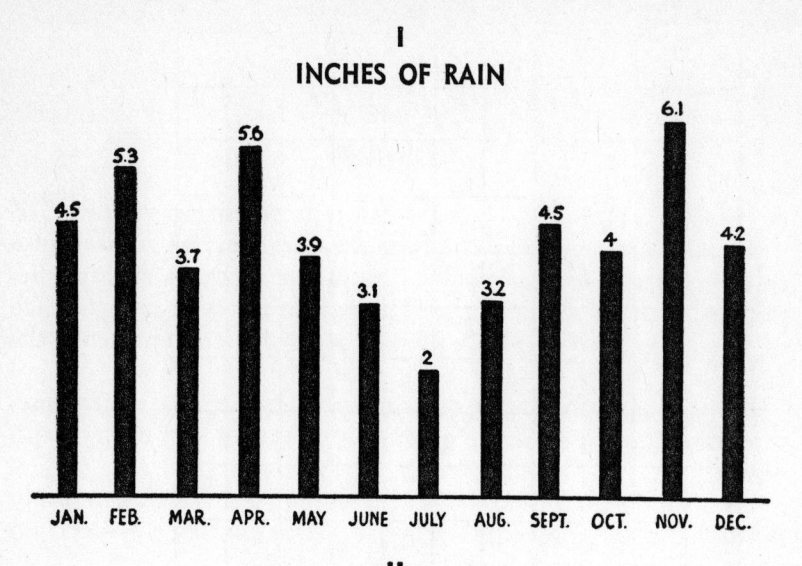

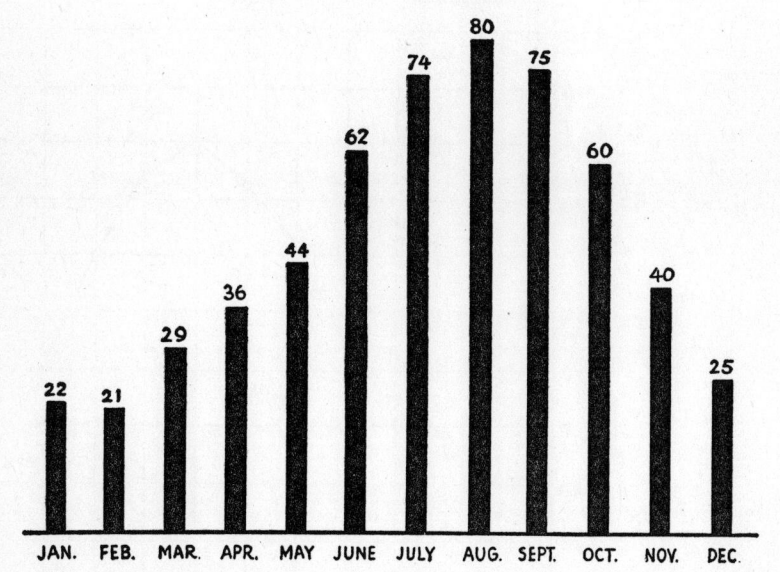

## I
### INCHES OF RAIN

| JAN. | FEB. | MAR. | APR. | MAY | JUNE | JULY | AUG. | SEPT. | OCT. | NOV. | DEC. |
|------|------|------|------|-----|------|------|------|-------|------|------|------|
| 4.5  | 5.3  | 3.7  | 5.6  | 3.9 | 3.1  | 2    | 3.2  | 4.5   | 4    | 6.1  | 4.2  |

## II
### DEGREES OF TEMPERATURE

| JAN. | FEB. | MAR. | APR. | MAY | JUNE | JULY | AUG. | SEPT. | OCT. | NOV. | DEC. |
|------|------|------|------|-----|------|------|------|-------|------|------|------|
| 22   | 21   | 29   | 36   | 44  | 62   | 74   | 80   | 75    | 60   | 40   | 25   |

72  MATHEMATICS MADE EASY

The foregoing graphs may be expressed by *curved*, instead of *vertical*, lines, as follows:

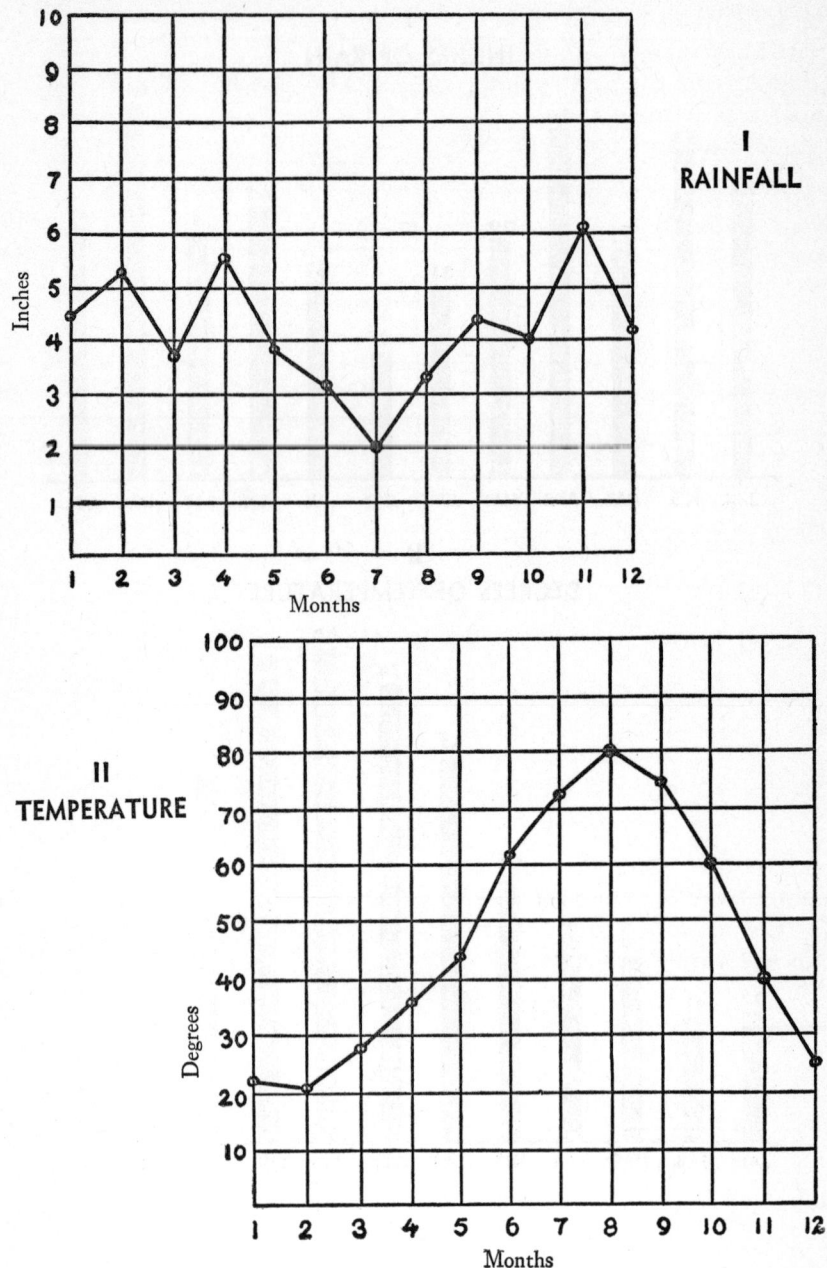

**I RAINFALL**

**II TEMPERATURE**

# GRAPHS

By using one and the same base for months, it is possible to represent *both* the rainfall and the temperature on a *single* graph. The rainfall will then be indicated by inches on the left-hand margin, and the temperature will be indicated by degrees on the right-hand margin. In the following graph, which illustrates this procedure, the rainfall curve is solid and the temperature curve is dotted.

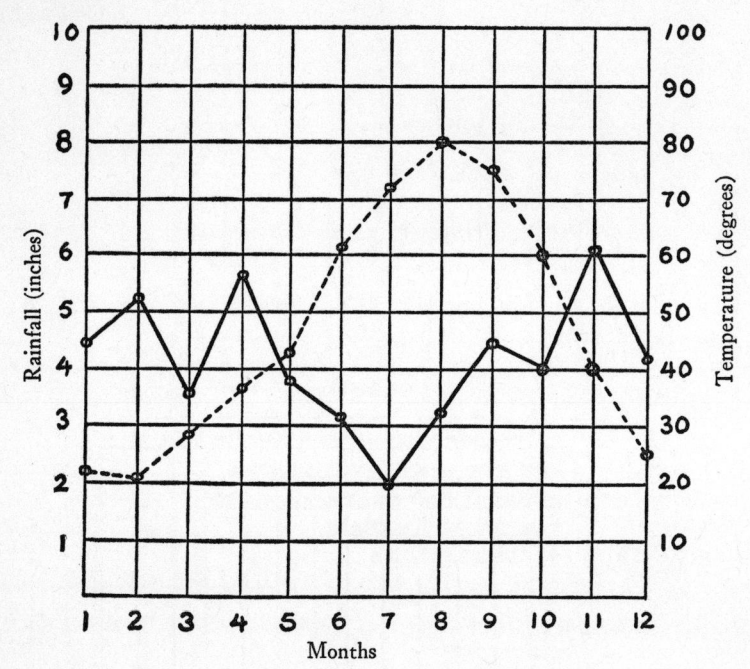

Another type of graph that is commonly used to represent statistics is that of the *horizontal bar*.

Let us, for example, consider the number of soldiers enlisted in the various countries during the World War of 1914–1918.

### Allies

| | |
|---|---|
| Russia . . . . . . . . | 12,000,000 |
| France . . . . . . . . | 8,400,000 |
| Great Britain . . . . . . | 8,900,000 |
| Italy . . . . . . . . | 5,600,000 |
| United States . . . . . . | 4,300,000 |

### Central Powers

| | |
|---|---|
| Germany | 11,000,000 |
| Austria-Hungary | 7,800,000 |
| Turkey | 2,800,000 |

This may be expressed in terms of millions, as follows:

### Allies

| | |
|---|---|
| Russia | 12 |
| France | 8.4 |
| Great Britain | 8.9 |
| Italy | 5.6 |
| United States | 4.3 |

### Central Powers

| | |
|---|---|
| Germany | 11 |
| Austria-Hungary | 7.8 |
| Turkey | 2.8 |

Represented by the horizontal bar graph, the statistics will appear as follows:

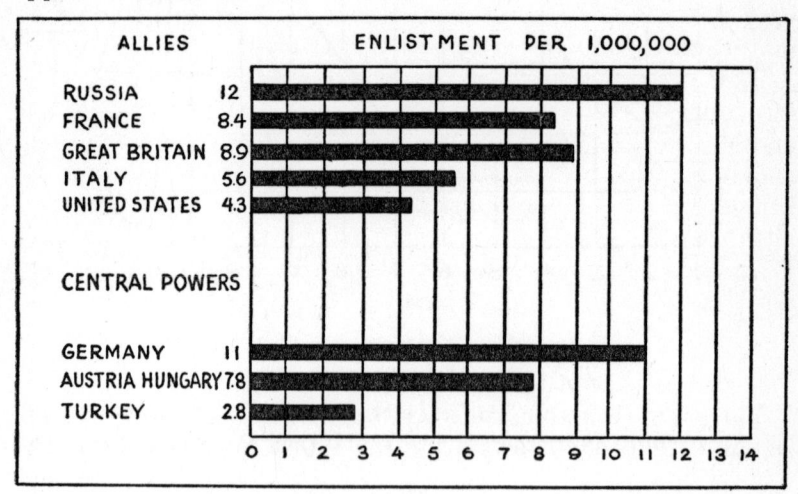

```
ALLIES              ENLISTMENT PER 1,000,000
RUSSIA         12
FRANCE         8.4
GREAT BRITAIN  8.9
ITALY          5.6
UNITED STATES  4.3

CENTRAL POWERS

GERMANY        11
AUSTRIA HUNGARY 7.8
TURKEY         2.8
              0 1 2 3 4 5 6 7 8 9 10 11 12 13 14
```

Nearly all other statistics may be reduced to similar simple graphs. It is rarely necessary to resort to graphs of a more complicated nature. Reduce your statistics to a simple group of figures, and the correct form of the graph will present itself to you without any trouble.

## CHAPTER XII
## Algebra

THE WORD *algebra*, from the Arabic *al-jabr*, means *the reunion of broken parts*. Algebra is a study of reunions. It is a *completion* of arithmetic.

Algebra not only *completes*, but *simplifies* arithmetic. Many a problem which would take considerable figuring by the arithmetic method, can be done in a few lines by the algebraic method. Algebra is like a tunnel cut through a mountain. It takes you to your destination by the shortest route.

And often, too, by the most *practical* route. Indeed, algebra may be said to be the most practical of the sciences. It is the very *foundation* of science. For the language of science is mathematics, and the grammar of mathematics is algebra.

Algebra is the basis of computation, invention, and construction. Chemists, physicists, architects, statisticians, civil and electrical and mechanical engineers, all depend upon their expert knowledge of algebra. Skyscrapers, steamships, roads, bridges, trains, automobiles, radios, telephones, airplanes—all these are built in accordance with algebraic formulae. Without algebra, our complex civilization today would be reduced to a state of primitive barbarism. Algebra is the handmaid of material progress.

### ALGEBRA VERSUS ARITHMETIC

There are three important differences between algebra and arithmetic:

1. In arithmetic we add, subtract, multiply, and divide *numbers*. In algebra we apply these operations not only to *numbers*, but to *letters* as well.

For example, in algebra we may say that a man walked 10 miles or $a$ miles, that he spent 50 dollars or $b$ dollars, that he is 62 years old or $x$ years old.

Again, in algebra we may say that 10 dollars is equal to $a$ times $b$ dollars, or that 25 years is equal to 5 times $c$ years. We would write these expressions as follows:

$10 = ab$
$25 = 5c$

(Note that when you multiply letters by letters, or numbers by letters, you omit the multiplication sign.)

Letters in algebra always represent numbers. The first letters of the alphabet (a, b, c, etc.) are generally used to express *known* quantities. The last letters of the alphabet (x, y, and z) are used to express *unknown* quantities. Algebra is the process of discovering the *unknown* quantities with the help of the *known* quantities.

2. The second important difference between algebra and arithmetic is this: In arithmetic there are *four* fundamental processes—addition, subtraction, multiplication, and division. In algebra there are *six* fundamental processes—addition, subtraction, multiplication, division, raising to powers, and extracting roots.

*Raising to powers.* When a number is multiplied by itself one or more times, it is raised to a power. If it is multiplied by itself once, it is squared, or raised to the 2nd power. If it is multiplied by itself twice, it is cubed, or raised to the 3d power. If it is multiplied by itself three times, it is raised to the 4th power, and so on. The power to which a number or a letter is raised is written in a smaller number in the upper right hand corner, thus:

$2 \times 2 = 2^2 = 4$
$2 \times 2 \times 2 = 2^3 = 8$
$2 \times 2 \times 2 \times 2 = 2^4 = 16$
$a \times a \times a = a^3$
$a \times a \times a \times a = a^4$

*Extracting roots.* The extraction of roots is the reverse of raising to powers. The square root of a given number is a number which, when multiplied by itself, will equal that given number. The cube (or 3d) root of a given number is a number which, when multiplied by itself twice, will equal that given

# ALGEBRA

number. The 4th root of a given number is a number which, when multiplied by itself three times, will equal that given number. And so on.

### TABLE OF SQUARE ROOTS

$\sqrt{1} = 1$  $\qquad$ $\sqrt{49} = 7$
$\sqrt{4} = 2$  $\qquad$ $\sqrt{64} = 8$
$\sqrt{9} = 3$  $\qquad$ $\sqrt{81} = 9$
$\sqrt{16} = 4$ $\qquad$ $\sqrt{100} = 10$
$\sqrt{25} = 5$ $\qquad$ $\sqrt{121} = 11$
$\sqrt{36} = 6$ $\qquad$ $\sqrt{144} = 12$

Other roots are expressed as follows:

$\sqrt[3]{8}$ (the cube root of 8) = 2
$\sqrt[4]{81}$ (the 4th root of 81) = 3
$\sqrt[5]{32}$ (the 5th root of 32) = 2

3. The third important difference between algebra and arithmetic is this: In arithmetic we deal with numbers which are *greater* than zero. In algebra we deal not only with numbers which are *greater* than zero, but also with numbers which are *less* than zero.

A number that is *greater* than zero is a *positive* number. A number that is *less* than zero is a *negative* number.

At first it may seem absurd to talk about a number that is less than zero. How can *anything* be less than *nothing?* Consider, however, the following facts: Suppose you have spent all your money. Your wealth in that case is zero. A bad fix indeed! But you might have been in an even worse fix if you had *borrowed* $250 and *spent* it. Your wealth in *that* case would have been *$250 less than zero*, or *minus $250*. To bring yourself back to zero, you would have been obliged *to earn $250 and to repay your debt*.

A *negative* number in algebra means that something is lacking. It shows that the computation is "in the red," that something must be added to bring it "out of the red."

Negative numbers are written with a minus sign, as follows:

$-10, \ -25, \ -a, \ -3x.$

## EXERCISE 69

Solve the following problems:

1. What is meant by a temperature of minus 10 degrees (written $-10°$)?
2. When the temperature is $-15°$ how much must it rise to be $0°$? to be $+7°$? to be $+15°$?
3. If the temperature falls from $-15°$ to $-23°$, how many degrees does it fall?
4. If the temperature is $-9°$, what will it be after a rise of $5°$?
5. If a man's net worth is $-\$8100$ and he saves $\$1500$ each year, what is his net worth at the end of 4 years?  7 years?
6. A man buys an automobile for $\$1000$ and sells it for $\$1200$. What is his gain?  What would his gain be if he had sold it for $\$800$?
7. If a point $21°$ north of the equator is considered positive, how would you indicate a point $74°$ south of the equator?
8. An airplane's cruising speed in still air is 250 miles per hour. What is its speed against a head wind of 40 miles per hour?
9. A man who was $\$500$ in debt contracted another debt of $\$800$. If his total assets were $\$1000$, what was his net worth?
10. A shaft is sunk to a depth of 450 feet from a plateau 300 feet above sea level. How far below sea level is the bottom of the shaft? If points above sea level are positive, and those below are negative, how would you represent the height of the plateau? of the bottom of the shaft?

## COMPUTATION OF NEGATIVE NUMBERS

1. Suppose you owed 6 dollars and paid back 4 dollars. How much would you still owe?  The answer, obviously, is 2 dollars. The algebraic way of expressing it is as follows:

$$-6+4=-2.$$

Now suppose you earned 5 dollars and spent 8 dollars. Your balance would be $5-8$, or $-3$ dollars.

In the above example, when you spend 8 dollars, you can say that you subtract $+8$ dollars. Or else you can say that you add $-8$ dollars. In algebra you express it as follows:

$$-(+8), \text{ or} +(-8).$$

Your whole example will now be written

$$5-(+8), \text{ or } 5+(-8).$$

The answer in either case is $-3$ dollars.

From the above you will note that, in addition and in subtraction, *a minus and a plus sign*, or *a plus and a minus sign*, are equivalent to *a minus sign*.

$6+(-3)=6-3=3.$
$6-(+3)=6-3=3.$

Now suppose you owed 5 dollars and removed, or subtracted, 3 dollars of that debt by paying it. You have *increased* your assets by *decreasing* your debt. In other words, your wealth now equals

$-5-(-3),$ or $-5+3,$ or $-2.$

From this you will note that, in addition and in subtraction, *two minus signs* are equivalent to *a plus sign*.

$8-(-4)=8+4=12.$
$-7-(-9)=-7+9=2.$

2. Consider, now, the following facts:

(a) A positive times a positive (like the friend of a friend) is positive.

*Plus times plus = plus.*

(b) A positive times a negative (like the friend of an enemy) is negative.

*Plus times minus = minus.*

(c) A negative times a positive (like the enemy of a friend) is negative.

*Minus times plus = minus.*

(d) A negative times a negative (like the enemy of an enemy) is positive.

*Minus times minus = plus.*

From the above we get the following formula:

$(+)\times(+)=+$
$(+)\times(-)=-$
$(-)\times(+)=-$
$(-)\times(-)=+$

$(4)\times(5)\ \ =+20$
$(4)\times(-5)=-20$
$(-4)\times(5)\ \ =-20$
$(-4)\times(-5)=+20$

80 MATHEMATICS MADE EASY

In accordance with this formula, the square root of a positive may be either a positive or a negative number. For example, the square root of 16 is $+4$ or $-4$, since $(+4)\times(+4)=16$, and $(-4)\times(-4)=16$.

3. In the division of positive and negative numbers, the same formula holds true as in multiplication.

$$\frac{+9}{+3}=+3$$
$$\frac{+9}{-3}=-3$$
$$\frac{-9}{+3}=-3$$
$$\frac{-9}{-3}=+3$$

### EXERCISE 70

A. Add the following:

1. $-73$    2. $\phantom{-}83$    3. $-72$    4. $-83$
    $73$        $-900$      $-42$       $730$

B. Perform the following subtractions:

1. $7-(+4)$    2. $7-(-4)$    3. $46-(-58)$
4. $73.6-(-26.4)$    5. $-19-(-31)$    6. $-19.71-(-12.42)$

C. Multiply:

1. $6\times(-50)$    2. $7\times(-57)$    3. $-9\times 80$
4. $-8\times(-50)$    5. $-11\times 73$    6. $-33\times(-12)$

D. Divide:

1. $-375$ by $15$    2. $-625$ by $-25$    3. $-729$ by $9$
4. $-12.1$ by $1.1$    5. $-741$ by $-3$    6. $891$ by $-99$

### Substituting Numbers for Letters

Let us look at the following examples:

1. If $a=2$, $b=3$, $c=5$, and $x=4$, find the value of the expression $a^2+2ax+x^2$.

Substituting the numbers for the letters, we have

$$2^2+2\times 2\times 4+4^2=4+16+16=36.$$

ALGEBRA 81

2. Using the same values for $a$, $b$, $c$, and $x$, find the value of $\dfrac{a^3}{b^2}$

$$\frac{2^3}{3^2} = \frac{2 \times 2 \times 2}{3 \times 3} = \frac{8}{9}$$

3. Still using the same values for $a$, $b$, $c$, and $x$, find the value of $\dfrac{bx}{a^2} - \sqrt{x}$

$$\frac{3 \times 4}{2^2} - \sqrt{4}$$

$$\frac{12}{4} - 2$$

$$3 - 2 = 1.$$

## EXERCISE 71

If $a=3$, $b=4$, $x=5$, and $y=6$, find the value of the following expressions:

1. $5a$
2. $3x$
3. $ax$
4. $xy$
5. $7ax$
6. $9by$
7. $x^2$
8. $3x^2$
9. $ax^2$
10. $9xy^2$
11. $a^2-b^2$
12. $x^2+2xy+y^2$
13. $x^2-2xy+y^2$
14. $a^3-b^3$
15. $x^3+y^3$
16. $x^3+3x^2y+3xy^2+y^3$
17. $5a^2b-3bxy+6abx$
18. $a^2+b^2+x^2+2ax+2bx+2ab$
19. $\dfrac{a^4}{a^3}$
20. $(a+b)(a-b)$

### Addition of Algebraic Numbers

1. Add the following:

$5ab+4ab-12ab+2ab+8ab-3ab$
$19ab-15ab = 4ab$

Answer, $4ab$

2. Add 7 shirts, 5 ties, 6 hats; 4 shirts, 2 ties, 3 hats, 4 dresses; 3 shirts, 5 dresses.

```
  7 sh. +5 t. +6 h.
  4 sh. +2 t. +3 h. +4 dr.
  3 sh.              +5 dr.
 ─────────────────────────
 14 sh. +7 t. +9 h. +9 dr.
```

3. In like manner, add $5a, 4bc, 3a^2d$; $4a, 3bc, 5a^2d, 7bcd$; $6a, 2bcd$.

$$5a+4bc+3a^2d$$
$$4a+3bc+5a^2d+7bcd$$
$$6a\phantom{+3bc+5a^2d}+2bcd$$
$$\overline{15a+7bc+8a^2d+9bcd}$$

4. Add $6a-5b+2c$ and $4a+2b-4c+5d$.

$$6a-5b+2c$$
$$4a+2b-4c+5d$$
$$\overline{10a-3b-2c+5d}$$

In adding algebraic numbers, you separate them into similar terms and then you add the terms separately.

### EXERCISE 72

Add the following:

1. 4 mi. and 7 mi.
2. $4a$ and $7a$
3. 4.10 and 7.10
4. 5 qt.$+6$ qt.$+7$ qt.
5. $5a+6a+7a$
6. $5.10+6.10+7.10$
7. $3ab+5ab+7ab$
8. $-2ab+6ab-3ab$
9. $-19xyz+24xyz+18xyz-15xyz$
10. $9(a+b)+10(a+b)$

### EXERCISE 73

Add the following:

1. $5°+13'$
   $9°+23'$

2. $5x+13y$
   $9x+23y$

3. $5.10+13.2$
   $9.10+23.2$

4. $x^3+5a^2b+5ab^2+\phantom{6}y^3$
   $5x^3+\phantom{5}a^2b+6ab^2+3y^3$

5. $x^4+\phantom{3}4x^3y+\phantom{2}6x^2y^2+\phantom{8}4xy^3+y^4$
   $4x^4+32x^3y+24x^2y^2+8xy^3+y^4$

### EXERCISE 74

Add the following:

1. $6a-7b-8c$; $-4a+3b-11c$; $-12a-15b+11c$
2. $16p-10q+14r$; $10p+18q-16r$; $-8p-10q+6r$; and $-28p+12q-2r$

## ALGEBRA

3. $x^2+xy+y^2$; $x^2-xy+y^2$; $-x^2+xy-y^2$; $x^2+y^2$
4. $3a^3+2a^2+2a+1$; $4a^3-2a^2+2a-2$; $9a^3+7a^2-a+14$
5. $9ab^2+7b^3$; $a^3+9a^2b+b^3$; $3a^3+9a^2b+9ab^2$
6. $2x^2+3b^2-5c^2+3d^2+5x^2-5b^2+2c^2-3d^2+19$
7. $x^3+3x^2y+3xy^2+y^3-x^3+3x^2y-3xy^2-y^3$
8. $6a^3-5a^2b+4ab^2-2b^3-5a^3+4a^2b-3ab^2+2b^3$
   $+4a^3-3a^2b+2ab^2-4a^3+5a^2b-3ab^2+2b^3$
9. $x^4-x^3+x^2-x+2-3x^4+3x^3+3x^2+3+3x^4-2x^3+2x^2-5x+4$
10. $14a^4-8b^4+6a^3b-4a^2b^2+7ab^3-14a^4+14ab^3-4a^3b+6a^2b^2-2b^4$
    $-6a^2b^2$

## SUBTRACTION OF ALGEBRAIC NUMBERS

To subtract algebraic numbers, remember the following simple rule: *Change the signs in the subtrahend, and then proceed as in addition.*

Examples:

1. From $10ab$ subtract $7ab$.   $10ab-(+7ab)$.
    $10ab$
    $\underline{7ab}$
    $3ab$

2. From $10ab$ subtract $-7ab$.   $10ab-(-7ab)$.
    $10ab$
    $\underline{-7ab}$
    $17ab$

3. From $-10ab$ subtract $-7ab$.   $-10ab-(-7ab)$.
    $-10ab$
    $\underline{-\ 7ab}$
    $-\ 3ab$

4. From $-10ab$ subtract $7ab$.   $-10ab-(+7ab)$.
    $-10ab$
    $\underline{7ab}$
    $-17ab$

5. From $9a-3b+4c$ subtract $4a+6b+2d$.
    $9a-3b+4c$
    $\underline{4a+6b\ \ \ \ \ +2d}$
    $5a-9b+4c-2d$

## EXERCISE 75

Subtract:

1. $8xy$
   $5xy$

2. $9y$
   $4y$

3. $4y$
   $9y$

4. $\phantom{-}4y$
   $-9y$

5. $5(x+y)$
   $4(x+y)$

6. $\phantom{-}11(a+b)$
   $-4(a+b)$

7. $-9(x+y)$
   $-6(x+y)$

8. $8a^2-9b$
   $4a^2+3b$

9. $4x^2-5x$
   $3x^2+2x$

10. $\phantom{-}3a^3-6$
    $-2a^3+3$

11. $\phantom{-}10a^2+8a-6$
    $-2a^2-6a+10$

12. $a^2-5ab+y^2$
    $a^2-5ab-y^2$

13. $\phantom{2}a+\sqrt{a}-2\sqrt{b}$
    $2a-2\sqrt{a}-2\sqrt{b}$

14. $3a^3-\frac{1}{2}a^2+\frac{1}{3}a-\frac{5}{6}$
    $2a^3+\frac{1}{2}a^2-\frac{1}{3}a-\frac{1}{6}$

15. $5x^4+32x^3y+24x^2y^2+8xy^3+y^4$
    $\phantom{5}x^4-\phantom{3}4x^3y+\phantom{2}6x^2y^2-4xy^3+y^4$

### REMOVING PARENTHESES

Consider the following three cases:

1. Suppose on Monday you earned $20 on a certain job, and on Tuesday you worked on two jobs and earned $10 and $9 on them. Your total earnings for the two days would be $20+($10+$9), or $20+$10+$9, or $39.

2. Suppose on Monday you earned $20, and on Tuesday you bought a hat for $4 and a pair of shoes for $6. Your balance would be $20-($4+$6), or $20-$4-$6, or $10.

3. Suppose on Monday you earned $20, and on Tuesday you gave a $10 bill for a pair of shoes and received $4 in change. Your balance would be $20-($10-$4), or $20-$10+$4, or $14.

From the above examples, you get the following rule: *Whenever you remove a parenthesis with a plus sign in front of it, you do not change the signs of the numbers inside the parenthesis. But whenever you remove a parenthesis with a minus sign in front of it, you change the signs of all the numbers inside the parenthesis.*

Remove the parentheses in the following examples:

1. $5+(8-3)-(4+2)$
   $5+8-3-4-2=4$

# ALGEBRA

2. $3a+(5-[2a-6])$

First remove the inner bracket. This will give you
$3a+(5-2a+6)$.

Then remove the parenthesis, and you get
$3a+5-2a+6 = a+11$.

3. $3a-(5-[2a-6])$

Remove the inner bracket, and you get
$3a-(5-2a+6)$.

Remove the parenthesis, and you get
$3a-5+2a-6 = 5a-11$.

### EXERCISE 76

Remove the parentheses and simplify:

1. $8+(11+4)$
2. $8+(11-4)$
3. $8x+(11x+4x)$
4. $8x+(11x-4x)$
5. $8x-(11x+4x)$
6. $8x-(11x-4x)$
7. $3x-(2x-1)$
8. $5x+(4-[2-3x])$
9. $37x-(14y+6x)$
10. $48a-(48-48a)$
11. $(2x+y)-(2x-y)$
12. $[a^2+b^2+c^2]-(a^2-b^2+c^2)$

## MULTIPLICATION OF ALGEBRAIC NUMBERS

Multiply 2 by 2.
$2 \times 2 = 4$, or $2^2$

Multiply 2 by 2 by 2.
$2 \times 2 \times 2 = 8$, or $2^3$

Multiply $2^2$ by $2^3$.
$(2 \times 2) \times (2 \times 2 \times 2) = 32$, or $2^5$

The small number in the upper right hand corner is called the *exponent*, from the Latin *exponere, to set forth*. It sets forth, or points out, the number of times a figure or a letter is multiplied by itself. Thus, $2^5$ means that 2 is multiplied by itself 5 times, $2 \times 2 \times 2 \times 2 \times 2$. Thus, also, $a^5$ means $a \times a \times a \times a \times a$.

When a letter appears without any exponent, the exponent (understood) is 1. Thus, $a = a^1$; $a \times a = a^1 \times a^1$, or $a^2$; $a \times a \times a = a^1 \times a^1 \times a^1$, or $a^3$.

From the above we note that when we multiply a letter (or a number) by itself, we *add* the exponents.

Thus:

$a^2 \times a^3 = a^{2+3} = a^5$
$a^4 \times a^5 = a^{4+5} = a^9$
$(x+y)^2 \times (x+y)^4 = (x+y)^{2+4} = (x+y)^6$

1. Multiply $4a^2b^3$ by $3ab^2$
   $4 \times 3 \times a^{2+1} \times b^{2+3} = 12a^3b^5$

2. Multiply $5a^{2b+4}$ by $2a^{b-3}$
   $5 \times 2 \times a^{2b+4-b-3} = 10a^{3b+1}$

3. Multiply $3(x+y)^2$ by $-4(x+y)^3$
   $3 \times -4 \times (x+y)^{2+3} = -12(x+y)^5$

4. Multiply $-8(b-c)^5$ by $-5(b-c)$
   $-8 \times -5 \times (b-c)^{5+1} = 40(b-c)^6$

## EXERCISE 77

| | 1. | 2. | 3. | 4. |
|---|---|---|---|---|
| Multiply | $-9$ | $-9a$ | $-3a$ | $5ab$ |
| by | $3$ | $3$ | $9$ | $-4$ |

| | 5. | 6. | 7. | 8. |
|---|---|---|---|---|
| Multiply | $-4ab$ | $-6x$ | $6x$ | $4ax$ |
| by | $5$ | $-2x$ | $2x$ | $-5ax$ |

| | 9. | 10. | 11. |
|---|---|---|---|
| Multiply | $-4byz$ | $-6a^2b$ | $5a^2$ |
| by | $5byz^2$ | $+7c^2d$ | $-4a^5$ |

| | 12. | 13. | 14. |
|---|---|---|---|
| Multiply | $x^n$ | $a^{2x}$ | $-3x^n$ |
| by | $x$ | $a^x$ | $-4x^5$ |

| | 15. | 16. | 17. |
|---|---|---|---|
| Multiply | $16x^{2a+3}$ | $7a^xb^y$ | $4(x+y)^3$ |
| by | $16x^{3a-2}$ | $8a^2b^2$ | $-(x+y)$ |

| | 18. | 19. | 20. |
|---|---|---|---|
| Multiply | $10(x+y)^3$ | $-6(x+y)^2$ | $17a^2b^3c^4d^5$ |
| by | $-8(x+y)^4$ | $-4(x+y)^3$ | $18a^3b^4c^5d^6$ |

## MULTIPLICATION OF POLYNOMIALS

A *polynomial* is a quantity consisting of two or more terms connected by plus or minus signs. For example:

$5x+2y$
$3a^2b-2bc+bcd$

Let us now consider the multiplication of polynomials.

1. Suppose you are asked to multiply 6 by 15. In algebra, this multiplication may be performed as follows:

$$6\times 15 = 6\,(10+5)$$
$$\begin{array}{r}10+5\\ 6\\ \hline 60+30=90\end{array}$$

2. The same rule applies in multiplying letters.

$$\begin{array}{r}2a+5b\\ \times 3a\\ \hline 6a^2+15ab\end{array}$$

3. Multiply, algebraically, 24 by 14.
$$24\times 14 = (20+4)(10+4)$$

$$\begin{array}{r}20+4\\ 10+4\\ \hline 200+40\phantom{+00}\\ +80+16\\ \hline 200+120+16=336\end{array}$$

4. Multiply $5a^2+2b$ by $4a+3b^2$

$$\begin{array}{l}5a^2+2b\\ 4a\ +3b^2\\ \hline 20a^3+8ab\\ \phantom{20a^3+8ab}+15a^2b^2+6b^3\\ \hline 20a^3+8ab+15a^2b^2+6b^3\end{array}$$

5. Multiply $2a+3b$ by $4a-7b$

$$\begin{array}{l}2a+3b\\ 4a-7b\\ \hline 8a^2+12ab\\ \phantom{8a^2}-14ab-21b^2\\ \hline 8a^2-2ab-21b^2\end{array}$$

And now let us look at the following three examples:

A. Multiply $(a+b)(a+b)$

$$\begin{array}{r} a+b \\ a+b \\ \hline a^2+ab \\ +ab+b^2 \\ \hline a^2+2ab+b^2 \end{array}$$

B. Multiply $(a-b)(a-b)$

$$\begin{array}{r} a-b \\ a-b \\ \hline a^2-ab \\ -ab+b^2 \\ \hline a^2-2ab+b^2 \end{array}$$

C. Multiply $(a+b)(a-b)$

$$\begin{array}{r} a+b \\ a-b \\ \hline a^2+ab \\ -ab-b^2 \\ \hline a^2\phantom{+ab}-b^2 \end{array}$$

From the above three examples, we note the following three important rules:

A. The square of the sum of two terms is equal to the square of the first term, plus twice the product of the first term by the second term, plus the square of the second term.

Examples:

$(a+4)^2 = a^2+8a+16$
$15^2 = (10+5)^2 = 100+(2\times10\times5)+25 = 225$

B. The square of the *difference* of two terms is equal to the square of the first term, *minus* twice the product of the first term by the second term, plus the square of the second term.

Examples:

$(a-4)^2 = a^2-8a+16$
$15^2 = (20-5)^2 = 400-(2\times20\times5)+25 = 225$

## ALGEBRA

C. The product of the sum and the difference of two terms equals the difference of their squares.

Examples:

$(a+5)(a-5) = a^2 - 25$
$24 \times 16 = (20+4)(20-4) = 400 - 16 = 384$
$28 \times 22 = (25+3)(25-3) = 625 - 9 = 616$

### EXERCISE 78

|  | 1. | 2. | 3. |
|---|---|---|---|
| Multiply by | $x+y$ <br> $a$ | $x+y+z$ <br> $a^2$ | $x^2+y^2+z$ <br> $ax^2$ |

|  | 4. | 5. | 6. |
|---|---|---|---|
| Multiply by | $4x-3y$ <br> $-2xy$ | $x-y+z$ <br> $-x$ | $x^2-2xy+y^2$ <br> $-5x^2y$ |

|  | 7. | 8. |
|---|---|---|
| Multiply by | $x^7-4x^4y^2+3xy^5$ <br> $18x^3y^5$ | $a^n b^n - 3ab - 14$ <br> $-4a^p y^p$ |

9.
Multiply by $\quad 3a^{4n}+4a^{3n}b-3a^{2n}b^2+2a^n b^3-5b^4$
$\quad\quad\quad -3a^{3n}$

10.
Multiply by $\quad 9(2x+3y)^2+6(2x+3y)+1$
$\quad\quad\quad 5(2x+3y)$

### EXERCISE 79

|  | 1. | 2. | 3. |
|---|---|---|---|
| Multiply by | $x+y$ <br> $x+y$ | $x-y$ <br> $x-y$ | $a+b$ <br> $a-b$ |

|  | 4. | 5. | 6. |
|---|---|---|---|
| Multiply by | $a-3$ <br> $a+2$ | $4x-5y$ <br> $3x-6y$ | $a^2-2ab+b^2$ <br> $a-b$ |

|  | 7. | 8. |
|---|---|---|
| Multiply by | $a^3-3a^2b+3ab^2-b^3$ <br> $a^2-2ab+b^2$ | $a^2+2ab+b^2$ <br> $a^2+2ab+b^2$ |

9.
Multiply by $\quad x^6+6x^5y+15x^4y^2+20x^3y^3+15x^2y^4+6xy^5+y^6$
$\quad\quad\quad x^2+2xy+y^2$

## EXERCISE 80

Multiply at sight:
1. $(a+b)^2$
2. $(x+y)^2$
3. $(m+n)^2$
4. $(a-b)^2$
5. $(x-y)^2$
6. $(m-n)^2$
7. $(a+b)(a-b)$
8. $(x+y)(x-y)$
9. $(m+n)(m-n)$
10. $21 \times 19$ [or $(20+1)(20-1)$]
11. $23 \times 17$
12. $35 \times 25$

## DIVISION OF ALGEBRAIC NUMBERS

1. Divide 16 by 4

$$16 = 2^4;\ 4 = 2^2$$
$$\frac{2^4}{2^2} = \frac{\not{2} \times \not{2} \times 2 \times 2}{\not{2} \times \not{2}} = 4,\ \text{or}\ 2^2$$

That is, $\frac{2^4}{2^2} = 2^{4-2} = 2^2$

2. Divide $a^6$ by $a^3$

$$\frac{a^6}{a^3} = \frac{\not{a} \times \not{a} \times \not{a} \times a \times a \times a}{\not{a} \times \not{a} \times \not{a}} = a^3$$

That is, $\frac{a^6}{a^3} = a^{6-3} = a^3$

In multiplication, as we have seen, we *add* the exponents. In division, on the other hand, we *subtract* the exponents.

3. Divide $15a^2b^3c^5$ by $3a^2b^2c^2$

$$\frac{15a^2b^3c^5}{3a^2b^2c^2} = 5a^{2-2}b^{3-2}c^{5-2} = 5bc^3$$

$15 \div 3 = 5$; $a^2 \div a^2 = a^0$, or 1 (anything divided by itself $= 1$); $b^3 \div b^2 = b^1$, or $b$; $c^5 \div c^2 = c^3$

The rule for signs in division is the same as in multiplication.

$+$ divided by $+ = +$
$+$ divided by $- = -$
$-$ divided by $+ = -$
$-$ divided by $- = +$

4. Divide $21x^2y^3z$ by $-7xy^3z$

$$\frac{21x^2y^3z}{-7xy^3z} = -3x$$

5. Divide $-36a^4$ by $6a$

$$\frac{-36a^4}{6a} = -6a^3$$

6. Divide $-49abcd$ by $-7abcd$.

$$\frac{-49abcd}{-7abcd} = 7$$

## EXERCISE 81

Divide:

1. $\dfrac{16x}{2x}$
2. $\dfrac{-18a}{6a}$
3. $\dfrac{27y}{-3y}$
4. $\dfrac{-28p^5}{-4p^3}$

5. $\dfrac{\Pi r^2}{\Pi}$
6. $\dfrac{4\Pi r^3}{2\Pi r}$
7. $\dfrac{.9ax^2}{.3ax}$
8. $\dfrac{-75xy^3z^5}{25xz^3}$

9. $\dfrac{-24a^5b^5c^5}{-6a^5bc^3}$
10. $\dfrac{-700xy}{140xy}$
11. $\dfrac{-169a^8b^9d}{-13a^8b}$

12. $\dfrac{65a^7b^8c^7}{13a^5b^7c^3}$
13. $\dfrac{(a+b)^6}{(a+b)^4}$
14. $\dfrac{(a-b)^4}{a-b}$

15. $\dfrac{18a^2b(x-y)^6}{3ab(x-y)^4}$
16. $\dfrac{x^x}{x^y}$
17. $\dfrac{85a^xb^yc^z}{17a^3b^2c}$

18. $\dfrac{-18a^{n+4}}{3a^{n+1}}$
19. $\dfrac{36a^7b^6c^5}{.12a^5b^5c^5}$
20. $\dfrac{9x^{6n}}{3x^{8n}}$

## DIVISION OF POLYNOMIALS

1. Divide $12x^3 - 16x^2 + 20x$ by $4x$

$$\frac{12x^3 - 16x^2 + 12x}{4x} = 3x^2 - 4x + 3$$

$$\frac{12x^3}{4x} = 3x^2$$

$$\frac{-16x^2}{4x} = -4x$$

$$\frac{12x}{4x} = 3$$

When you divide a polynomial by a single term, you divide each term in the polynomial by that single term.

2. Divide $a^2+3a-28$ by $a-4$

When you divide a polynomial by a polynomial, you proceed as in long division in arithmetic, as follows:

$$\begin{array}{r} a+7\phantom{00000} \\ a-4\overline{\smash{\big)}a^2+3a-28} \\ \underline{a^2-4a\phantom{0000}} \\ 7a-28 \\ \underline{7a-28} \\ 0 \end{array}$$ Answer, $a+7$

Explanation:
$a^2 \div a = a$
$a \times a = a^2$
$a \times -4 = -4a$
$a^2 - a^2 = 0$
$3a - (-4a) = 7a$

Bring down the $-28$, and you get $7a-28$
$7a \div a = +7$
$7 \times a = 7a$
$7 \times -4 = -28$

This leaves no remainder.

Compare this to long division, and you will note the similarity of the process, step by step:

$$\begin{array}{r} 345\phantom{0} \\ 27\overline{\smash{\big)}9315} \\ \underline{81\phantom{00}} \\ 121\phantom{0} \\ \underline{108\phantom{0}} \\ 135 \\ \underline{135} \\ 0 \end{array}$$ Answer, 345

3. Divide $a^2+a^2b+2ab+ab^2+b^2$ by $a+ab+b$

$$\begin{array}{r} a+b\phantom{0000000000} \\ a+ab+b\overline{\smash{\big)}a^2+a^2b+2ab+ab^2+b^2} \\ \underline{a^2+a^2b+\phantom{0}ab\phantom{00000000}} \\ ab+ab^2+b^2 \\ \underline{ab+ab^2+b^2} \\ 0 \end{array}$$ Answer, $a+b$

ALGEBRA

4. Divide $a^3-8b^3$ by $a-2b$

$$
\begin{array}{r}
a^2+2ab+4b^2\phantom{000000} \\
a-2b\overline{\smash{\big)}a^3\phantom{00000000}-8b^3} \\
\underline{a^3-2a^2b\phantom{000000000}} \\
2a^2b\phantom{0000}-8b^3 \\
\underline{2a^2b-4ab^2\phantom{0000}} \\
4ab^2-8b^3 \\
\underline{4ab^2-8b^3} \\
0
\end{array}
$$

Answer, $a^2+2ab+4b^2$

## EXERCISE 82

Divide:

1. $\dfrac{81ac-54bc}{9c}$

2. $\dfrac{a^3-5a^2}{-a}$

3. $\dfrac{4a^5-6a^3+15a}{-a}$

4. $\dfrac{-6a^3b+9a^2b^2-12ab^3}{3ab}$

5. $\dfrac{-45a^2b^2c^3+85a^4b^2c^2}{5ab^2c^2}$

6. $\dfrac{3a^2b^2-30a^3b^3+6a^4b^4}{3a^2}$

7. $\dfrac{.04x^2-.06xy}{.5x}$

8. $\dfrac{a^2(a^2+1)+(a^2+1)}{a^2+1}$

9. $\dfrac{15a^{3n-3}-10a^{3n-2}+20a^{3n-1}+5a^{3n}}{5a^{2n-1}}$

10. $\dfrac{198a^4b^2-132a^3b^3-99a^2b^4+242ab^5}{11ab}$

## EXERCISE 83

Divide:

1. $\dfrac{x^2-7x+12}{x-3}$

2. $\dfrac{x^2-2x-63}{x+7}$

3. $\dfrac{x^2-23x+90}{x-5}$

3. $\dfrac{2x^2+5x-12}{x+4}$

4. $\dfrac{15x^2-2x-8}{3x+2}$

5. $\dfrac{a^4-b^4}{a-b}$

6. $\dfrac{a^3+3a^2b+3ab^2+b^3}{a^2+2ab+b^2}$

7. $\dfrac{x^3-y^3}{x-y}$

8. $\dfrac{x^4+4x^3y+6x^2y^2+4xy^3+y^4}{x+y}$

94  MATHEMATICS MADE EASY

9. $\dfrac{a^8+8a^7b+28a^6b^2+56a^5b^3+70a^4b^4+56a^3b^5+28a^2b^6+8ab^7+b^8}{a^3+3a^2b+3ab^2+b^3}$

10. $\dfrac{x^3-3xyz+y^3+z^3}{x+y+z}$

## FACTORING

Any numbers which, when multiplied together, will give a certain product, are called *factors* of that product.

Thus, 2 and 5 are factors of 10; 2, 3, and 5 are factors of 30; $a$ and $b$ are factors of $ab$.

We shall here consider four different kinds of factoring, under sections A, B, C, and D:

### A

1. Factor $ab-ac+ad$

You will note that $a$ is common to all the three terms—in other words, that you can divide $ab$, $-ac$, and $ad$ by $a$.

Perform this division:

$$\dfrac{ab}{a}=b$$

$$\dfrac{-ac}{a}=-c$$

$$\dfrac{ad}{a}=d$$

Now express this algebraically:

$a(b-c+d)$

2. Factor $3b^2-9b^4$

$3b^2$ is common to both terms.

Taking this $3b^2$ out as one of the factors, we get $1-3b^2$ as the other factor. Expressed algebraically, the answer is as follows:

$3b^2(1-3b^2)$

3. Factor $2a^4b^2+6a^3b-4a^5b^4$

$2a^3b(ab+3-2a^2b^3)$

4. Factor $4(a+b)a+5(a+b)b$

$(a+b)(4a+5b)$

## EXERCISE 84

Factor the following:

1. $4a^2 + 12a^3$
2. $10y^2 - 15y^4$
3. $a^2 + 2a$
4. $7x + 21x^3$
5. $3y + 9y^2 - 9y^3$
6. $8x^2 - 6x^5$
7. $3a^4 + a^3b - a^2b^2$
8. $x^4 + 5x^3 - 4x^2$
9. $x^2y - 2x^2y^2$
10. $\frac{1}{2}a^3 + \frac{1}{4}a^2$
11. $10x^4y^3 - 35x^3y^4$
12. $2x^4y^3z - 2x^3y^3z^3 + 4x^2y^4z^2$
13. $x^ny^3 - 4x^{2n}y^2 + 6x^{3n}y$
14. $2x^5 - 6x^4 + 14x^3$
15. $5x^3y^3 - 10x^6y^4 + 15x^5y^5$
16. $x(a+b) + y(a+b)$
17. $a^2(x+y) + b^2(x+y)$
18. $8(x+y)a + 3(x+y)b$

### B

Recall the formulae that we have noted on page 88:

$$(a+b)^2 = a^2 + 2ab + b^2$$
$$(a-b)^2 = a^2 - 2ab + b^2$$

Translating these formulae into the language of algebraic factoring, we learn that the factors of $a^2 + 2ab + b^2$ are $(a+b)^2$ or $(a+b)(a+b)$, and that the factors of $a^2 - 2ab + b^2$ are $(a-b)^2$ or $(a-b)(a-b)$.

Factor $x^2 + 4x + 4$
$(x+2)^2$ or $(x+2)(x+2)$

Factor $25a^2 - 40ab + 16b^2$
$(5a - 4b)^2$

You can use this method whenever you have a perfect square—that is, when the *middle term* is *twice* the product of the square roots of the other two terms. ($-40ab = 2 \times 5a \times -4b$)

## EXERCISE 85

Factor the following:

1. $9x^2 + 6x + 1$
2. $x^2 + 8x + 16$
3. $49x^2 + 14x + 1$
4. $49x^2 + 14xy + y^2$
5. $81x^2 + 36xy + 4y^2$
6. $121a^2 + 66ab + 9b^2$
7. $64a^2 - 16ab + b^2$
8. $25x^2 - 60xy + 36y^2$
9. $144p^2 - 216pq + 81q^2$
10. $(x^2 + 2xy + y^2)^2$
11. $a^2x + 2abx + b^2x$
12. $16(a+b)^2 + 8(a+b) + 1$

## C

And now recall this formula:

$(a+b)(a-b) = a^2 - b^2$

The factors of $a^2 - b^2$ are $(a+b)(a-b)$

You can use this method of factoring whenever you have the difference of two squares.

Factor $x^2 - 9$

$(x+3)(x-3)$

Factor $a^8 - 256$

The square root of $a^8$ is $a^4$

The square root of 256, or $2^8$, is 16, or $2^4$

Hence $a^8 - 256 = (a^4 + 16)(a^4 - 16)$

But $a^4 - 16$ is again the difference of two squares. This, when factored, equals $(a^2 + 4)(a^2 - 4)$.

Hence $a^8 - 256 = (a^4 + 16)(a^2 + 4)(a^2 - 4)$

But, once again, $a^2 - 4$ is the difference of two squares. This can be resolved into the factors $(a+2)(a-2)$.

Our complete answer, therefore, is as follows:

$a^8 - 256 = (a^4 + 16)(a^2 + 4)(a+2)(a-2)$

Factor $a^8 b^8 - c^8$

$(a^4 b^4 + c^4)(a^2 b^2 + c^2)(ab+c)(ab-c)$

## EXERCISE 86

Factor the following:

1. $x^2 - 16$
2. $x^2 - 9y^2$
3. $4a^2 - 25b^2$
4. $16x^2 - 36y^2$
5. $49a^2 - 64b^2$
6. $81x^2 - 100y^2$
7. $121x^2 - 1$
8. $x^2 - 144y^2$
9. $\frac{1}{4}a^2 - b^2$
10. $2\frac{1}{4}x^2 - 6\frac{1}{4}y^2$
11. $.36a^2 - .0049b^2$
12. $(a+b)^2 - (x+2y)^2$
13. $x^2 + 2xy + y^2 - a^2$
14. $x^3 - 16x$
15. $a^4 - b^4$*
16. $16x^4 - 1$
17. $x^8 - y^8$
18. $256a^4 - 81b^4$
19. $\frac{1}{16}x^4 - \frac{16}{81}y^4$
20. $(x^2 + 2xy + y^2)^2 - 1$

*After factoring, it will be found that one of the factors is itself factorable. Factor as completely as possible this and the expressions which follow it.

# ALGEBRA

## D

1. Factor $a^2+10a+24$

This is not a perfect square, yet it can be factored by inspection, as follows:

$(a+\ )(a+\ )$

The missing terms must be such that their sum is 10, and their product is 24. Only two such numbers will meet these requirements. These numbers are 6 and 4.

The answer, therefore, is $(a+6)(a+4)$.

To prove this you multiply the two factors:

$$\begin{array}{r} a+6 \\ a+4 \\ \hline a^2+6a \\ +4a+24 \\ \hline a^2+10a+24 \end{array}$$

2. Factor $a^2-a-20$

$(a-\ )(a+\ )$

Here we have a *minus* and a *plus*, because the product is a *minus*. [Remember the formula, $(-)\times(+)=-$.] Now the two terms must be such that their difference is $-1$, and their product is $-20$. By inspection you find that these two terms are $-5$ and $+4$. Your answer, therefore, is $(a-5)(a+4)$. Proving this, you find that it is correct:

$$\begin{array}{r} a-5 \\ a+4 \\ \hline a^2-5a \\ +4a-20 \\ \hline a^2-\ a\ -20 \end{array}$$

3. Factor $x^2-8x+15$

$(x-\ )(x-\ )$

We have two *minus* signs because the product is *plus*. $(-)\times(-)=+$.

By inspection we notice that the two missing terms are $-5$ and $-3$.

$x^2-8x+15=(x-5)(x-3)$

## EXERCISE 87

Factor the following:

1. $x^2+5x+6$
2. $x^2+8x+15$
3. $x^2-x-12$
4. $x^2+x-6$
5. $x^2-5x-14$
6. $x^2-13x+40$
7. $x^2-13x+22$
8. $x^2-13x-48$
9. $x^2-13x+36$
10. $x^2+5x-36$

## SIMPLE EQUATIONS

The equation is the basis of algebra. Practically all the constructions and inventions are founded upon equations. Indeed, the very riddle of the universe is based upon an equation—Life+Death=What? The unknown quantity, the mystery, is $x$. Get the value of $x$, and you have solved the mystery.

In order to learn the solution of the algebraic equations, let us look at the following arithmetic equations:

1. $10-4=6$
   $10=4+6$

2. $10=7+3$
   $10-7=3$
   $10-3=7$

3. $5+4=9$
   $5=9-4$
   $4=9-5$

From the above examples you will note that when you move a term from one side of an equation to the other side, you must change its sign. If it is plus, it becomes minus. If it is minus, it becomes plus.

Thus, in the first example, when the $-4$ is moved from the left side of the equation to the right side, it becomes $+4$. In the second equation, when the $+7$ is moved from the right side of the equation to the left side, it becomes $-7$. The same is true of the $+3$. In the third equation, when the $+4$ is moved from the right side of the equation to the left side, it becomes $-4$. The same is true of the 5.

Let us now look at the following algebraic equations:

1. $x-7=0$
   $x=0+7$
   $x=7$

2. $x+6=10$
   $x=10-6$
   $x=4$

3. $x-4=5$
   $x=5+4$
   $x=9$

4. $x+5-2x-4=9-3x$

In order to solve for $x$, we bring all the $x$ terms on one side of the equation and all the numbers on the other side.

$x-2x+3x=-5+4+9$
$2x=8$
$x=4$

5. $(x+3)^2-(x+2)^2=x+8$
   $(x^2+6x+9)-(x^2+4x+4)=x+8$
   $x^2+6x+9-x^2-4x-4=x+8$
   $x^2+6x-x^2-4x-x=-9+4+8$
   $x=3$

6. $5(x+4)-6(x-3)=6x+3$
   $5x+20-6x+18=6x+3$
   $5x-6x-6x=-20-18+3$
   $-7x=-35$
   $x=5$

7. $12(x-2)(x+2)=x(12x-12)$
   $12(x^2-4)=12x^2-12x$
   $12x^2-48=12x^2-12x$
   $12x^2-12x^2+12x=48$
   $12x=48$
   $x=4$

8. $\dfrac{x^3-8}{x-2}-(x-1)^2=15$

Dividing $x^3-8$ by $x-2$, we get
$x^2+2x+4$
$x^2+2x+4-(x-1)^2=15$
$x^2+2x+4-(x^2-2x+1)=15$
$x^2+2x+4-x^2+2x-1=15$
$4x=12$
$x=3$

## EXERCISE 88

Solve for $x$:
1. $x-5=6$
2. $2x-13=x$
3. $3x^2-14x=3x^2-15x+6$
4. $x+6=19$
5. $4x=30-6x$
6. $x+14-30=0$
7. $15x-21+21x-15=108$
8. $10x-14+6x=18$
9. $6x-21=24+15x$
10. $48-6x=50-8x$
11. $32x-14=30x-6$
12. $10x+72-18x-12=0$
13. $18x-46=26-6x$
14. $7x-5+14x=4+x+31$
15. $5x-7+7x-3=38$
16. $8x+12-2x=4x+42-x$
17. $7x-31=x-7$
18. $6x-x-44+3x=4x$
19. $8+2x-11=x+8$
20. $5x-4+9x-6=2x+8+3x$

## EXERCISE 89

Solve for $x$:
1. $(x+6)^2-(x+5)^2=x+14$
2. $4(x-2)(x-3)-(2x-3)^2=3x+4$
3. $10(x-3)-14(6-x)=42-6(8-x)$
4. $12(x-1)(x+1)=x(12x+16)$
5. $(2x-6)^2=(2x+1)^2$
6. $(x-1)(x+3)=(x+11)(x-3)$
7. $(x+2)(x+1)=(x+10)(x-3)$
8. $(3x-2)(x+1)=3(x+1)^2-5x-5$
9. $(4x+1)(3x+2)=(6x+14)(2x-2)$
10. $3(x+1)(x+2)=(3x-1)(x+3)+16$
11. $\dfrac{2x^2+x-36}{x-4}=\dfrac{x^3-1}{x^2+x+1}+6x$
12. $\dfrac{x^3+3x^2+3x+1}{x+1}=x^2+29$
13. $\dfrac{x^3-1}{x-1}-(x+1)^2=47$
14. $\dfrac{8x^3+27}{2x+3}=(2x+1)^2-8x-2$
15. $\dfrac{x^4+4x^3+6x^2+4x+1}{x^2+2x+1}-2x=x^2-9x+73$

## SIMPLE EQUATION PROBLEMS
### A

1. Mary earns $x$ dollars a week. Her father earns $15 a week more. How much does her father earn? How much do they earn together?

Her father earns $x+15$ dollars.
Together they earn $x+x+15$, or $2x+15$ dollars.

2. Of three consecutive numbers, $x+1$ is the largest. What are the three numbers?

1st number $= x+1$
2nd number $= 1$ less than $x+1$, or $x$
3d number $= 1$ less than $x$, or $x-1$

3. Of three consecutive numbers, $x+1$ is the smallest. What are the three numbers?

$x+1, x+2, x+3$

4. By how much does $x$ exceed 5?
To enable us to solve this, let us give a definite number to $x$. Let $x=10$. By how much does 10 exceed 5? Obviously by $10-5$, or 5.

Hence $x$ exceeds 5 by $x-5$

5. By how much does 5 exceed $b$?
Suppose $b=2$. Then 5 exceeds 2 by $5-2$, or 3. 5 exceeds $b$ by $5-b$.

## EXERCISE 90

Solve the following problems:

1. Jones has $x$ dollars, and Smith has three times as many. How many has Smith? How many have both together?
2. The sum of all the salaries earned in an office is $1000. The bookkeeper's salary is $x$ dollars. What is the sum of the rest of the salaries?
3. The difference between two numbers is 25. The smaller number is $x$. What is the larger number? What is their sum?
4. Of three consecutive numbers, $x$ is the smallest. What are the other two numbers? What are the other two numbers if $x$ is the largest?
5. Of three consecutive odd numbers $2n+1$ is the smallest. What are the other numbers?
6. Of three consecutive even numbers $2n$ is the smallest. What are the other numbers?
7. By how much does $x$ exceed 10? By how much does 10 exceed $x$?

8. What is the fifth part of $x$? of $a$? the nth part of $x$?

9. Jones has $x$ dollars, and Smith has eight dollars less than twice as many. How many has Smith?

10. A man sold a car for $1000 and lost $x$ dollars. How much did the car cost? For how much would he have had to sell it in order to make a profit of $y$ dollars?

11. Jones is $x$ years old. How old was he 5 years ago? How old will he be 6 years from now? How old, $y$ years from now?

12. How many nickels are there in $x$ dollars and $y$ dimes?

13. Jones is $x$ years old, and Smith is $y$ years old. What will be the sum of their ages 9 years from now?

14. How much does a man have left if he starts with $15 and spends $1.35? How much if he starts with $x$ dollars and spends $y$ cents?

15. An automobile travels at the rate of $x$ miles per hour. How far will it travel in 2 hours? In $a$ hours?

16. An automobile travels $x$ miles in $y$ hours. How far does it travel in 1 hour. In $z$ hours?

17. What is the interest on $x$ dollars at $y$ percent for $z$ years?

18. If a bushel of wheat costs $x$ dollars, how much will $a$ bushels of wheat cost?

19. When two numbers are multiplied, their product is $a$. One of the numbers is $x$. What is the other number?

20. When $x$ is divided by another number, the quotient is $a$. What is the other number?

## EXERCISE 91

Express the following facts as algebraic equations:

1. Three times $x$ is 10.
2. One-fifth of $x$ is 35.
3. Eighteen subtracted from three times $x$ is the same as two added to $x$.
4. 15 is as much smaller than $x$ as 25 is larger than $x$.
5. If Brown's age is $x+12$, Smith's age is $2x+9$, and Robinson's age is $3x+6$, express the following:
   (a) Robinson is twice as old as Brown.
   (b) Robinson is as much older than Smith as Smith is older than Brown.
   (c) Fifteen years ago, Robinson was as old as Smith is now.
   (d) Twenty years ago, Robinson was four times as old as Brown.
   (e) Thirty years ago, Robinson was as old as Brown is now.
   (f) Fifteen years from now, Robinson will be as old as the combined present ages of Brown and Smith.

6. If Brown has $4x+\$500$, Smith has $7x$ dollars, and Robinson has $8x-\$100$, express the following:
   (a) The sum of their money is $19,400.
   (b) If Robinson gains $100, and Brown loses $400, Robinson will then have twice as much as Brown.
   (c) Robinson has $900 more than Smith.
   (d) If Brown loses $1000, he will have half as much as Smith has now.
   (e) Brown and Smith together have $3600 more than Robinson.
   (f) If Brown pays $1400 to Robinson, he will then have only one-fourth as much as Robinson.

## B

This group of problems involves wages, capital, taxes, expenses, profits, losses, and all sorts of numbers in general. Let us see how problems of this nature are solved:

1. John and Harry together have saved up $4500 for their college career. John has saved up $900 more than Harry. How much has each of them saved?

   Let $x=$ Harry's savings
   Then $x+900=$ John's savings
   $x+x+900=$ their combined savings
   $$2x+900=4500$$
   $$2x=4500-900=3600$$
   $$x=1800$$
   $$x+900=2700$$
   Answer: John, $2700; Harry, $1800.

2. Smith sells four houses, then buys a house for $12000 and has $48000 left. For how much did he sell each house?

   Let $x=$ the amount he gets for selling one house.
   $4x=$ the amount he gets for selling the four houses.
   $4x-12000=$ the amount he has left after he buys the house.

   But this amount $=48000$
   Hence $4x-12000=48000$
   $$4x=48000+12000=60000$$
   $$x=15000 \qquad \text{Answer, \$15000.}$$

3. Three times a number equals the number increased by 24. What is the number?

Let $x =$ the number
$$3x = x + 24$$
$$3x - x = 24$$
$$2x = 24$$
$$x = 12$$

Answer, 12.

4. Brown is 40 years old. His son is 10 years old.
(a) In how many years will the son be half as old as the father?
(b) How many years ago was the father seven times as old as the son?

(a) Let $x =$ the number of years it will take for the son to be half as old as the father.
At that time the son will be $x + 10$ years old.
At that time the father will be $x + 40$ years old.
$x + 10$ will be half as much as $x + 40$.
Or, to put it in another way, $x + 40$ will be twice as much as $x + 10$.
Putting this into an equation, we get

$$x + 40 = 2(x + 10)$$
$$x + 40 = 2x + 20$$
$$x - 2x = -40 + 20$$
$$-x = -20$$
$$x = 20$$

Answer, in 20 years.

(b) Let $x =$ the number of years ago when the father was seven times as old as the son.

$$40 - x = 7(10 - x)$$
$$40 - x = 70 - 7x$$
$$-x + 7x = -40 + 70$$
$$6x = 30$$
$$x = 5$$

Answer, 5 years ago.

ALGEBRA

5. A, B, and C have $70. A has $10 less than twice the sum that B has, and B has $1 more than twice the sum that C has. How much has each?
Let $x=$ the sum that C has
$2x+1=$ the sum that B has
$2(2x+1)-10=$ the sum that A has

$$x+2x+1+4x+2-10=70$$
$$7x=70-1-2+10$$
$$7x=77$$
$$x=11, \text{ the sum that C has}$$
$$22+1=23, \text{ the sum that B has}$$
$$46-10=36, \text{ the sum that A has}$$
Answer: A, $36; B, $23; C, $11.

6. A man has $2.75 in dimes and quarters. If he has 20 coins in all, how many are dimes and how many are quarters?
Let $x=$ the number of dimes
$10x=$ the *number of cents* represented by these 10 dimes.
$20-x=$ the number of quarters
$25(20-x)=$ the *number of cents* represented by these quarters

$$10x+25(20-x)=275 \text{ cents}$$
$$10x+500-25x=275$$
$$-15x=275-500$$
$$-15x=-225$$
$$15x=225$$
$$x=15$$
$$20-x=5$$
Answer: 15 dimes, 5 quarters.

## EXERCISE 92

Solve the following problems:

1. The combined capital of Brown and Smith is $1000. Brown has three times as much as Smith. How much has each?
2. The combined capital of Brown and Smith is $900. Brown has $100 more than Smith. How much has each?
3. Brown and Smith pay together $600 in taxes. Brown pays $100 more than Smith. How much does each pay?
4. Ten increased by five times a certain number equals 50. Find the number.

5. Brown starts the day with $25 and then sells three wallets. He then has $40. For how much did he sell each wallet?

6. Nine times a certain number is diminished by 12, the remainder being 24. What is the number?

7. Brown sells three hats and spends $8, having $22 left. For how much did he sell each hat?

8. Four times a number equals the number increased by 48. What is the number?

9. The sum of two numbers is 56, and one of them is four less than three times the other. What are the numbers?

10. Eight times a certain number equals 121 diminished by three times the number. What is the number?

11. Three consecutive numbers add up to 33. What are the numbers?

12. Three consecutive odd numbers add up to 57. What are the numbers?

13. Three consecutive even numbers add up to 180. What are the numbers?

14. Brown is twice as old as Smith, and the sum of their ages is 75 years. How old is each?

15. Brown is four years more than twice as old as Smith. In sixteen years, Brown will be three times as old as Smith is now. How old is each?

16. A man is 35 years old, and his son is 10 years old. In how many years will the son be half as old as his father? How many years ago was the father six times as old as his son?

17. A bookkeeper saves one-tenth of his weekly salary, or $1 more than is saved by a salesman. The salesman's salary is $5 per week more than the bookkeeper's, but the salesman saves only one-thirteenth of his salary. How much does each earn? How much does each save?

18. The sum of three numbers is 65. The first is eight less than twice the second number; the second is one more than three times the third number. What are the numbers?

19. Smith began a business with five times as much capital as Jones. After a year, Smith had lost $2500, and Jones had gained $1000; and Smith then had only twice as much as Jones. With how much capital did each start the year?

20. A man has $9.80 in dollars and dimes. If he has four times as many dimes as dollars, how many of each has he?

21. A man has $1.30 in dimes and nickels. If he has 22 coins altogether, how many are dimes and how many are nickels?

## ALGEBRA

22. In the division of partnership profits, Smith receives $700 less than Jones, and Jones receives $1400 less than Robinson. Robinson and Smith together receive $4300. How much does each receive?

23. The four salesmen of an automobile agency together sold 25 automobiles in one week. The second sold twice as many as the first; the third, twice as many as the second; and the fourth, three more than the third. How many did each sell?

24. Five men agreed to contribute equal amounts to raise a sum of money. Two of them failed to do so, and each of the others therefore had to pay $80 more than originally planned. How much did each agree to pay at the beginning?

25. Suppose only one had failed to pay, with the result that each still had to pay $80 more than planned. How much had each planned to pay?

### C

The following group of problems deals with motion, both in space and in time.

1. Two boys, A and B, 180 miles apart, start to travel on bicycles toward each other. A travels at the rate of 10 miles an hour. B travels at the rate of 8 miles an hour. How many miles does each travel before they meet?

Let $10x =$ the number of miles A travels.
" $8x =$ " " " " B "
But both together travel 180 miles.
Therefore, $10x + 8x = 180$
$$18x = 180$$
$$x = 10$$
$10x = 100$ miles, distance A travels.
$8x = 80$ miles, " B "

2. A train leaves New York for Boston at the rate of 46 miles an hour. Thirty minutes later, an automobile leaves for Boston at the rate of 50 miles an hour. How long will it take the automobile to overtake the train?

In order to solve this and similar problems, you will find it helpful to learn the following formula:

$D = TR$.   Distance = Time × Rate.

That is, if a train travels 250 miles in 5 hours, you know from the formula, $250 = 5 \times R$, that it travels at the rate of 50 miles an hour.

From the above formula, you also get the following:

$$T = \frac{D}{R} \left(5 = \frac{250}{50}\right).$$
$$R = \frac{D}{T} \left(50 = \frac{250}{5}\right).$$

With this formula in mind, let us now solve the problem:

Let $x$ = the Time, or the number of hours, that the automobile travels.

Then $x + \frac{1}{2}$ = the Time, or the number of hours, that the train travels.

$50x$ = the Distance that the automobile travels.

$46(x + \frac{1}{2})$ = the Distance that the train travels.

But when the automobile overtakes the train, they have both traveled the same Distance.

Hence $50x = 46(x + \frac{1}{2})$
$50x = 46\left(\frac{2x+1}{2}\right)$
$50x = 23(2x+1)$
$50x = 46x + 23$
$4x = 23$
$x = 5\frac{3}{4}$ hours, or 5 hrs. 45 min.

3. At what time between 3 and 4 o'clock are the hands of a watch opposite each other?

Applying the formula, $D = TR$, we get the following solution:

Let $x$ = the number of minute-spaces—or the Distance—passed by the minute-hand from 3 o'clock to the required Time.

Since the hour-hand is 15 spaces in advance of the minute hand at 3 o'clock, and since at the required Time it will be 30 spaces away from the minute-hand, it will have traveled 45 minute-spaces *less* than the minute-hand.

Hence $x - 15 - 30$, or $x - 45$ = the number of minute-spaces—or the Distance—passed by the hour-hand from 3 o'clock to the required Time.

But the minute-hand moves 12 times as much—that is, it covers 12 times as much Distance—as the hour-hand.

# ALGEBRA

Therefore, $x = 12(x-45)$
$x = 12x - 540$
$-11x = -540$
$11x = 540$
$x = 49\frac{1}{11}$

Answer, $49\frac{1}{11}$ minutes after 3 o'clock.

## EXERCISE 93

Solve the following problems:

1. A train leaves New York for Chicago at the rate of 44 miles per hour. Thirty minutes later, another train leaves for Chicago at the rate of 50 miles per hour. How long will it take the second train to overtake the first?

2. Two trains start from Cleveland at the same time but in opposite directions. If one travels twice as fast as the other, and they are 272 miles apart at the end of 3 hours, how fast does each train travel?

3. Smith and Jones begin to walk in the same direction at the same time, but Smith has a lead of 5 miles. If Smith walks at the rate of 3 miles per hour, and Jones at the rate of 4 miles per hour, in how many hours will Jones overtake Smith?

4. The distance by automobile road between New York and Albany is 153 miles. If an automobile sets out from Albany at 30 miles per hour and another sets out at the same time from New York at 35 miles per hour, how many miles from New York will they be when they meet? (Assume that neither makes any stops.)

5. The distance by automobile road between New York and Baltimore is 192 miles. If an automobile sets out from Baltimore at 39 miles per hour, and another sets out from New York at 33 miles per hour, how many miles from New York will they be when they meet?

6. The distance by automobile road between New York and Buffalo is 412 miles. A man begins to drive from Buffalo at the rate of 28 miles per hour and stops one hour for food, gasoline, etc. Another man begins at the same time from New York at 32 miles per hour, and stops $1\frac{1}{2}$ hours on the way. How many miles from New York will they be when they meet?

7. At what time between 1 and 2 o'clock will the hands of a clock be together?

Suggestion: The minute-hand travels 60 spaces per hour; the hour-hand, five spaces. The hour-hand has a lead of five spaces.

8. At what time between (a) 2 and 3 o'clock, (b) 3 and 4 o'clock, and (c) 4 and 5 o'clock will the hands of a clock be together?

9. Smith and Jones walk towards each other from two towns 24 miles apart. Smith starts at 9 A.M. and Jones at 10 A.M., and Jones walks one mile per hour faster than Smith. If they meet at 1 P.M., how fast does each walk?

10. Smith starts to walk from a town at the rate of 3 miles per hour. One hour later, Jones sets out in the same direction from the same point at the rate of 30 miles per hour. One hour after Jones's departure, a train sets out in the same direction from the same point at the rate of 40 miles per hour. If Smith started at 9 A.M. when does Jones overtake him? When does the train overtake Jones? How far from the town are all three when the train overtakes Jones?

## SIMULTANEOUS EQUATIONS

A *simultaneous* equation is an equation that contains more than one unknown quantity. We shall here consider equations with two unknown quantities, $x$ and $y$. Such equations can be solved in two ways:

    A. By addition or subtraction.
    B. By substitution.

### A

Solve for $x$ and $y$, eliminating by addition or subtraction:

1. $x+y=9$
   $x-y=1$

Adding the two equations, we get

$$x+x+y-y=9+1$$
$$2x=10$$
$$x=5$$
$$5+y=9$$
$$y=9-5$$
$$y=4$$

                Answer, $x=5$
                            $y=4$

2. $3x+2y=17$
   $x+4y=19$

In order to eliminate the $y$'s, we multiply the first equation by 2. This gives us

$$6x+4y=34$$
$$x+4y=19$$

# ALGEBRA

Since the $y$'s have the same sign, we now *subtract* the second equation from the first (by changing the signs of all the terms in the second equation and then proceeding as in addition). This gives us

$$5x = 15$$
$$x = 3$$
$$3 + 4y = 19$$
$$4y = 19 - 3 = 16$$
$$y = 4$$

Answer, $x = 3$
$y = 4$

3. $2\frac{1}{4}x + 3\frac{3}{4}y = 39$
$6\frac{3}{4}x - 2\frac{1}{4}y = 9$
$$\frac{9x}{4} + \frac{15y}{4} = 39$$
$$\frac{27x}{4} - \frac{9y}{4} = 9$$

Multiplying each equation by 4, we get
$9x + 15y = 156$
$27x - 9y = 36$

Multiplying the first equation by 3
$27x + 45y = 468$
$27x - \phantom{0}9y = \phantom{0}36$
$54y = 432$
$y = 8$
$9x + 120 = 156$
$9x = 156 - 120 = 36$
$x = 4$

Answer, $x = 4$
$y = 8$

## B

Solve for $x$ and $y$, eliminating by substitution:

1. $x + 2y = 16$
$2x + 3y = 26$

In the first equation, $x = 16 - 2y$.

Substituting this value for $x$ in the second equation, we get

$2(16-2y)+3y=26$
$32-4y+3y=26$
$-y=-32+26$
$-y=-6$
$y=6$
$x+12=16$
$x=16-12=4$

Answer, $x=4$
$y=6$

2. $3x+2y=29$
$2x+4y=38$
In the first equation,
$3x=29-2y$
$x=\dfrac{29-2y}{3}$

Substituting this value for $x$ in the second equation, we get

$2\left(\dfrac{29-2y}{3}\right)+4y=38$
$\dfrac{58-4y}{3}+4y=38$
$58-4y+12y=114$
$8y=56$
$y=7$
$3x+14=29$
$3x=15$
$x=5$

Answer, $x=5$
$y=7$

# EXERCISE 94
## A

Solve for $x$ and $y$, eliminating by addition or subtraction:

1. $x+y=7$
$x-y=-1$

2. $x+2y=19$
$2x+3y=31$

3. $3x+2y=34$
$5x-2y=14$

4. $2x+y=17$
$3x-y=3$

5. $2x+3y=30$
$x-3y=-21$

6. $2x+3y=41$
$5x-4y=-24$

# ALGEBRA

7. $9x+7y=76$
$3x-2y=-5$

8. $4x+y=50$
$5x-2y=56$

9. $4x+7y=47$
$3x+9y=54$

10. $4x-7y=10$
$7x-4y=67$

11. $10x-12y=12$
$11x+7y=296$

12. $10x+3y=91$
$8x-y=15$

13. $3\frac{1}{5}x+2\frac{2}{5}y=176$
$8\frac{1}{6}x-4\frac{3}{5}y=21$

14. $8x+3y=1096$
$7x-2y=626$

15. $5x-2y=28$
$13x-3y=108$

## B

Solve for $x$ and $y$, eliminating by substitution:

1. $x+5y=39$
$2x+3y=29$

2. $x-3y=-12$
$3x+2y=19$

3. $x-4y=6$
$5x+3y=99$

4. $3x+2y=49$
$2x+5y=73$

5. $5x-3y=53$
$7x-8y=40$

6. $x+5y=83$
$2x+3y=61$

7. $35x-17y=20$
$8x-4y=4$

8. $5x-10y=20$
$8x-9y=67$

9. $5x+7y=132$
$7x-y=12$

10. $6x-7y=9$
$24x-43y=-9$

11. $\frac{1}{4}x+\frac{1}{5}y=32$
$\frac{1}{6}x+\frac{1}{7}y=22$

12. $9x-2y=11$
$4x-y=4$

13. $2x+7y=84$
$3x-4y=10$

14. $5x+8y=148$
$9x-y=20$

15. $2x=5y-19$
$3x=131-7y$

16. $\frac{1}{5}x+\frac{1}{10}y=2\frac{1}{2}$
$\frac{1}{2}x-\frac{1}{3}y=-\frac{1}{2}$

## SIMULTANEOUS EQUATION PROBLEMS

It is often necessary to use two unknown quantities in order to solve an algebraic problem. The following are a few sample problems of this type:

1. The sum of two numbers is 17; their difference, 3. Find the numbers.

$x+y=17$
$x-y=3$
$2x=20$
$x=10$
$10+y=17$
$y=7$      Answer, 10 and 7.

2. A man hired 6 men and 2 boys for a day for $42; and the next day, 4 men and 7 boys for $39. How much did he pay each per day?

Let $x=$ the number of dollars he paid each man per day.
Let $y=$ the number of dollars he paid each boy per day.

$6x+2y = 42$
$4x+7y = 45$
$12x+4y = 84$ (we get this by multiplying the 1st equation by 2)
$12x+21y = 135$ (we get this by multiplying the 2nd equation by 3)
$\quad -17y = -51$
$\qquad y = 3$
$\quad 6x+6 = 42$
$\qquad 6x = 36$
$\qquad\; x = 6$          Answer, $6 to each man; $3 to each boy.

3. A grocer has 2 grades of coffee, worth 40 cents and 25 cents per pound. How many pounds of each must he use to make a mixture of 100 pounds worth 31 cents a pound?

Let $x=$ the number of pounds worth 40¢ a pound.
"   $y=$ "    "    "    "    "   25¢ "    "

$$x+y=100$$
$$40x+25y=31\times 100 = 3100$$

Multiply 1st equation by 40:    $40x+40y=4000$
$\qquad\qquad\qquad\qquad\qquad\qquad 40x+25y=3100$
$\qquad\qquad\qquad\qquad\qquad\qquad\quad 15y=900$
$\qquad\qquad\qquad\qquad\qquad\qquad\qquad y=60$
$\qquad\qquad\qquad\qquad\qquad\quad x+60=100$
$\qquad\qquad\qquad\qquad\qquad\qquad\quad x=40$

Answer, 40 pounds worth 40¢ a pound.
$\qquad\quad$ 60 pounds    "    25¢ "    "

4. Four boys and one man can do a job in 40 days; and three boys and six men can do it in 16 days. How long will it take 10 boys to do the job? How long will it take 10 men to do the job?

Let $x=$ the number of days it will take *one boy* to do the job.

$\dfrac{1}{x}=$ the part of the job *one boy* can do in *one day*.

$\dfrac{4}{x}=$ the part of the job *four boys* can do in *one day*.

$\dfrac{3}{x}=$ the part of the job *three boys* can do in *one day*.

# ALGEBRA

Let $y$ = the number of days it will take *one man* to do the job.

$\dfrac{1}{y}$ = the part of the job *one man* can do in *one day*.

$\dfrac{6}{y}$ = the part of the job *six men* can do in *one day*.

Now 4 boys and 1 man can do the job in 40 days. Therefore they can do $\frac{1}{40}$ of the job in 1 day.

And 3 boys and 6 men can do it in 16 days. Therefore they can do $\frac{1}{16}$ of the job in 1 day.

With this information, we can now form the simultaneous equations:

$$\dfrac{4}{x}+\dfrac{1}{y}=\dfrac{1}{40}$$

$$\dfrac{3}{x}+\dfrac{6}{y}=\dfrac{1}{16}$$

Multiply each term of the 1st equation by 6.

$$\dfrac{24}{x}+\dfrac{6}{y}=\dfrac{6}{40}$$

$$\dfrac{3}{x}+\dfrac{6}{y}=\dfrac{1}{16}$$

$$\dfrac{21}{x}=\dfrac{6}{40}-\dfrac{1}{16}$$

$$\dfrac{21}{x}=\dfrac{12}{80}-\dfrac{5}{80}=\dfrac{7}{80}$$

Multiplying both sides of the equation by $80x$, we get

$7x = 1680$

$x = 240$

It will take 1 boy 240 days to do the job.
It will take 10 boys 24 days to do the job.
Substituting 240 for $x$ in the 1st equation, we have

$$\dfrac{4}{240}+\dfrac{1}{y}=\dfrac{1}{40}$$

$$\dfrac{1}{60}+\dfrac{1}{y}=\dfrac{1}{40}$$

$$\dfrac{1}{y}=\dfrac{1}{40}-\dfrac{1}{60}=\dfrac{3}{120}-\dfrac{2}{120}=\dfrac{1}{120}$$

$y = 120$

It will take 1 man 120 days to do the job.
It will take 10 men 12 days to do the job.

## EXERCISE 95

Solve the following problems involving two unknown quantities:

1. The sum of two numbers is 15; their difference, 9. Find the numbers.

2. A man deposited in his bank $80 in ten- and five-dollar bills. The number of bills was ten. How many of each did he deposit?

3. The receipts from a baseball game were $3850. Seats in the grandstand were $1.10, and those in the bleachers were 55¢. If as many had bought seats for the grandstand as for the bleachers, the receipts would have been $4950. How many people bought each kind of seat?

4. A man hired 5 men and 2 boys for a day for $31; and the next day, 4 men and 5 boys for $35. How much did he pay each per day?

5. A grocer has two grades of coffee, worth 32¢ and 20¢ per pound. How many pounds of each must he use to make a mixture of 100 pounds worth 29¢ per pound?

6. A man drives an automobile a certain distance and discovers that if he had traveled ten miles per hour faster he would have saved one hour; but he would have lost two hours if he had traveled ten miles per hour slower. How far had he traveled?

7. If a rectangle were 3 in. narrower and 6 in. longer, its area would remain unchanged; and the same would be the case if it were 4 in. narrower and 9 in. longer. What are its dimensions?

8. The members of a club bought a clubhouse and noted that if there had been fifty more members, they would have paid $12 less per member; and that if there had been 100 members more, each would have paid $20 less. How many members were there in the club, and how much did the clubhouse cost?

9. The sum of the digits of a two-figure number is 9. If $4\frac{1}{2}$ times the unit digit is added to the number, the digits become interchanged. What is the number?

Suggestion: The number is $10x+y$.

10. Two men begin to drive in the same direction from towns 100 miles apart. One overtakes the other after 10 hours of driving; but if they had driven towards each other, they would have met in two hours. How fast does each travel?

11. Smith takes 6 hours more than Brown to drive a distance of 280 miles, but if he doubled his speed he could do it in one hour less than Brown. How fast does each travel?

12. A tank can be filled by two pipes if one runs for 3 hours, and

# ALGEBRA

the other 4 hours; or if the first runs 2 hours, and the other 9 hours. How long will it take each pipe separately to fill the tank?

13. Three pounds of coffee and five pounds of tea cost $2.90. If the price of coffee should increase 20% and the price of tea decline 20%, the same items would cost 22¢ less. How much does each cost per pound?

14. If Smith gives Brown $10, Brown will then have twice as much as Smith. If Brown gives Smith $40, Smith will then have three times as much as Brown. How much has each?

15. A number of two figures is equal to twelve times the sum of its digits. If 36 is subtracted from the number, the digits become interchanged. What is the number?

16. Three boys and one man can do a job in 48 days; and 4 boys and 8 men can do it in 12 days. How long will it take 15 men to do the job?

17. The perimeter of a rug is 54 feet. Three times the length added to four times the width equals 90 feet. What are the dimensions of the rug?

18. The cost of publishing a certain magazine is 12¢ per copy, and it is sold to the newsdealers at 10¢ per copy. The amount received for advertising is 30% of the amount the dealers pay for magazines in excess of 10,000 copies. What is the smallest number of magazines the publishers can sell without sustaining a loss?

19. A theater charges $1.10 for orchestra seats and 83¢ for balcony seats. At a sell-out performance, all 1500 seats were sold for a total of $2615 in receipts. How many seats were there in the orchestra and how many in the balcony?

20. If 8 is added to a two-figure number, and the sum is divided by the sum of the digits of the number, the quotient is 9. If the number is divided by the units digit, the quotient is 41. What is the number?

## ANSWERS
### EXERCISE 69

1. 10° below zero
2. 15°; 22°; 30°
3. 8°
4. −4°
5. −$2100; +$2400
6. $200; −$200
7. −74°
8. 210 miles per hour
9. −$300
10. 150 feet; +450 feet; −150 feet.

### EXERCISE 70A

1. 0
2. −817
3. −114
4. 647

### EXERCISE 70B

1. 3
2. 11
3. 104
4. 100
5. 12
6. −7.29

### EXERCISE 70C

1. $-300$
2. $-399$
3. $-720$
4. $400$
5. $-803$
6. $396$

### EXERCISE 70D

1. $-25$
2. $25$
3. $-81$
4. $-11$
5. $247$
6. $-9$

### EXERCISE 71

1. $15$
2. $15$
3. $15$
4. $30$
5. $105$
6. $216$
7. $25$
8. $75$
9. $75$
10. $1620$
11. $-7$
12. $121$
13. $1$
14. $-37$
15. $341$
16. $1331$
17. $180$
18. $144$
19. $3$
20. $-7$

### EXERCISE 72

1. 11 mi.
2. $11a$
3. 11.10
4. 18 qt.
5. $18a$
6. 18.10
7. $15ab$
8. $ab$
9. $8xyz$
10. $19(a+b)$

### EXERCISE 73

1. $14°+36'$
2. $14x+36y$
3. $14.10+36.2$
4. $6x^3+6a^2b+11ab^2+3y^4$
5. $5x^4+36x^3y+30x^2y^2+12xy^3+2y^4$

### EXERCISE 74

1. $-10a-19b-8c$
2. $-10p+10q+2r$
3. $2x^2+xy+2y^2$
4. $16a^3+7a^2+3a+13$
5. $4a^3+18a^2b+18ab^2+8b^3$
6. $7x^2-2b^2-3c^2+19$
7. $6x^2y$
8. $a^3+a^2b-4ab^2+2b^3$
9. $6x^2-6x+9$
10. $2a^3b-4a^2b^2+21ab^3-10b^4$

### EXERCISE 75

1. $3xy$
2. $5y$
3. $-5y$
4. $13y$
5. $x+y$
6. $15(a+b)$
7. $-3(x+y)$
8. $4a^2-12b$
9. $x^2-7x$
10. $5a^3-9$
11. $12a^2+14a-16$
12. $2y^2$
13. $-a+3\sqrt{a}$
14. $a^3-a^2+\frac{2}{3}a-\frac{2}{3}$
15. $4x^4+36x^3y+18x^2y^2+12xy^2$

### EXERCISE 76

1. $23$
2. $15$
3. $23x$
4. $15x$
5. $-7x$
6. $x$
7. $x+1$
8. $8x+2$
9. $31x-14y$
10. $96a-48$
11. $2y$
12. $2b^2$

### EXERCISE 77

1. $-27$
2. $-27a$
3. $-27a$
4. $-20ab$
5. $-20ab$
6. $12x^2$
7. $12x^2$
8. $-20a^2x^2$
9. $-20b^2y^2z^3$
10. $-42a^2bc^3d$
11. $-20a^7$
12. $x^{n+1}$
13. $a^{3x}$
14. $12x^{m+5}$
15. $256x^{5a+1}$
16. $56a^{x+2}b^{y+2}$
17. $-4(x+y)^4$
18. $-80(x+y)^7$
19. $24(x+y)^5$
20. $306a^5b^7c^9d^{11}$

# ALGEBRA

### EXERCISE 78

1. $ax+ay$
2. $a^2x+a^2y+a^2z$
3. $ax^4+ax^2y^2+ax^2z$
4. $-8x^2y+6xy^2$
5. $-x^2+xy-xz$
6. $-5x^4y+10x^3y^2-5x^2y^3$
7. $18x^{10}y^5-72x^7y^7+54x^4y^{10}$
8. $-4a^{p+n}b^ny^p+12a^{p+1}by^p+56a^py^p$
9. $-9a^{7n}-12a^{6n}b+9a^{5n}b^2-6a^{4n}b^3+15a^{3n}b^4$
10. $45(2x+3y)^3+30(2x+3y)^2+5(2x+3y)$

### EXERCISE 79

1. $x^2+2xy+y^2$
2. $x^2-2xy+y^2$
3. $a^2-b^2$
4. $a^2-a-6$
5. $12x^2-39xy+30y^2$
6. $a^3-3a^2b+3ab^2-b^3$
7. $a^5-5a^4b+10a^3b^2-10a^2b^3+5ab^4-b^5$
8. $a^4+4a^3b+6a^2b^2+4ab^3+b^4$
9. $x^8+8x^7y+28x^6y^2+56x^5y^3+70x^4y^4+56x^3y^5+28x^2y^6+8xy^7+y^8$

### EXERCISE 80

1. $a^2+2ab+b^2$
2. $x^2+2xy+y^2$
3. $m^2+2mn+n^2$
4. $a^2-2ab+b^2$
5. $x^2-2xy+y^2$
6. $m^2-2mn+n^2$
7. $a^2-b^2$
8. $x^2-y^2$
9. $m^2-n^2$
10. 399 $[20^2-1^2]$
11. 391
12. 875

### EXERCISE 81

1. 8
2. $-3$
3. $-9$
4. $7p^2$
5. $r^2$
6. $2r^2$
7. $3x$
8. $-3y^3z^2$
9. $4b^4c^2$
10. $-5$
11. $13b^8d$
12. $5a^2bc^4$
13. $(a+b)^2$
14. $(a-b)^3$
15. $6a(x-y)^2$
16. $x^{n-y}$
17. $5a^{x-3}b^{y-2}c^{z-1}$
18. $-6a^3$
19. $300a^2b$
20. $3x^{8n}$

### EXERCISE 82

1. $9a-6b$
2. $-a^2+5a$
3. $-4a^4+6a^2-15$
4. $-2a^2+3ab-4b^2$
5. $-9ac+17a^3$
6. $b^2-10ab^3+2a^2b^4$
7. $.08x-.12y$
8. $a^2+1$
9. $3a^{n-2}-2a^{n-1}+4a^n+a^{n+1}$
10. $18a^3b-12a^2b^2-9ab^3+22b^4$

### EXERCISE 83

1. $x-4$
2. $x-9$
3. $x-18$
4. $5x-4$
5. $a^3+a^2b+ab^2+b^3$
6. $a+b$
7. $x^2+xy+y^2$
8. $x^3+3x^2y+3xy^2+y^3$
9. $a^5+5a^4b+10a^3b^2+10a^2b^3+5ab^4+b^5$
10. $x^2-xy-xz+y^2-yz+z^2$

### EXERCISE 84

1. $4a^2(1+3a)$
2. $5y^2(2-3y^2)$
3. $a(a+2)$
4. $7x(1+3x^2)$
5. $3y(1+3y-3y^2)$
6. $2x^2(4-3x^3)$
7. $a^2(3a^2+ab-b^2)$
8. $x^2(x^2+5x-4)$
9. $x^2y(1-2y)$
10. $\frac{1}{2}a^2(a+\frac{1}{2})$
11. $5x^3y^3(2x-7y)$
12. $2x^2y^3z(x^2-xz^2+2yz)$
13. $x^ny(y^2-4x^ny+6x^{2n})$
14. $2x^3(x^2-3x+7)$
15. $5x^5y^3(x^3-2xy+3y^2)$
16. $(x+y)(a+b)$
17. $(a^2+b^2)(x+y)$
18. $(x+y)(8a+3b)$

## EXERCISE 85

1. $(3x+1)^2$
2. $(x+4)^2$
3. $(7x+1)^2$
4. $(7x+y)^2$
5. $(9x+2y)^2$
6. $(11a+3b)^2$
7. $(8a-b)^2$
8. $(5x-6y)^2$
9. $(12p-9q)^2$
10. $(x+y)^4$
11. $x(a+b)^2$
12. $[4(a+b)+1]^2$

## EXERCISE 86

1. $(x+4)(x-4)$
2. $(x+3y)(x-3y)$
3. $(2a+5b)(2a-5b)$
4. $(4x+6y)(4x-6y)$
5. $(7a+8b)(7a-8b)$
6. $(9x+10y)(9x-10y)$
7. $(11x+1)(11x-1)$
8. $(x+12y)(x-12y)$
9. $(\frac{1}{2}a+b)(\frac{1}{2}a-b)$
10. $(\frac{3}{5}x+\frac{5}{2}y)(\frac{3}{5}x-\frac{5}{2}y)$
11. $(.6a+.07b)(.6a-.07b)$
12. $(a+b+x+2y)(a+b-x-2y)$
13. $(x+y+a)(x+y-a)$
14. $x(x+4)(x-4)$
15. $(a^2+b^2)(a+b)(a-b)$
16. $(4x^2+1)(2x+1)(2x-1)$
17. $(x^4+y^4)(x^2+y^2)(x+y)(x-y)$
18. $(16a^2+9b^2)(4a+3b)(4a-3b)$
19. $(\frac{1}{4}x^2+\frac{4}{9}y^2)(\frac{1}{2}x+\frac{2}{3}y)(\frac{1}{2}x-\frac{2}{3}y)$
20. $(x^2+2xy+y^2+1)(x+y+1)(x+y-1)$

## EXERCISE 87

1. $(x+3)(x+2)$
2. $(x+5)(x+3)$
3. $(x-4)(x+3)$
4. $(x+3)(x-2)$
5. $(x-7)(x+2)$
6. $(x-8)(x-5)$
7. $(x-11)(x-2)$
8. $(x-16)(x+3)$
9. $(x-9)(x-4)$
10. $(x+9)(x-4)$

## EXERCISE 88

1. 11
2. 13
3. 6
4. 13
5. 3
6. 16
7. 4
8. 2
9. $-5$
10. 1
11. 4
12. $7\frac{1}{2}$
13. 3
14. 2
15. 4
16. 10
17. 4
18. 11
19. 11
20. 2

## EXERCISE 89

1. 3
2. 1
3. 6
4. $-\frac{3}{4}$
5. $-\frac{5}{4}$
6. 5
7. 8
8. 9
9. 6
10. 7
11. 2
12. 14
13. $-47$
14. 5
15. 8

## EXERCISE 90

1. $3x$; $4x$
2. $\$1000-x$
3. $x+25$; $2x+25$
4. $x+1$ and $x+2$; $x-1$ and $x-2$
5. $2n+3$ and $2n+5$
6. $2n+2$ and $2n+4$
7. $x-10$; $10-x$
8. $\frac{x}{5}$; $\frac{a}{5}$; $\frac{x}{n}$
9. $2x-8$
10. $\$1000+x$; $\$1000+x+y$
11. $x-5$; $x+6$; $x+y$
12. $20x+2y$
13. $x+y+18$
14. $\$13.65$; $100x-y$ cents
15. $2x$; $ax$
16. $\frac{x}{y}$; $\frac{xz}{y}$
17. $xyz$
18. $ax$
19. $\frac{a}{x}$
20. $\frac{x}{a}$

# ALGEBRA

## EXERCISE 91

1. $3x=10$
2. $\dfrac{x}{5}=35$
3. $3x-18=x+2$
4. $25-x=x-15$
   (b) $3x+6-(x+9)=2x+9-(x+12)$
   (d) $3x+6-20=4(x+12-20)$
   (f) $3x+6+15=x+12+2x+9$
   (b) $8x=2(4x+\$500-\$400)$
   (d) $4x+\$5000-\$1000=\tfrac{1}{2}(7x)$
   (f) $4x+\$500-\$1400=\dfrac{8x-\$100+\$1400}{4}$
5. (a) $3x+6=2(x+12)$
   (c) $3x+6-15=2x+9$
   (e) $3x+6-30=x+12$
6. (a) $4x+\$500+7x+8x-100=\$19{,}400$
   (c) $8x-\$100-\$900=7x$
   (e) $4x+\$500+7x=8x-\$100+\$3600$

## EXERCISE 92

1. Brown, $750; Smith, $250.
2. Brown, $500; Smith, $400.
3. Brown, $350; Smith, $250.
4. 8
5. $5
6. 4
7. $10
8. 16
9. 41 and 15
10. 11
11. 10, 11, and 12
12. 17, 19, and 21
13. 58, 60, and 62
14. 50 and 25 years
15. 44 and 20
16. 15 years; 5 years
17. The salesman earns $65 and saves $5; the bookkeeper earns $60 and saves $6.
18. 30, 19, and 6
19. $2500 and $1500
20. 28 dimes and 7 dollars
21. 4 dimes and 18 nickels
22. Smith receives $1100; Jones, $1800; Robinson, $3200.
23. 2, 4, 8, and 11 automobiles respectively.
24. $120
25. $320

## EXERCISE 93

1. 3 hours, 40 minutes
2. 28 and 56 miles per hour
3. 5 hours
4. $82\tfrac{5}{18}$ miles
5. 88 miles
6. $212\tfrac{4}{15}$ miles
7. $5\tfrac{5}{11}$ minutes past 1 o'clock
8. (a) $10\tfrac{10}{11}$ minutes past 2 o'clock; (b) $16\tfrac{4}{11}$ minutes past 3 o'clock; (c) $21\tfrac{9}{11}$ minutes past 4 o'clock.
9. Smith, 3 miles per hour; Jones, 4 miles per hour.
10. Jones overtakes Smith at 6 minutes and 40 seconds past 10 o'clock. The train overtakes Jones at 2 P.M. at a point 120 miles from the town; Smith is then 15 miles from the town.

## EXERCISE 94A

1. $x=3; y=4$
2. $x=5; y=7$
3. $x=6; y=8$
4. $x=4; y=9$
5. $x=3; y=8$
6. $x=4; y=11$
7. $x=3; y=7$
8. $x=12; y=2$
9. $x=3; y=5$
10. $x=13; y=6$
11. $x=18; y=14$
12. $x=4; y=17$
13. $x=25; y=40$
14. $x=110; y=72$
15. $x=12; y=16$

## EXERCISE 94B

1. $x=4; y=7$
2. $x=3; y=5$
3. $x=18; y=3$
4. $x=9; y=11$
5. $x=16; y=9$
6. $x=8; y=15$
7. $x=3; y=5$
8. $x=14; y=5$
9. $x=4; y=16$
10. $x=5; y=3$
11. $x=72; y=70$
12. $x=3; y=8$
13. $x=14; y=8$
14. $x=4; y=16$
15. $x=18; y=11$
16. $x=9; y=15$

## EXERCISE 95

1. 12 and 3
2. 6 ten-dollar bills; 4 five-dollar bills
3. 2000 in the grandstand; 3000 in the bleachers
4. $5 for a man; $3 for a boy.
5. 75 lb. at 32¢; 25 lb. at 20¢.
6. 120 miles
7. 18 in. by 12 in.
8. 200 members; $12,000
9. 36
10. 30 and 20 miles per hour
11. 20 and 35 miles per hour
12. $3\frac{3}{8}$ and 19 hours
13. Coffee, 30¢ per pound; tea, 40¢ per pound.
15. 84
16. 8 days
17. 18 ft. by 9 ft.
18. 30,000
19. 1000 in the orchestra; 500 in the balcony
20. 82

# GEOMETRY

## CHAPTER XIII
# Geometry

*Geometry* means the *measure of land*. *Plane Geometry* is the measure, or the study, of land surfaces. It deals with lines, angles, triangles, quadrilaterals, squares, polygons, and circles.

A *triangle* is a figure having *three angles*: △.

A *quadrilateral* is a figure having *four sides*: ▢.

A *polygon* (from the Greek *poly*, many, and *gon*, side) is a figure of any number of sides. A figure of *five sides* is a *pentagon*—⬠; a figure of *six sides* is a *hexagon*—⬡; and so forth. A *regular polygon* is a polygon with equal sides and equal angles.

### POINTS AND LINES

All geometry—that is, all the measuring of land, begins with a *point*. Geometrically speaking, a point has no size—no length or breadth or thickness. For practical purposes, we represent a point by a dot.

A *line* is the path of a moving point.

A *straight line* is the *shortest path* between two points.

### ANGLES

An *angle* is a *corner* produced by the meeting of two straight lines: ∠.

The *vertex* of an angle is the point at which the two lines meet, or converge.

An angle may be designated by three capital letters, as follows:

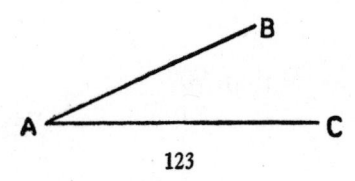

It is then read as BAC, or as CAB. The vertex letter should always be read in the middle.

Sometimes an angle is designated by a single small letter or by a number placed inside, between the two lines, as follows:

These angles are called *angle a*, and *angle 1*.

All angles are parts of a circle, as you will see from the following figure:

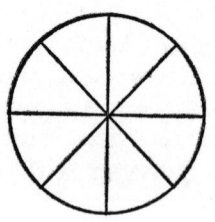

A *circle* is divided into 360 equal parts, or *degrees*. Half a circle contains 180 degrees (written 180°). A quarter circle contains 90°.

An angle that marks off a quarter circle is a *90° angle*, or a *right angle*.

An angle that contains *less than* 90° is an *acute angle*.

An angle that contains *more than* 90° is an *obtuse angle*.

Right angle    90°

Acute angle    Less than 90°    LESS THAN 90°

Obtuse angle    More than 90°    MORE THAN 90°

# GEOMETRY

Two angles are *complementary* if their sum is equal to 90°.

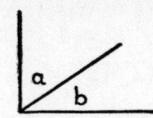

Angles a and b are *complementary*. That is, each of these angles is complementary to the other.

Two angles are *supplementary* if their sum is equal to 180°. They are sometimes called *straight angles*.

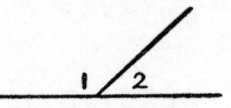

Angles 1 and 2 are *supplementary*. That is, each of these angles is supplementary to the other.

## MEASURING COMPLEMENTARY AND SUPPLEMENTARY ANGLES

1. The complement of an angle is eight times as large as itself. How large is the angle?

   Let $x$ = the angle
   $8x$ = the complement
   $x + 8x = 90°$
   $9x = 90°$
   $x = 10°$  Answer, 10°.

2. Find two supplementary angles with a difference of 70°.

   Let $x$ = the smaller angle
   $x + 70°$ = the larger angle
   $x + x + 70° = 180°$
   $2x = 180° - 70°$
   $2x = 110°$
   $x = 55°$
   $x + 70 = 125°$

   Answer, 55° and 125°

Angles are measured in degrees, minutes, and seconds. There are sixty seconds in a minute, and sixty minutes in a degree. A second is designated by two strokes ("), and a minute is designated by one stroke ('). An angle of 40 degrees, 25 minutes, and 12 seconds is written as follows: 40° 25′ 12″.

3. Find the complement of 34° 22′ 49″.

From 90° subtract 34° 22′ 49″.

```
   90°
 − 34°     22′      49″
```

From the 90° borrow 60′, and from the 60′ borrow 60″. This will give you 89° 59′ 60″.

```
   89°     59′      60″
 − 34°     22′      49″
   55°     37′      11″
```

## EXERCISE 96

Solve the following problems:

1. Find the supplement of
(a) 48°   (b) 63°   (c) 96°   (d) 103°
(e) 89° 54′ 26″   (f) 143° 15′ 58″

2. Find the complement of
(a) 71°   (b) 61°   (c) 87°   (d) 53°
(e) 49° 35′ 18″   (f) 64° 26′ 43″

3. The complement of an angle is twice as large as the angle itself. How large is the angle?

4. The complement of an angle is four times as large as the angle itself. How large is the angle?

5. The complement of an angle is five times as large as the angle itself. How large is the angle?

6. The supplement of an angle is nine times as large as the angle itself. How large is the angle?

7. The supplement of an angle is seventeen times as large as the angle itself. How large is the angle?

8. The complement of an angle is one-eighth of the angle itself. How large is the angle?

9. The complement of an angle is one-fourteenth of the angle itself. How large is the angle?

10. The supplement of an angle is one-eleventh of the angle itself. How large is the angle?

11. Find two complementary angles with a difference of ten degrees.

12. Find two complementary angles with a difference of
(a) 6°   (b) 12°   (c) 26°   (d) 38°
(e) 49°   (f) 37°   (g) 19° 16′   (h) 39° 17′ 26″

13. Find two supplementary angles with a difference of
(a) 8°      (b) 14°      (c) 28°        (d) 46°
(e) 51°     (f) 49°      (g) 23° 18'    (h) 73° 15' 42"

Two angles that have a common side and a common vertex—that is, two angles that *lie next to each other*—are *adjacent angles*.

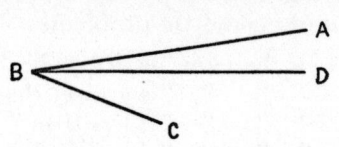

Angles ABD and DBC are adjacent, because they have a common side, BD, and a common vertex, B.

Two angles are *vertical* when their sides intersect.

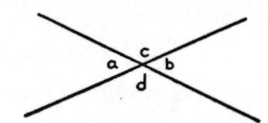

Angles a and b are vertical. Also, angles c and d are vertical.

When an angle equals 90°—that is, when it is a right angle—the sides are *perpendicular* to each other.

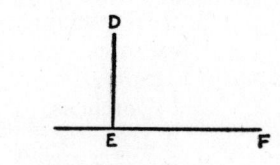

∠DEF = 90°
DE is perpendicular to EF.

### GENERAL DEFINITIONS

*Propositions.* A *proposition* is a geometric statement which has to be demonstrated or proved.

*Theorem.* A *theorem* is the same as a *proposition*.

*Corollaries.* A *corollary* is a theorem that is logically derived from another theorem.

The *hypothesis* is the part of the theorem that is given in order to help the solution of the rest of the theorem.

## GEOMETRIC SYMBOLS

In order to save time, we use symbols and abbreviations instead of writing out the geometric terms in full. Thus, *triangle* is written △; *angle* is written ∠; *circle* is written ⊙; and so on. Following is a list of the more common symbols used in the solution of geometric problems:

⊥ stands for the term "is perpendicular to."
\> " " " " "is greater than."
< " " " " "is less than."
∴ " " " " "therefore."
∥ " " " " "is parallel to."
= " " " " "is equal to."
≠ " " " " "is not equal to."
⌒ " " " " "arc."
≅ " " " " "is congruent to."
~ " " " " "is similar to."

## GEOMETRIC ABBREVIATIONS

The following abbreviations are commonly used in geometry:

ax. for axiom.
circum. " circumference.
comp. " complement.
cor. " corollary.
corr. " corresponding.
ex. " exercise.
ext. " exterior.
hy. " hypotenuse.
hyp. " hypothesis.
int. " interior.
isos. " isosceles.
rt. ∠ " right angle.

## AXIOMS

An *axiom* is a fact that requires no proof. For example, it is an axiom that all living things must die. In geometry it is important to learn the following axioms, a knowledge of which will save considerable trouble in the solution of various problems:

1. Things equal to the same thing are equal to each other.
2. If equals are added to equals, the sums are equal.

# GEOMETRY

3. If equals are subtracted from equals, the remainders are equal.
4. If equals are multiplied by equals, the products are equal.
5. If equals are divided by equals, the quotients are equal.
6. The whole is equal to the sum of its parts.
7. The whole is greater than any of its parts.
8. One quantity may be substituted for another equal quantity in an equation.
9. One straight line, and only one, can be drawn between two points.
10. A straight line is the shortest distance between two points.
11. All right angles are equal.
12. Two intersecting straight lines cannot both be parallel to a third straight line.
13. A geometric figure may be moved from one position to another without change of shape or size.
14. Two straight lines can intersect at only one point.

We shall have occasion again and again to cite these axioms. For the sake of brevity, we shall always refer to them by number.

## TRIANGLES

The following figures represent the various kinds of triangles:

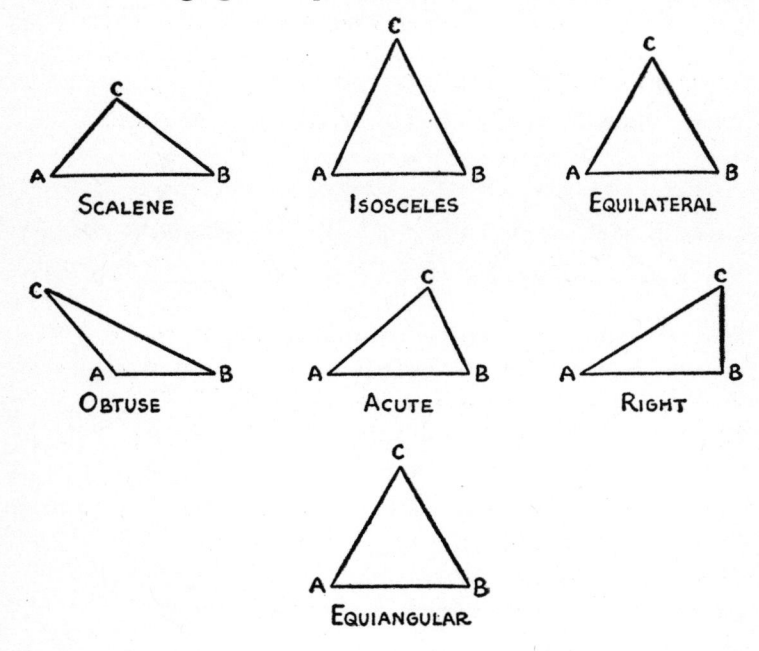

SCALENE    ISOSCELES    EQUILATERAL

OBTUSE    ACUTE    RIGHT

EQUIANGULAR

There are several kinds of triangles:

1. *Scalene*—a triangle whose three sides are all of different lengths.
2. *Isosceles*—a triangle which has two equal sides.
3. *Equilateral*—a triangle whose three sides are all equal.
4. *Obtuse*—a triangle which has one obtuse angle.
5. *Acute*—a triangle whose three angles are all acute.
6. *Right*—a triangle which has one right angle.
7. *Equiangular*—a triangle whose three angles are all equal.

The *base* of a triangle is the *bottom* side—that is, the side upon which it appears to rest.

The *arms* of a triangle are the other two sides.

The *hypotenuse* is the side opposite the *right angle* in a right triangle. In the above right triangle, AC is the hypotenuse.

The *vertex angle* is the angle opposite the base.

The *altitude* of a triangle is the length of a line drawn perpendicularly from the vertex angle to the base.

The *sum of the angles* of a triangle is always 180°.

In their relation to one another, triangles may be *equal*, or *equivalent*, or *similar*.

Two triangles are *equal* when they will *exactly coincide* if one is placed upon the other. The sides and the angles of the one will fall *directly* upon the sides and the angles of the other. The two following triangles, ABC and DEF, are *equal*:

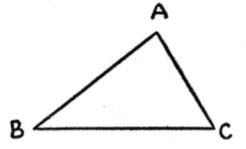

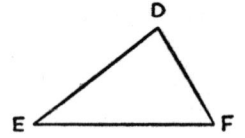

Two triangles are *similar* when their *angles* are equal. Their sides need not necessarily be equal. All equal triangles are similar, but not all similar triangles are equal. The two *above* triangles are both *equal* and *similar*. The two *following* triangles are merely *similar*:

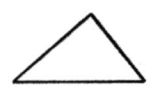

# GEOMETRY

Two triangles are *equivalent* when their *areas* are equal. Such triangles need not necessarily be equal or similar. All equal triangles are obviously equivalent triangles, but not all equivalent triangles are equal triangles. The two following triangles are equivalent:

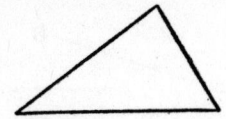

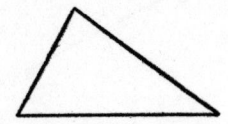

## HOW TO PROVE A GEOMETRIC THEOREM

To prove a geometric theorem, proceed as follows:
1. Write out the theorem, or proposition.
2. Draw the diagram.
3. State the thing that is given, or admitted, in the proposition. This is called the *hypothesis*.
4. State the thing that you must prove.
5. Proceed with the proof. Write the statements on the left, and the reasons for these statements on the right.

### PROPOSITION I

*All vertical angles are equal.*

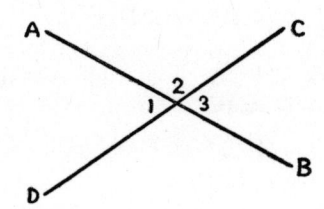

*Given:* Vertical angles, 1 and 3, formed by the intersection of the lines AB and CD.

*To Prove:* $\angle 1 = \angle 3$
*Proof:*  $\angle 1 + \angle 2 = 180°$   All straight lines $= 180°$
        $\angle 3 + \angle 2 = 180°$   " " " "
        $\angle 1 = 180° - \angle 2$   Transposing and changing signs
        $\angle 3 = 180° - \angle 2$   " " " "
∴   $\angle 1 = \angle 3.$   Axiom 1.

## EXERCISE 97

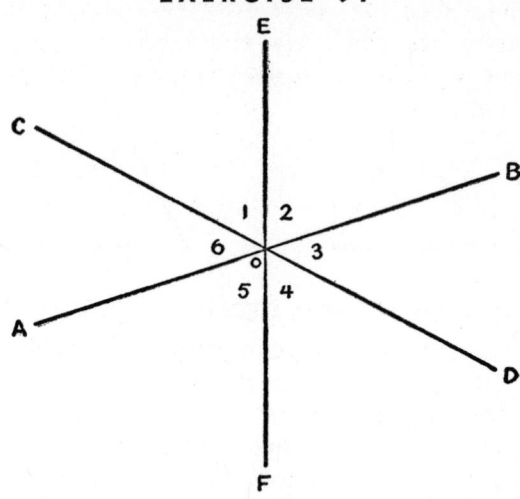

In the diagram above, three straight lines intersect at 0.

1. Which angle is equal to
(a) ∠1  (b) ∠2  (c) ∠3  (d) ∠4  (e) ∠5  (f) ∠6

2. Which angle is equal to
(a) ∠COB  (b) ∠EOD  (c) ∠BOF  (d) ∠DOA  (e) ∠FOC
(f) ∠AOE

3. If ∠1=48° and ∠3=47°, how large is
(a) ∠2  (b) ∠4  (c) ∠5  (d) ∠6
(e) ∠COB  (f) ∠EOD  (g) ∠BOF  (h) ∠DOA
(i) ∠FOC  (j) ∠AOE

## PROPOSITION II

*Two triangles are equal if two angles and the enclosed side of one equal, respectively, two angles and the enclosed side of the other.* (Angle, side and angle of one △ are equal to angle, side and angle of the other △. This is generally expressed as follows: a.s.a. = a.s.a.)

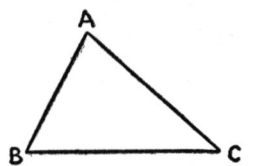

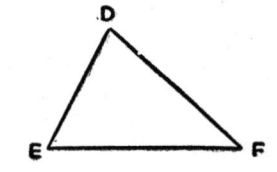

GEOMETRY 133

*Given:* △ABC and DEF with AB=DE, ∠A= ∠D, and ∠B= ∠E.
*To Prove:* △ABC= △DEF.
*Proof:* Place △ABC upon △DEF so that AB shall coincide with its equal DE. } Hypothesis. Axiom 13.
   Then AC will fall along DF. } Since ∠A= ∠D by hypothesis.
   And BC will fall along EF. } Since ∠B= ∠E by hypothesis.
   Point C will fall upon point F. } Axiom 14.
   ∴ △ABC= △DEF.    Triangles are equal if they coincide exactly.

## EXERCISE 98

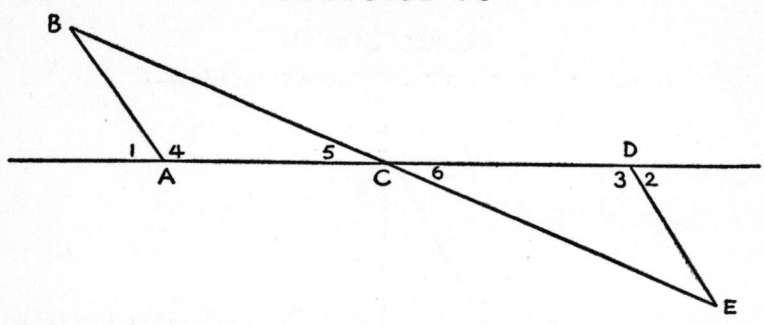

*Given:* AD and BE intersecting at C; AC=CD; ∠1= ∠2
*To Prove:* AB=DE

2. If AB=5 in., BC=8 in., AC=4 in., ∠1=43°, and ∠5=23°, find:
(a) CD     (b) DE     (c) EC     (d) ∠3     (e) ∠6

## PROPOSITION III

*Two triangles are equal if two sides and the included angle of one are equal, respectively, to two sides and the included angle of the other.* (s.a.s.=s.a.s.)

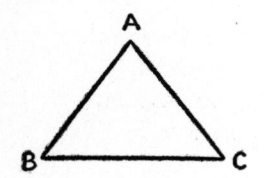

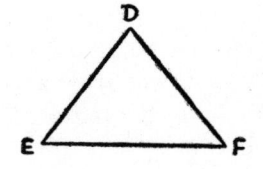

*Given:* △ABC and DEF with AB=DE, BC=EF, and ∠B=∠C.
*To Prove:* △ABC=△DEF.
*Proof:* Place △ABC upon △DEF ⎫ Hypothesis.
so that BC shall coincide with its ⎬ Axiom 13.
equal EF. ⎭

Then BA (or AB) will fall along ⎱ ∠B=∠E, by hyp.
ED (or DE). ⎰

Point A will fall on point D.    } AB=DE, by hyp.
AC will coincide with DF.        } Axiom 9.
∴   △ABC=△DEF.                   Triangles are equal if they coincide exactly.

## PROPOSITION IV

*The base angles of an isosceles triangle are equal.*

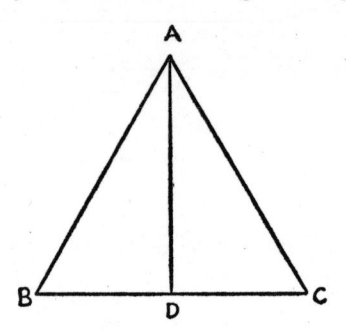

*Given:* ABC is an isosceles △.
*To Prove:* ∠B=∠C.
*Proof:* Draw the line AD to bisect ∠BAC.
Then ∠BAD=∠CAD.         By construction.
     AB=AC.              Hyp. The sides of an isos. △.
     AD=AD.              Identity.
     △ABD=△ACD.          s.a.s.=s.a.s.
∴    ∠B=∠C.              Corresponding parts of equal △.

Corollary. *If the base angles of a triangle are equal, the sides opposite are equal. That is, the triangle is isosceles.*

Note: Corollaries are so obvious, and so logically derived from their theorems, that they do not as a rule have to be proved.

## EXERCISE 99

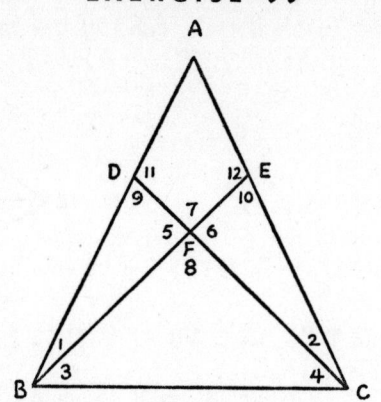

1. In the diagram above, AB=AC and ∠1=∠2. Prove that BE=CD.
2. Prove (a) that AD=AE; (b) that FD=FE.
3. If AB=20 in., AD=7½ in., BF=12½ in., and FE=4½ in., find
(a) AC  (b) AE  (c) CD  (d) FD
4. If ∠A=54°, ∠B=63°, ∠1=21°, ∠5=84°, and ∠9=75°, find
(a) ∠C  (b) ∠2  (c) ∠3  (d) ∠4  (e) ∠6
(f) ∠7  (g) ∠8  (h) ∠10  (i) ∠11  (j) ∠12

## EXERCISE 100

Prove that the bisector of the vertex angle of an isosceles triangle bisects the base and is perpendicular to the base.

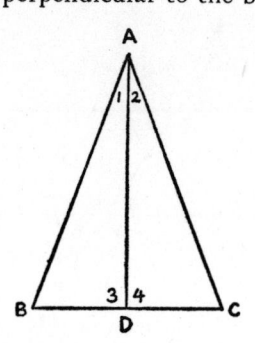

*Given:* AB=AC; ∠1=∠2.
*To Prove:* BD=DC;  ∠3 and ∠4 are rt. ∠s

## PROPOSITION V

*Two triangles are equal if three sides of one are equal, respectively, to three sides of the other.  (s.s.s = s.s.s.)*

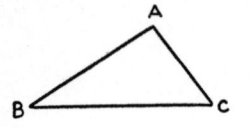

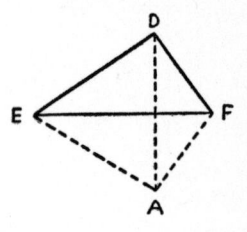

**Given:** △ABC and DEF, with AB = DE, BC = EF, and AC = DF.
**To Prove:** △ABC = △DEF.
**Proof:** Place △ABC so that BC shall coincide with EF and A and D shall lie on opposite sides of EF. } Hypothesis. Axiom 13.

| | |
|---|---|
| Draw AD. | Axiom 9. |
| △AFD is isosceles | AF = DF, by hyp. |
| ∠FAD = ∠FDA. | Proposition IV. |
| △AED is isosceles | AE = DE, by hyp. |
| ∠EAD = ∠EDA | Proposition IV. |
| ∠FAD + ∠EAD = ∠FDA + ∠EDA | Axiom 2. |
| Or,   ∠A = ∠D | Substitution. |
| ∴ △ABC = △DEF | s.a.s. |

## PARALLEL LINES

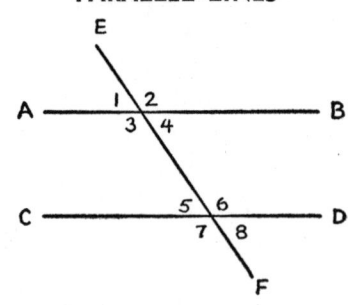

In the above figure, EF intersects AB and CD. It is therefore called a transversal. A *transversal* is a line that intersects two or more lines. This intersection produces a number of angles, and the angles are named as follows:

1, 2, 7, and 8 are *exterior* angles.
3, 4, 5, and 6 are *interior* angles.
1 and 8 are *alternate exterior* angles.
2 and 7 are     "          "          "
3 and 6 are *alternate interior* angles.
4 and 5 are     "         "         "
1 and 5 are *corresponding* angles.
3 and 7 are          "           "
2 and 6 are          "           "
4 and 8 are          "           "

Lines AB and CD in the above figure are parallel. *Parallel lines* are lines which never meet.

Two straight lines parallel to a third line are parallel to each other. Note, for example, the parallel lines in a striped coat.

## PROPOSITION VI

*The exterior angle of a triangle is greater than either of the opposite interior angles.*

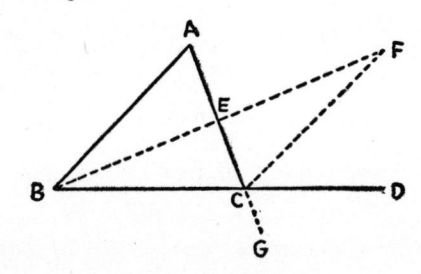

*Given:* △ABC and the exterior ∠ACD.
*To Prove:* ∠ACD > ∠A or ∠B.
*Proof:* Let E be the middle point of AC. Draw BE and produce it until EF = BE. Draw FC.
In the △ ABE and CFE,

| | |
|---|---|
| BE = EF. | Construction. |
| AE = EC. | Construction. |
| ∠AEB = ∠CEF | Vertical ∠s. |
| △ABE = △CFE | s.a.s. = s.a.s. |
| ∠ECF = ∠A | Corresponding parts of equal △ are equal. |
| ∠ACD > ECF | Axiom 7. |
| ∴ ∠ACD > A | Substitution. |

And now, by joining A to the midpoint of BC, and continuing it by the same process as outlined above, we can prove that $\angle BCG > \angle B$.
But $\angle ACD = \angle BCG$                 Vertical $\angle s$.
∴ $\angle ACD > B$                       Substitution.

## PROPOSITION VII

*Two lines are parallel if the alternate interior angles made by a transversal are equal.*

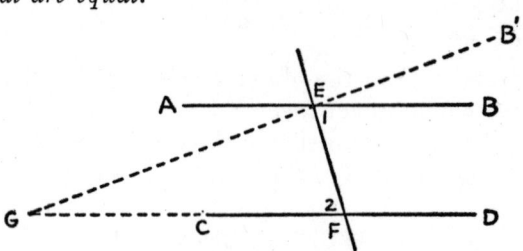

*Given:* AB and CD are crossed by a transversal at points E and F so that $\angle 1 = \angle 2$.
*To Prove:* AB‖CD.
*Proof:* Suppose they are not parallel. In that case they meet at some point. Let that point be G.
Then $\angle B'EF$, or $\angle 1$, is greater than $\angle 2$.   } Proposition VI.
But $\angle 1 = \angle 2$.                                               Hyp.
∴ AB and CD cannot meet, and hence are parallel.

**Corollary.** *The alternate interior angles of parallel lines are equal.*

## PROPOSITION VIII

*Two lines are parallel if the corresponding angles made by a transversal are equal.*

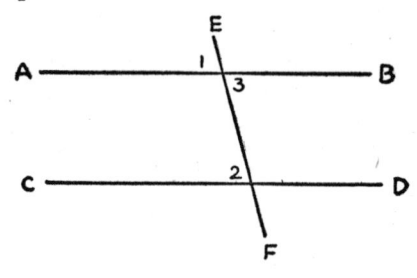

*Given:* AB and CD are crossed by a transversal, EF, so that ∠1 = ∠2.
*To Prove:* AB‖CD.
*Proof:* ∠1 = ∠2.                    Hyp.
   ∠1 = ∠3.                    Vertical ∠s. Prop. I.
   ∠2 = ∠3.                    Axiom 1.
  ∴ AB ‖ CD.                    Proposition VII.

## PROPOSITION IX

*The sum of the angles of a triangle is equal to two right angles (180°).*

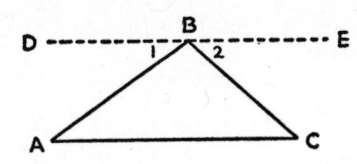

*Given:* △ABC.
*To Prove:* ∠A + ∠B + ∠C = 180°
*Proof:* Through point B, draw DE‖AC.
     ∠1 = ∠A                    Corollary to Prop. VII.
     ∠2 = ∠C                    "     "     "     "
   ∠1 + ∠B + ∠2 = 180°            Axiom 2.
  ∴ ∠A + ∠B + ∠C = 180°            Substitution.

**Corollary 1.** *A triangle can have only one obtuse or one right angle.*

Otherwise, the sum of the angles of the △ would be more than 180°.

**Corollary 2.** *The acute angles of a right triangle are complementary.*

That is, their sum = 90°.

**Corollary 3.** *If two triangles have two angles of the one equal to two angles of the other, the third angles are equal.*

**Axiom 3.** If equals are subtracted from equals, the remainders are equal.

**Corollary 4.** *Two triangles are equal if two angles and the side opposite one of the angles are equal respectively to two angles and the corresponding side of the other.* (a.a.s = a.a.s.)

∠A = ∠D    Hyp.
∠B = ∠E    Hyp.
∠C = ∠F    Ax. 3.
△ABC = △DEF    Prop. II.

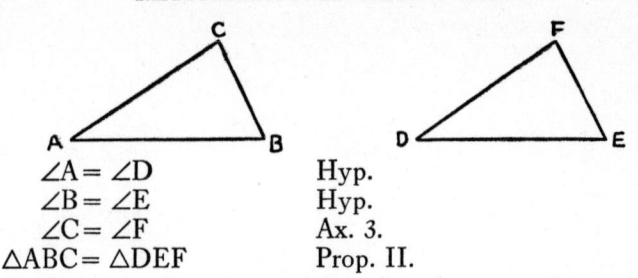

**Corollary 5.** *Each angle of an equiangular triangle equals 60°.*
$180° \div 3 = 60°$

**Corollary 6.** *Two right triangles are equal if the hypotenuse and an acute angle of the one are equal to the hypotenuse and an acute angle of the other.*
See Corollary 4.

**Corollary 7.** *Two right triangles are equal if an arm and an acute angle of one triangle are equal to an arm and an acute angle of the other triangle.*

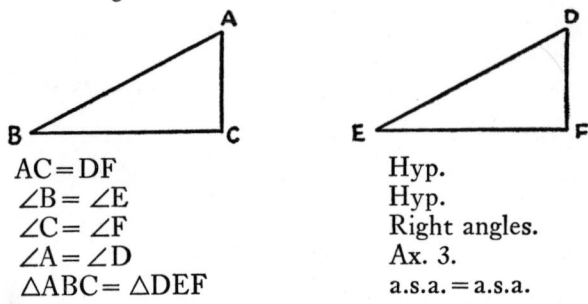

AC = DF    Hyp.
∠B = ∠E    Hyp.
∠C = ∠F    Right angles.
∠A = ∠D    Ax. 3.
△ABC = △DEF    a.s.a. = a.s.a.

**Corollary 8.** *Each angle in an equilateral triangle equals 60°.*

**Corollary 9.** *An equilateral triangle consists of two equal right triangles whose acute angles equal, respectively, 30° and 60°.*

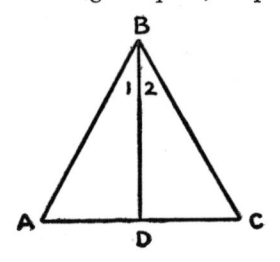

△ABC consists of rt. △ ABD and CBD.
ZA = 60°          See Corollary 8.
ZC = 60°             "      "      "
∠BDA = 90°       Rt. ∠.
∠BDC = 90°         "     "
∠1 = 30°          Ax. 3.
∠2 = 30°           "     "
AB = BC           Equal sides of equilateral △.
BD = BD           Identity.
△ABD = △CBD      s.a.s. = s.a.s.

## EXERCISE 101

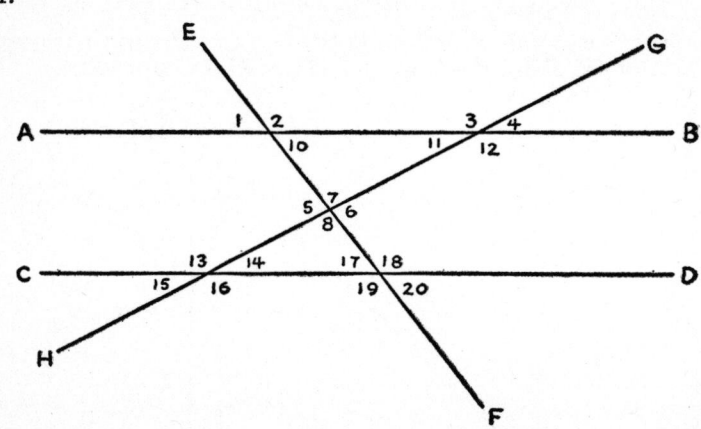

1.

In the diagram above, AB∥CD, and EF and GH are transversals. If ∠1 = 48° and ∠4 = 34°, find:

(a) ∠2   (b) ∠3   (c) ∠5   (d) ∠6
(e) ∠7   (f) ∠8   (g) ∠9   (h) ∠10
(i) ∠11  (j) ∠12  (k) ∠13  (l) ∠14
(m) ∠15  (n) ∠16  (o) ∠17  (p) ∠18
(q) ∠19  (r) ∠20

2. Prove that an equiangular △ is also equilateral.
3. Prove that if one acute ∠ of a right △ is 45°, the △ is isosceles.
4. (a) Prove that if one acute ∠ of a right △ is 30°, the side opposite the 30° ∠ equals $\frac{1}{2}$ the hypotenuse.

Suggestion: Prolong BC so that BC=CD; and draw AD. Now show that △ABD is equilateral.

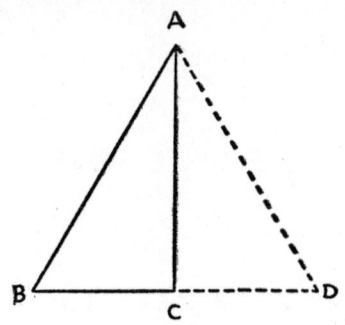

(b) Prove the converse. If BC=½AB, ∠BAC=30°.

5. An obelisk casts a shadow of 100 ft. at a time when the sun is at an ∠ of 45° above the horizon. How tall is the obelisk?

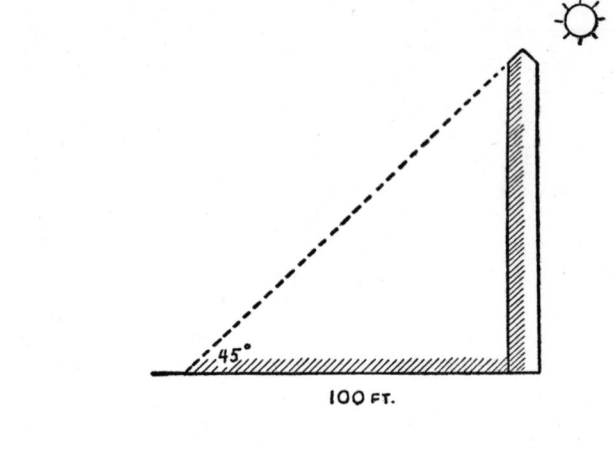

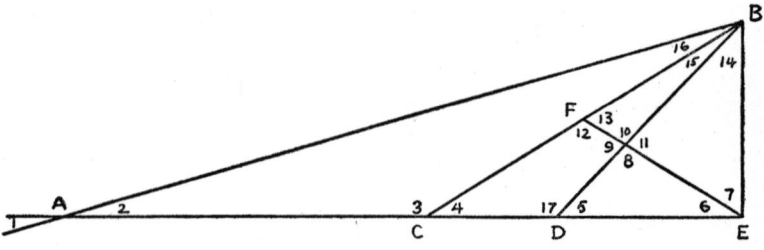

6. In the diagram above, BE is ⊥ to AE; BE=BF=FC=DE; AC=twice FE. Prove that:

(a) $\angle 4 = 30°$  (b) $\angle FBE = 60°$  (c) $\angle 13 = 60°$
(d) $FE = FC$   (e) $AC = CB$    (f) $\angle 1 = 15°$

7. Give the size of the following $\angle$s:

(a) $\angle 2$      (b) $\angle 3$      (c) $\angle 5$      (d) $\angle 6$
(e) $\angle 7$      (f) $\angle 8$      (g) $\angle 9$      (h) $\angle 10$
(i) $\angle 11$     (j) $\angle 12$     (k) $\angle 13$     (l) $\angle 14$
(m) $\angle 15$     (n) $\angle 16$     (o) $\angle 17$     (p) $\angle ABD$

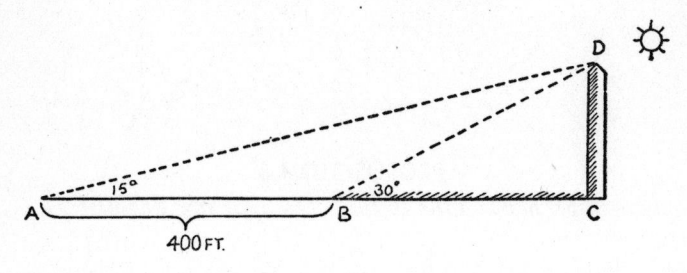

8. While the sun is 30° above the horizon, a man measures 400 ft. in a straight line from the edge of the shadow cast by an obelisk and notes that the top of the obelisk is then 15° above the horizon. What is the height of the obelisk?

9. A hill is 440 ft. high, and the road up it is a 30° grade. If an automobile travels 30 miles per hour up the hill, how long will it take to complete the ascent?

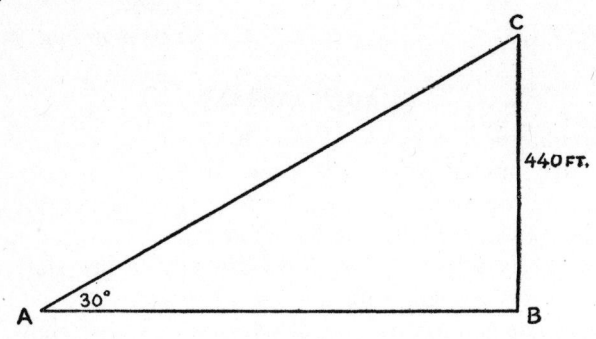

10. A man wishes to measure across a river from A to B, directly opposite points. He turns at right angles and measures a convenient distance to C, and then the same distance to D. He turns once more at right angles and arrives at a point E from which he can sight B and

C on a straight line. He then takes DE as the distance across the river. Prove that this is correct.

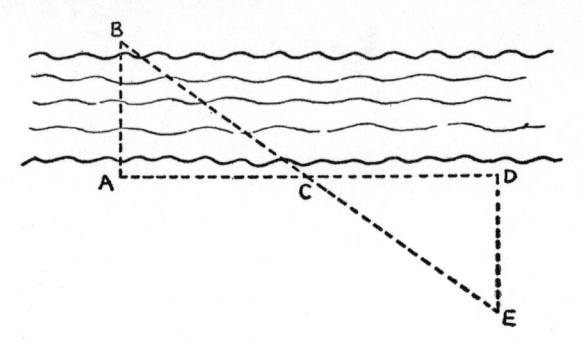

## PROPOSITION X

*Two lines perpendicular to the same line are parallel.*

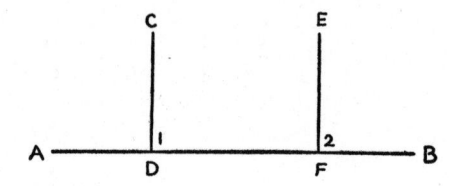

Given: CD and EF ⊥ to AB
To Prove: CD is parallel to EF
Proof: ∠1 = ∠2           Rt. ∠s.
∴ CD∥EF           Corresponding ∠s are =.

## QUADRILATERALS

A *quadrilateral* is a figure of *four sides*.

There are seven kinds of quadrilaterals: *the square, the rectangle, the trapezoid, the isosceles trapezoid, the parallelogram, the rhombus, and the irregular quadrilateral.*

The *square* is a quadrilateral whose angles are right angles and whose sides are all equal.

The *rectangle* is a quadrilateral whose angles are right angles, but whose sides are not necessarily equal. Every square is a rectangle, but not every rectangle is a square.

The *trapezoid* is a quadrilateral having only two parallel sides.

The *isosceles trapezoid* is a trapezoid whose nonparallel sides

GEOMETRY 145

are equal. The parallel sides are called the *bases* of the trapezoid.

The *parallelogram* is a quadrilateral whose opposite sides are parallel.

The *rhombus* is an equilateral parallelogram.

The *irregular quadrilateral* is a quadrilateral whose sides are all unequal and nonparallel.

The following figures illustrate the seven different kinds of quadrilaterals:

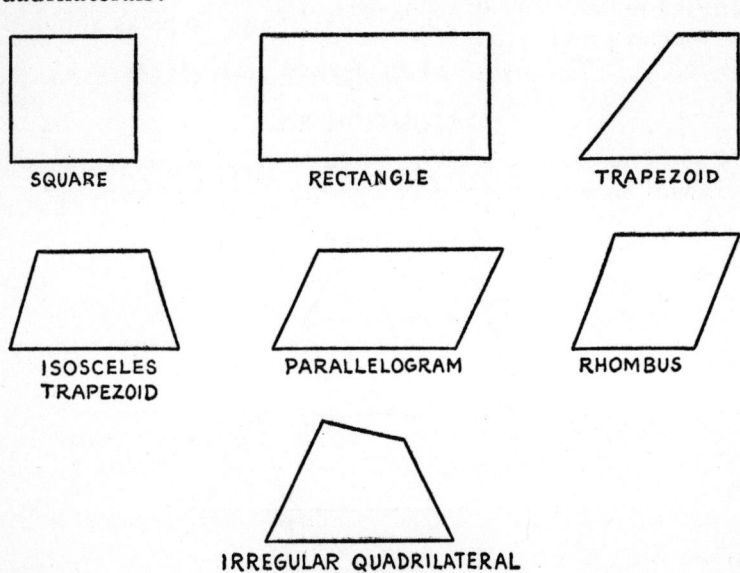

SQUARE    RECTANGLE    TRAPEZOID

ISOSCELES TRAPEZOID    PARALLELOGRAM    RHOMBUS

IRREGULAR QUADRILATERAL

## PROPOSITION XI

*The opposite sides and the opposite angles of a parallelogram are equal.*

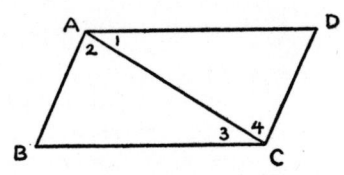

*Given:* □ABCD.
*To Prove:* AD=BC, AB=CD, ∠A= ∠C, ∠B= ∠D.

*Proof:* Draw AC.

| | |
|---|---|
| AD‖BC, and AB‖CD. | Opp. sides of a ▱. |
| ∠1 = ∠3, and ∠2 = ∠4. | Alt. int. ∠s. |
| AC = AC | Identity. |
| △ABC = △ADC | a.s.a. = a.s.a. |
| AD = BC }<br>AB = CD } | Corresponding sides of equal △. |
| ∠1 + ∠2 = ∠3 + ∠4 | Ax. 2. |
| ∠A = ∠C | Substitution. |

In like manner, by drawing BD, we can prove ∠B = ∠D. } Same steps as above.

**Corollary.** *Parallels included between parallels are equal.*

## PROPOSITION XII

*If three or more parallels intercept equal segments on one transversal, they intercept equal segments on every transversal.*

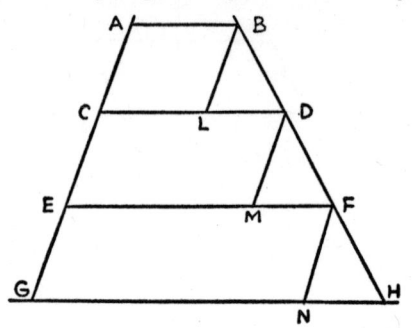

*Given:* AB‖CD‖EF‖GH
" AC = CE = EG
*To Prove:* BD = DF = FH
*Proof:* Draw BL, DM, and FN‖AG.
Then BL‖DM‖FN.

| | |
|---|---|
| | Lines ‖ to the same line are ‖ to each other. |
| ∠LBD = ∠MDF = ∠NFH. | Corresponding ∠s of ‖ lines. |
| ∠BDL = ∠DFM = ∠FHN. | " " " " |
| BL = AC, DM = CE, FN = EG. | Parallels included between parallels are equal. |
| AC = CE = EG | Hyp. |
| BL = DM = FN. | Axiom 1. |
| △BLD = △DMF = FNH. | s.a.s. = s.a.s. |
| ∴ BD = DF = FH. | Corresponding sides of = △. |

# GEOMETRY

**Corollary 1.** *A line parallel to one side of a triangle, and bisecting another side, also bisects the third side.*

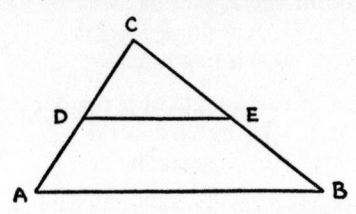

**Corollary 2.** *A line parallel to the bases of a trapezoid, and bisecting one of the nonparallel sides, also bisects the other nonparallel side.*

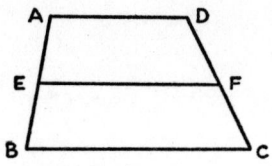

## PROPOSITION XIII

*The sum of the interior angles of a polygon having n sides is $n-2$ straight angles (that is, $n-2$ times $180°$.)*

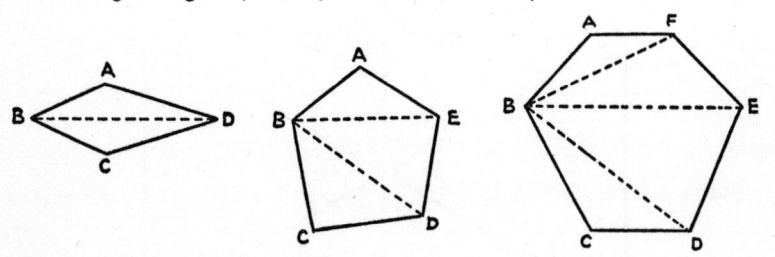

*Given:* A polygon of $n$ sides.
*To Prove:* The sum of its $\angle$s $= n-2$ str. $\angle$s.
*Proof:* In the above polygons, draw diagonals from B to each of the other vertices except A and C.

Each side, with the exception of AB and BC, becomes the base of a $\triangle$ whose vertex is at B. Hence there are $n-2$ $\triangle$s formed. (When $n$ is 4, there are 2 $\triangle$s; when $n$ is 5, there are 3 $\triangle$s; when $n$ is 6, there are 4 $\triangle$s; etc.)

But the sum of the interior $\angle$s of each $\triangle$ is $180°$.      Prop. IX.

∴ The sum of the interior $\angle$s of the polygon is $n-2$ times $180°$, or $n-2$ str. $\angle$s.

## EXERCISE 102

**1.** What is the sum of the angles of
(a) a triangle
(b) a quadrilateral
(c) a pentagon
(d) a hexagon
(e) a heptagon
(f) an octagon

**2.** What is the size of each angle of a regular
(a) triangle
(b) quadrilateral
(c) pentagon
(d) hexagon
(e) heptagon
(f) octagon

**3.** How many sides has a regular polygon each angle of which equals
(a) 162°
(b) 144°
(c) 90°
(d) 150°
(e) 157°30′
(f) 135°
(g) 160°
(h) 140°
(i) 108°
(j) 156°
(k) 120°
(l) 165°

**4.** The sum of two angles of a triangle is 80°, and their difference is 56°. How many degrees in each angle of the triangle?

**5.** The angles of a pentagon are $2x$, $3x$, $4x$, $5x$, and $6x$. How many degrees in each angle?

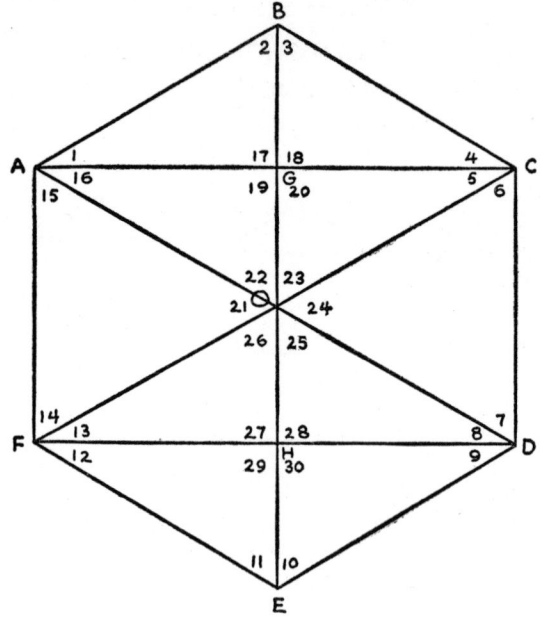

**6.** *Given:* regular hexagon ABCDEF with lines joining A and C, F and D; A and D, F and C, intersecting at O; and O and B and O and E.

GEOMETRY 149

*To Prove:* (a) $\angle 1 = 30°$    (b) $\angle FAG = 90°$    (c) $AF \parallel CD$
(d) $AC \parallel FD$    (e) $CO = OF$ and $AO = OD$    (f) $AD = FC$
(g) $CO = AO$    (h) $\angle 2 = \angle 3$    (i) $\angle 17 = 90°$    (j) $OB \parallel AF$
(k) $BOE$ is a straight line    (l) $GH = AF$    (m) $GO = OH$
(n) $BG = \frac{1}{2}AB$    (o) $OA = AB$
(p) $\angle 21 = \angle 22 = \angle 23 = \angle 24 = \angle 25 = \angle 26 = 60°$    (q) $FC \parallel AB$

## PROPORTION

In measuring land and water distances, such as the height of a mountain, the width of a river, the length of a race course, and so on, proportion plays a very important part. For distances are measured by means of similar, or proportional, triangles. For example, suppose a building throws a shadow of 10 feet, and a 1-foot rule that you hold perpendicularly to the ground throws a shadow of 1 inch. How tall is the building? In other words, 1 inch is to 1 foot as 10 feet is to the height of the building. Since 1 inch is $\frac{1}{12}$ of a foot, 10 feet is $\frac{1}{12}$ of the height of the building. The height of the building, therefore, is 120 feet.

Representing this graphically, we have the following similar triangles:

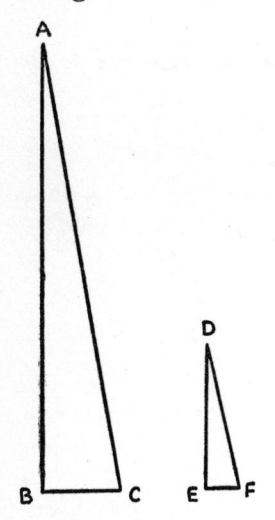

$AB$ = the height of the building.
$BC$ = the length of its shadow.
$DE$ = the length of the rule.
$EF$ = the length of *its* shadow.

The above example, as we have seen, has been solved by *ratio*, or *proportion*.

A *proportion* is a statement of the equality that exists between two *ratios*.

Thus, in the above example, 120 is to 12 as 10 is to 1. This proportion can be written in two ways, as follows:

(a) 120:12=10:1

(b) $\dfrac{120}{12}=\dfrac{10}{1}$

The first and the fourth terms of a proportion are called the *extremes;* the second and the third, the *means.* In the proportion, 120:12=10:1, 120 and 1 are the *extremes,* and 12 and 10 are the *means.*

When the means of a proportion are equal, either of the means is called the *mean proportional* between the first and the last terms. Thus, in the proportion, $x:y=y:z$, $y$ is the mean proportional between $x$ and $z$.

The proportion $x:y=y:z$ is read "$x$ is to $y$ as $y$ is to $z$." But when written $\dfrac{x}{y}=\dfrac{y}{z}$, it is read "$x$ over $y$ equals $y$ over $z$." The two forms are identical in value and in meaning.

## PROPOSITION XIV

*In any proportion, the product of the means is equal to the product of the extremes.*

Given: $a:b=c:d$.
To prove: $ad=bc$.

Proof: $\dfrac{a}{b}=\dfrac{c}{d}$   Hyp.

Multiplying both members of the equation by $bd$,   } Axiom 4.
$\dfrac{adb}{b}=\dfrac{bcd}{d}$

∴ $ad=bc$.

You will see the simple logic of this theorem when you substitute numbers for the letters. Let $a=2$, $b=3$, $c=4$, and $d=6$.

2:3=4:6
2×6=3×4
12=12

# GEOMETRY

## SOLVING EQUATIONS BY PROPORTION

Find the value of $x$ in the following proportions:

1. $5:6 = x:12$
   $6x = 60$
   $x = 10.$

2. $x:4 = 5:2$
   $2x = 20$
   $x = 10$

3. $7:x = 28:8$
   $28x = 56$
   $x = 2$

4. $6:5 = 30:x$
   $6x = 150$
   $x = 25$

## SIMILAR TRIANGLES

Two triangles are similar when their corresponding angles are equal and their corresponding sides are proportional.

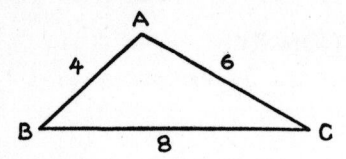

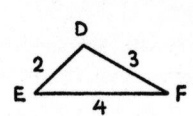

The above △ are similar because:
$\angle A = \angle D$
$\angle B = \angle E$
$\angle C = \angle F$
AB:DE = AC:DF = BC:EF  (4:2 = 6:3 = 8:4).

## PROPOSITION XV

*A line parallel to one side of a triangle divides the other two sides into segments that are proportional.*

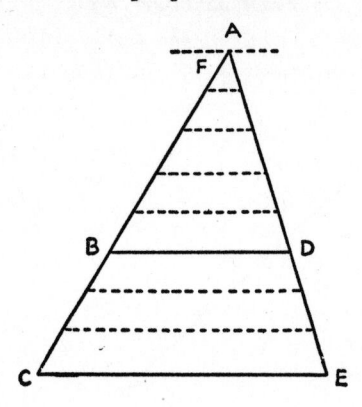

*Given:* In △ ACE, BD∥CE
*To Prove:* AB:BC=AD:DE
*Proof:* Take AF as a unit of measure. This unit of measure is contained 5 times in AB, and 3 times in BC.

$$\frac{AB}{BC}=\frac{5}{3}$$

Using this unit as a constant measure, draw, at the various points of division, lines that are parallel to CE.

These lines are ∥ to BD and to each other.

AD is divided into 5 equal parts, and DE is divided into 3 equal parts. } Prop. XII.

$$\frac{AD}{DE}=\frac{5}{3}$$

∴ $\frac{AB}{BC}=\frac{AD}{DE}$   Ax. 1.

## PROPOSITION XVI

*A mean proportional between two quantities is equal to the square root of their product.*

*Given:*    $x:y=y:z$
*To Prove:*  $y=\sqrt{xz}$
*Proof:*    $x:y=y:z$    Hyp.
         $y^2=xz$     Prop. XIV.
         $\sqrt{y^2}=\sqrt{xz}$ } Extracting the square
         $y=\sqrt{xz}$   root of both numbers.

Corollary. *If three terms of a proportion are equal to three corresponding terms of another proportion, the fourth terms are equal.*

## PROPOSITION XVII

*Two triangles are similar if the three angles of one are equal, respectively, to the three angles of the other.*

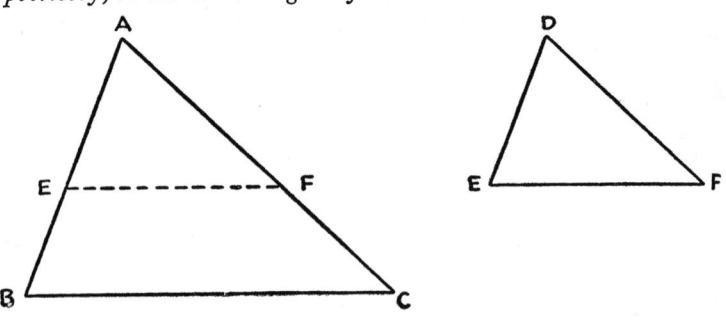

*Given:* △ABC and △DEF
    ∠A = ∠D
    ∠B = ∠E
    ∠C = ∠F
*To Prove:* △ABC∽DEF.
*Proof:* Place △DEF upon △ABC, so that ∠D coincides with ∠A, and △DEF takes the position of △AEF.

| | |
|---|---|
| ∠AEF = ∠DEF. | Identity. |
| ∠DEF = ∠B | Hyp. |
| ∠AEF = ∠B | Ax. 1. |
| EF ∥ BC | Since the corresponding ∠ are equal. |
| AB:AE = AC:AF | Proposition XV. |
| AB:DE = AC:DF | Substitution. |

In like manner, by placing △DEF upon △ABC so that ∠E coincides with ∠B, we can show that
    AB:DE = BC:EF

∴ $\dfrac{AB}{DE} = \dfrac{BC}{EF} = \dfrac{AC}{DF}$     Ax. 1.

But ∠A = ∠D ⎫
    ∠B = ∠E ⎬     Hyp.
    ∠C = ∠F ⎭

∴ △ABC∽DEF.     Their corresp. ∠ are =, and their corresp. sides are proportional.

**Corollary 1.** *Two triangles are similar if two angles of one are equal, respectively, to two angles of the other.*

**Corollary 2.** *Two right triangles are similar if an acute angle of one is equal to an acute angle of the other.*

**Corollary 3.** *A line parallel to one side of a triangle cuts off a triangle similar to the given triangle.*

**Corollary 4.** *If two triangles are similar to a third triangle, they are similar to each other.*

## PROPOSITION XVIII

*Two triangles are similar if an angle of one is equal to an angle of the other, and the sides including these angles are proportional.*

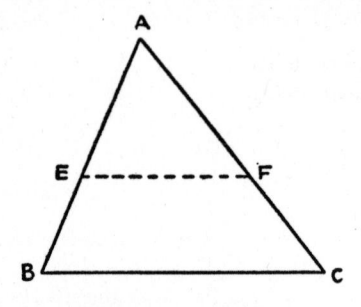

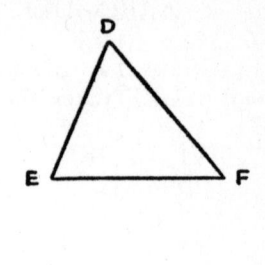

**Given:** △ABC and △DEF
$\angle A = \angle D$
AB:DE = AC:DF

**To Prove:** △ABC ∽ △DEF.

**Proof:**
Place △DEF upon △ABC, so that ∠D coincides with ∠A and △DEF takes the position of △AEF.

| | |
|---|---|
| AB:DE = AC:DF | Hyp. |
| AB:AE = AC:AF | Sub. |
| EF ∥ BC | Corollary to Prop. XV. |
| ∠B = ∠AEF ⎫<br>∠C = ∠AFE ⎭ | Corresp. ∠s of ∥ lines. |
| ∴ △ABC ∽ △DEF. | Prop. XVII. |

## PROPOSITION XIX

*Two triangles are similar if their corresponding sides are proportional.*

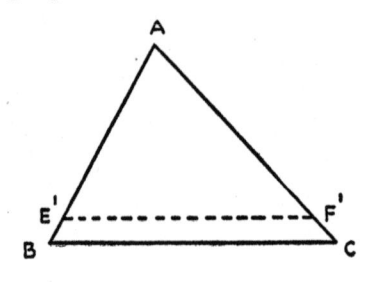

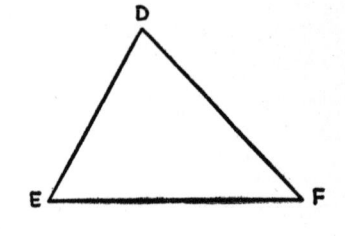

# GEOMETRY

*Given:* △ABC and △DEF
$$\frac{AB}{DE} = \frac{AC}{DF} = \frac{BC}{EF}$$
*To Prove:* △ABC∽DEF.
*Proof:* On AB and AC, lay off AE′=DE and AF′=DF.
  Draw E′F′.

| | |
|---|---|
| AB:DE = AC:DF. | Hyp. |
| AB:AE′ = AC:AF′. | Sub. |
| △AE′F′ ∽ △ABC. | Prop. XVII. |
| AB:AE′ = BC:E′F′ | Corresp. sides of ∽△. |
| EF = E′F′ | Corollary to Prop. XVI. |
| ∴ △DEF = AE′F′ | s.a.s. = s.a.s. |
| △DEF ∽ ABC | Substitution. |

## EXERCISE 103

In the following examples we shall see some of the practical applications of ratios, proportions, and similar triangles:—

1. Prove that if four quantities are in proportion, they are in proportion by:   That is, if $a:b=c:d$
  (a) alternation          then (a) $a:c=b:d$
  (b) inversion                 (b) $b:a=d:c$
  (c) composition               (c) $a+b:b=c+d:d$
  (d) division                  (d) $a-b:b=c-d:d$

2. Find the value of $x$ in the following:
  (a) $1:4=3:x$            (i) $x:16=6:4$
  (b) $3:6=5:x$            (j) $12:x=2:9$
  (c) $3:8=x:80$           (k) $1\frac{1}{2}:2=x:4$
  (d) $10:4=x:8$           (l) $5.1:x=3:10$
  (e) $28:x=8:2$           (m) $x:1.8=1.6:7.2$
  (f) $15:10=x:4$          (n) $x+2:18=3:2$
  (g) $15:x=3:5$           (o) $x+9:x+1=x+1:x-3$
  (h) $21:x=7:4$

3. In two similar triangles, the sides of the first are 18, 16, and 14; while the longest side of the second triangle is 12. What are the other sides of the second triangle?

4. The perimeter (the length of the three sides) of an isosceles triangle is 34 in., and the ratio of one of the equal arms to the base is as 7:3. What are the three sides of the triangle?

5. A map is drawn to the scale of 100 miles = 3 in. How far apart are two towns that are separated on the map by
(a) 2 in.   (b) 6 in.   (c) 8 in.   (d) 5 in.
(e) $1\frac{1}{4}$ in.   (f) $3\frac{1}{2}$ in.   (g) $\frac{7}{8}$ in.   (h) $2\frac{3}{16}$ in.
(i) $1\frac{5}{16}$ in.   (j) $2\frac{9}{16}$ in.

6. On the same map, how many inches apart would two towns be that were actually at a distance from each other of
(a) 50 mi.   (b) 80 mi.   (c) 45 mi.   (d) 120 mi.
(e) 93 mi.   (f) 62 mi.   (g) 861 mi.   (h) 431 mi.
(i) 742 mi.   (j) 984 mi.

7. If a man averages 30 mi. an hour in his automobile, how long would it take him to cover each of the distances in Problem 5? (Answer in hrs., mins., and secs.)

8. If the railroad fare is $2\frac{1}{2}$¢ per mile, how much would it cost to travel by train each of the distances in Problem 5?

9. A building throws a shadow of seven feet. You are six feet tall and throw a shadow of two feet. How high is the building?

10. You are two blocks away from a church steeple, 90 feet high, which you can just see over the top of a smokestack one block away. If you are slightly more than six feet tall, and the blocks are of equal length, how high is the smokestack?

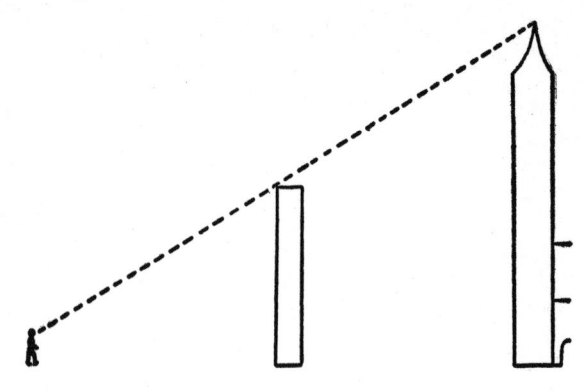

11. As you look at a mountain 12,000 feet high, you can just see the rim of the sun shining over its summit. You are six feet tall and cast a shadow of 5 feet. How far are you from the mountain?

# GEOMETRY

## RIGHT TRIANGLES

A right triangle, as we have seen, is a triangle that contains one right angle.

The following propositions, dealing with some of the properties of right triangles, are among the most important in all mathematics. Builders, inventors, surveyors, mechanics, scientists, carpenters, designers, and even the average layman, can find thousands of practical applications of the right triangle, the relations of its sides, and the computations of its angles.

In order to understand the right triangle, we must know how to extract the square root of a number. Let us, therefore, consider the extraction of the square root.

Before we extract the square root, however, let us first square a number of two digits. Suppose we are asked to square 57.

$$57 = 50+7$$
$$57^2 = (50+7)^2 = (50+7)(50+7)$$
$$\phantom{57^2 = }50+7$$
$$\phantom{57^2 = }50+7$$
$$\overline{50^2+(50\times 7)\phantom{+7^2}}$$
$$\phantom{50^2+}(50\times 7)+7^2$$
$$\overline{50^2+2(50\times 7)+7^2}$$
$$= 2500 + 2\times 350 + 49$$
$$= 2500 + \phantom{2\times}700 + 49$$
$$= 3249$$

This is exactly like the algebraic example $(a+b)^2$.

$(a+b)^2 = a^2+2ab+b^2$.

The square of the sum of two algebraic terms equals the square of the first term, plus twice the product of the first and the second terms, plus the square of the second term.

Similarly, the square of a number of two digits equals the square of the first (or the *tens*) digit, plus twice the product of the first and the second (or the *tens* and the *units*) digits, plus the square of the second (or *units*) digit.

And now let us extract the square root of 3249. The process, as we shall see, is the reverse of the above.

1. First we separate 3249, from right to left, into groups of two figures each: 32 49.

The first period, 32, contains the square of the *tens* number of the required root.

The second period, 49, contains the square of the *units* number of the required root.

*Each period represents one digit of the square root.*

We now proceed with the extraction of the square root:

$$\begin{array}{r|rr} & 32 & 49(57 \\ & 25 & \\ \hline 100+7 & 7 & 49 \\ 107 & 7 & 49 \end{array}$$

Explanation: The first period, 32, contains the square of the *tens* digit of the root. Since the greatest square in 32 is 25, the square root of 25, or 5, is the *tens* digit in the root.

Subtracting the square of the *tens* digit, or 25, from 32, and bringing down the 49, we get 7 49. This represents twice the product of the *tens* and the *units* digits, plus the square of the units. Therefore, if we divide 749 by twice the tens (that is, by 100, which is 2 times 5 tens), we shall find approximately the *units* digit. This digit is 7. Now twice the *tens* times the *units*, plus the square of the units, is equal to $2 \times (50 \times 7) + 7^2$, or $(2 \times 50 + 7) \times 7$, or $(100+7) \times 7$. Hence we add 7 to 100 and multiply by 7. The product is 749, and this completes the square of 57.

Extract the square root of 6241

$$\begin{array}{r|rr} & 62 & 41(79 \\ & 49 & \\ \hline 140+9 & 13 & 41 \\ 149 & 13 & 41 \end{array}$$

To check this work, $79^2 = 6241$.

Let us now return to our right angle triangles. Our knowledge of square roots, as we shall see, will be of great help in the solution of some of our geometric problems.

## PROPOSITION XX

*In any right triangle, the perpendicular from the vertex of the right angle to the hypotenuse divides the triangle into two triangles that are similar to each other and to the given triangle.*

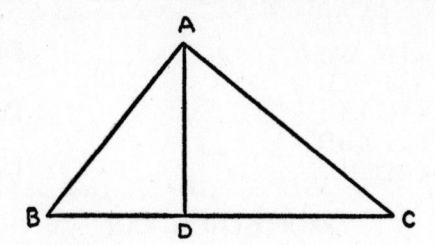

*Given:* The rt. △ABC.
  AD⊥ to the hypotenuse BC.
*To Prove:* △ABD∽CAD∽ABC
*Proof:* Each of the three △ is a rt. △.
In △ABD and ABC, ∠B = ∠B.           Identity.
∴ △ABD∽△ABC.                         Prop. XVII, Cor. 2.
In △CAD and ABC, ∠C = ∠C.            Identity.
∴ △CAD∽ABC.                          Prop. XVII, Cor. 2.
∴ △ABD∽CAD.                          Prop. XVII, Cor. 4.

The perpendicular from the vertex of a triangle to the base is called the *altitude* of the triangle.

## PROPOSITION XXI

*In a right triangle, the altitude upon the hypotenuse is the mean proportional between the segments of the hypotenuse, and either arm is the mean proportional between the hypotenuse and the segment adjacent to that arm.*

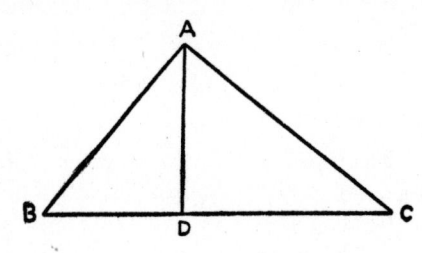

*Given:* The rt. △ABC.
     AD⊥ to the hypotenuse BC
*To Prove:* 1. BD:DA=DA:DC
         2. BC:AC=AC:DC
         3. BC:AB=AB:BD
*Proof:* △ABC∽△ABD∽△ACD           Prop. XX.
1. In △ABD and ACD,
     BD:DA=DA:DC               Defin. of sim. △.
2. In △ABC and ACD,
     BC:AC=AC:DC.              Defin. of sim. △.
3. In △ABC and ABD,
     BC:AB=AB:BD.              Defin. of sim. △.

## PROPOSITION XXII

*The sum of the squares of the arms of a right triangle is equal to the square of the hypotenuse.*

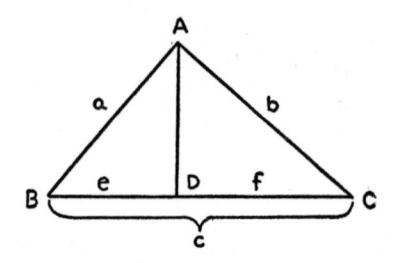

*Given:* Rt. △ABC, with its rt. ∠ at A.
*To Prove:* $a^2+b^2=c^2$
*Proof:* Draw AD⊥BC.
   $e:a=a:c$                   Prop. XXI.
   $a^2=c\times e$             Prod. of means = prod. of extremes.
In like manner,
   $b^2=c\times f$
   $a^2+b^2=(c\times e)(c\times f)$
   $a^2+b^2=c(e+f)$
But $e+f=c$
   ∴ $a^2+b^2=c\times c$        Substitution.
   $a^2+b^2=c^2$

Corollary 1. *The square of either arm of a right triangle is equal to the square of the hypotenuse, minus the square of the other arm.* $a^2=c^2-b^2$; $b^2=c^2-a^2$

Corollary 2. *The hypotenuse of a right triangle is equal to the square root of the sum of the squares of the arms.* $c=\sqrt{a^2+b^2}$

Corollary 3. *Either arm of a right triangle is equal to the square root of the difference between the square of the hypotenuse and the square of the other arm.* $a=\sqrt{c^2-b^2}$; $b=\sqrt{c^2-a^2}$

Let us illustrate all this with a concrete example. Take a right triangle whose arms are equal to 3 and to 4 respectively:

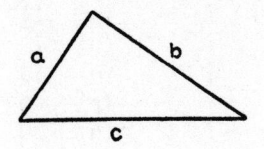

Prop. $a=3$
$b=4$
$c=?$
$a^2+b^2=c^2$
$3^2+4^2=c^2$
$9+16=c^2$
$25=c^2$

Cor. 1. $a^2=c^2-b^2$
$9=25-16$
$b^2=c^2-a^2$
$16=25-9$

Cor. 2. $c=\sqrt{a^2+b^2}$
$c=\sqrt{9+16}$
$c=\sqrt{25}=5$

Cor. 3. $a=\sqrt{c^2-b^2}$
$a=\sqrt{25-16}$
$a=\sqrt{9}=3$

$b=\sqrt{c^2-a^2}$
$b=\sqrt{25-9}$
$b=\sqrt{16}=4$

Corollary 4. *In a right-angle triangle whose acute angles are equal to 30° and 60° respectively, the hypotenuse equals twice the shorter arm.*

## EXERCISE 104

Solve the following problems:

1. In the following right triangles, find the missing side (answer to the nearest hundredth):

|  | Arm | Arm | Hypotenuse |  | Arm | Arm | Hypotenuse |
|---|---|---|---|---|---|---|---|
| (a) | 6 | 8 | ? | (k) | 15 | ? | 25 |
| (b) | 5 | 12 | ? | (l) | $\frac{3}{10}$ | ? | $\frac{1}{2}$ |
| (c) | 10 | 11 | ? | (m) | $1\frac{1}{5}$ | ? | $1\frac{3}{10}$ |
| (d) | 14 | 10 | ? | (n) | 7 | ? | 11 |
| (e) | 18 | 9 | ? | (o) | 10 | ? | 19 |
| (f) | 7 | 16 | ? | (p) | 6 | ? | 14 |
| (g) | 9 | 12 | ? | (q) | 20 | ? | 52 |
| (h) | 15 | 36 | ? | (r) | 64 | ? | 81 |
| (i) | 7 | 15 | ? | (s) | 19 | ? | 33 |
| (j) | 9 | 16 | ? | (t) | 16 | ? | 24 |

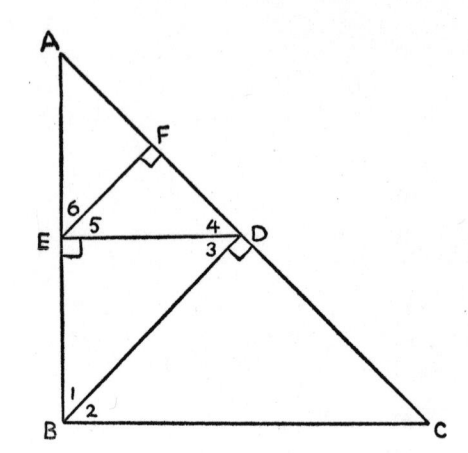

2. In the diagram above, $\angle$s B, D, E, and F are right angles; $\angle 5 = 45°$.
(a) What is the relation of EF to BD? Why?
(b) of ED to BC? (c) of $\angle 5$ to $\angle 6$? (d) of $\angle 5$ to $\angle 3$?
(e) What is the size of each acute angle in the diagram?
(f) What is the relation of FA to FE? (g) of FA to FD?
(h) of BD to DA? (i) of AE to EB? (j) of AB to BC?
(k) If ED is six inches long, find the length to the nearest hundredth of (1) AE (2) AD (3) AB (4) AC

GEOMETRY 163

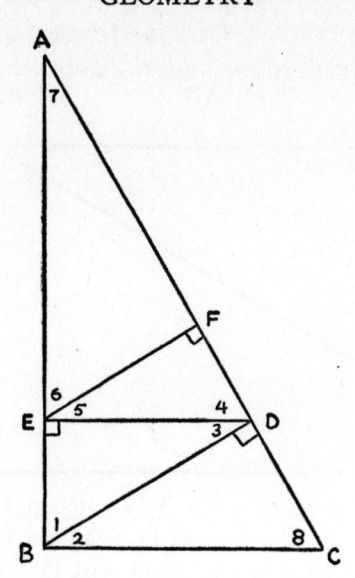

3. In the diagram above, ∠s B, D, E, and F are right angles; ∠4=60°.
   (a) What is the relation of EF to BD? Why?
   (b) of ED to BC?
   (c) of ∠5 to ∠3?   (d) of ∠3 to ∠2?
   (e) How many degrees in
       (1) ∠1    (2) ∠2    (3) ∠3    (4) ∠4    (5) ∠5
       (6) ∠6    (7) ∠A    (8) ∠C
   (f) What is the relation of EF to AE?   (g) of FD to ED?
   (h) of EB to BD?   (i) of DC to BC?   (j) of BC to AC?
   (k) If FD is six inches long, find the length to the nearest hundredth inch of
       (1) ED    (2) EF    (3) AE    (4) AF    (5) BD
       (6) EB    (7) BC    (8) DC    (9) AB    (10) AC
       (11) CF   (12) AD

4. In the diagram on the top of the next page, ∠s A and D are each 90°; ∠C=60°; ∠DBC=90°.
   (a) What is the sum of the ∠s of ABCD?
   (b) of ∠s A, D, and C?   (c) How many degrees in ∠B?
   (d) in ∠DBC?   (e) in ∠DBA?   (f) in ∠A?   (g) in ∠BDA?
   (h) in ∠BDC?   (i) What is the relation of AD to BD?

(j) of BC to CD? (k) If AD is ten inches long, find the length to the nearest hundredth inch of
(1) DB (2) AB (3) BC (4) DC

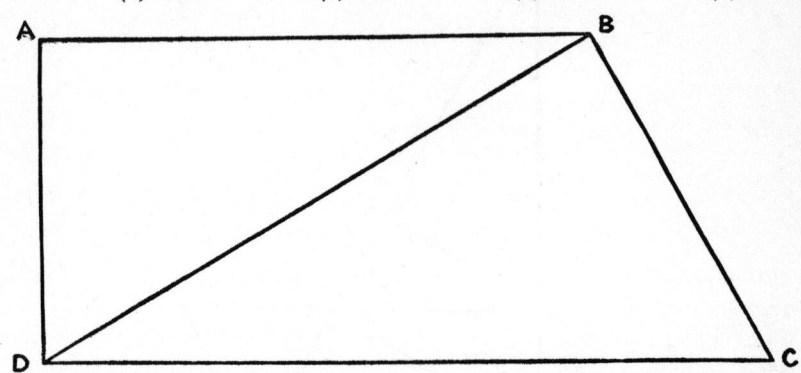

5. In the diagram below, ∠s A, C, E, and G are each 90°; ∠B=165°; ∠F=135°; FE=ED; FD=AF+AB; FB=2AF.
(a) What is the sum of the ∠s of ABCDEF?
(b) How many degrees in ∠D? (c) in ∠E? (d) in ∠1?
(e) in ∠2? Why? (f) in ∠F? (g) in ∠AFG?
(h) What is the relation of AF to BG? (i) of FG to AB?
(j) of GD to GB? Why? (k) How many degrees in ∠3?
(l) in ∠4? (m) ∠D? (n) ∠5? (o) ∠6?

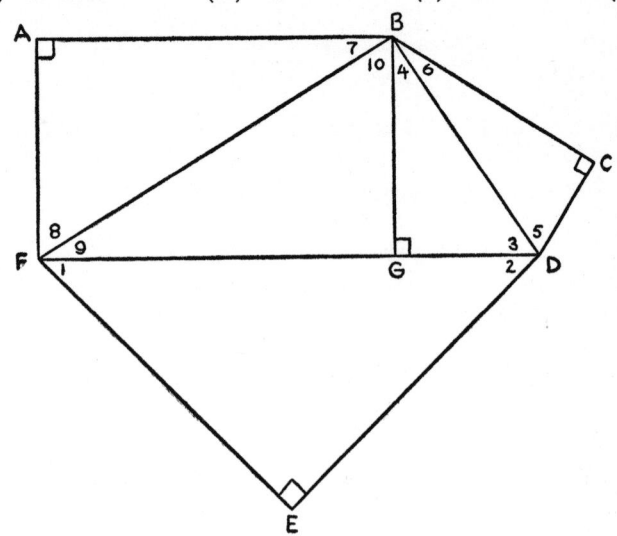

(p) What is the relation of CD to BD?   (q) of AF to BF?
(r) How many degrees in ∠7?   (s) in ∠8?   (t) ∠9?
(u) ∠10?   (v) If CD = 16 inches, find the length to the nearest hundredth inch of
(1) BD   (2) BC   (3) BG   (4) BF
(5) AB   (6) FD   (7) FE
(w) What is the shortest distance between E and side AB (assuming CD = 16 inches)?

## AREAS

1. The area of a square is equal to the square of its sides. For example, if each side is 5 inches, the area is 25 square inches.

2. The area of a rectangle is equal to the product of its sides. If it is 5 inches long and 3 inches wide, its area is 15 square inches.

3. The area of a parallelogram is equal to the product of its base times its altitude (the perpendicular distance from the base to the opposite side).

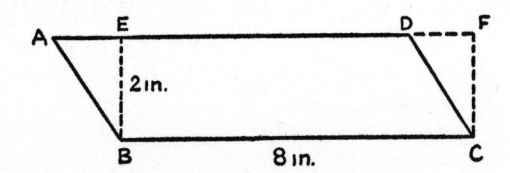

△AEB = △DFC.   s.AB, ∠A, ∠EBA = s.DC, ∠FDC, ∠FCD
∴ Parallelogram ABCD = rectangle BEFC.
∴ Area of parallelogram ABCD = 8 in. × 2 in., or 16 sq. in.

4. The area of a triangle is equal to half the product of the base and the altitude.

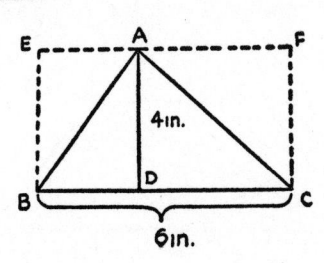

$\triangle ADB = \frac{1}{2}$ rectangle ADBE
$\triangle ADC = \frac{1}{2}$ rectangle ADCF
$\therefore \triangle ABC = \frac{1}{2}$ rectangle BEFC
$\therefore$ Area of $\triangle ABC = \frac{1}{2}(6 \text{ in.} \times 4 \text{ in.}) = 12$ sq. in.

5. When the base of a triangle is unknown, but the sides are known, we get the area as follows:

We multiply half the sum of the sides in succession by the three remainders obtained through subtracting each side separately from the half sum of the sides, and we then take the square root of this product.

For example, find the area of a triangle whose sides are respectively 5 in., 7 in., and 8 in.

Half the sum of the sides is $\frac{1}{2}$ of $(5+7+8)$, or 10.

$10-5$ (the first side)  $= 5$
$10-7$ (the second side) $= 3$
$10-8$ (the third side) $= 2$

The area $= \sqrt{10 \times 5 \times 3 \times 2} = \sqrt{300} = 17.32+$

That is, the area is about 17.32 sq. in.

This method of computing the area of a triangle is too complicated for demonstration so far as the practical purposes of this book are concerned. It is sufficient to remember the formula, which is as follows:

Area $= \sqrt{s(s-a)(s-b)(s-c)}$
$s = \frac{1}{2}$ the sum of the sides, or $\frac{1}{2}$ the perimeter.
$s-a =$ the perimeter minus side $a$.
$s-b =$ the perimeter minus side $b$.
$s-c =$ the perimeter minus side $c$.

In the above example, the formula is expressed thus:
$\sqrt{10(10-5)(10-7)(10-8)}$.

6. The area of a trapezoid is equal to one half the sum of its parallel sides times its altitude.

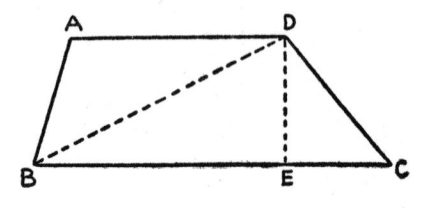

# GEOMETRY

In the trapezoid ABCD, draw BD to divide the trapezoid into △ DBC and DBA.

Area of △DBC = $\frac{1}{2}$ base (BC) × altitude (DE)
Area of △DBA = $\frac{1}{2}$ base (AD) × altitude (DE)
Area of △DBC + △DBA = $\frac{1}{2}$ bases (BC+AD) × altitude (DE)
Suppose BC = 5 in., AD = 3 in., and DE = 2 in.

The area = $\frac{1}{2}(5+3) \times 2 = \frac{8 \times 2}{2} = 8$ sq. in.

7. The area of an irregular polygon may be determined by dividing it into triangles and by adding the areas of the triangles.

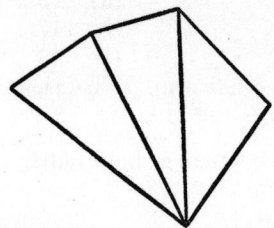

8. The circumference of a circle is equal to about $3\frac{1}{7}$ times the diameter. A more exact ratio is 3.14159265+; but for practical purposes, $3\frac{1}{7}$ is close enough. This ratio is called $\pi$ (pronounced pi, with a long *i*).

9. The radius of a circle is $\frac{1}{2}$ the diameter, or a line drawn from the center to the circumference.

10. The area of a circle is equal to the square of the radius times $\pi$, or $\pi r^2$.

For example, if the radius of a circle is 7 inches, the area is $3\frac{1}{7} \times 7^2$, or $\frac{22}{7} \times 49$, or 154 sq. in.

11. The cubic contents of a cylindrical tank are equal to the area of the circular base times the depth of the tank.

Note: 1 cubic foot contains 7.48+ gallons. For practical purposes, let us call it $7\frac{1}{2}$ gallons.

Example:

Find the number of gallons of water in a cylindrical tank 40 feet in diameter and 35 feet deep.

Radius = 20 ft.
Area = $3\frac{1}{7} \times 20^2$

Volume = 35 × 3⅐ × 20² cu. ft.
But there are 7½ gallons to a cu. ft.
∴ Contents = 35 × 3⅐ × 20² × 7½
= 330,000 gallons.

## EXERCISE 105

1. Find the area to the nearest hundredth square inch of the right triangles of which there follow one arm and the hypotenuse:

| | Arm | Hypotenuse | | Arm | Hypotenuse |
|---|---|---|---|---|---|
| (a) | 9 | 15 | (f) | 16 | 20 |
| (b) | 10 | 26 | (g) | 19 | 32 |
| (c) | 15 | 21 | (h) | 18 | 36 |
| (d) | 8 | 12 | (i) | 17 | 24 |
| (e) | 7 | 15 | (j) | 13 | 19 |

*Suggestion:* Find the other arm. The area = ½ the product of the arms of a right triangle.

2. Find the area to the nearest hundredth inch of a 45° right △ if the hypotenuse is:
(a) 14    (b) 15    (c) 16    (d) 17
(e) 18    (f) 19    (g) 20    (h) 21
(i) 22    (j) 23

*Suggestion:* The △ will be isosceles.

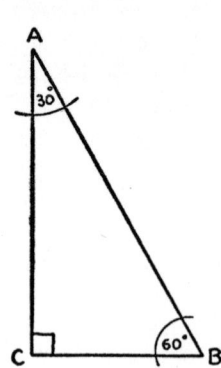

3. In the △ diagrammed above, ∠C = 90°, ∠A = 30°, ∠B = 60°. Find the area if
(a) AB = 14    (b) AB = 15    (c) AB = 16    (d) AB = 17
(e) AC = 18    (f) AC = 19    (g) AC = 20    (h) AC = 21
(i) BC = 22    (j) BC = 23    (k) BC = 24    (l) BC = 26

# GEOMETRY

4. In the △ diagrammed below, $\angle A = \angle C$. Find the area to the nearest hundredth square inch:

| | Perimeter | Side | | Perimeter | Side |
|---|---|---|---|---|---|
| (a) | 42 | $a = 18$ | (f) | 28 | $b = 12$ |
| (b) | 46 | $a = 19$ | (g) | 32 | $b = 14$ |
| (c) | 52 | $a = 20$ | (h) | 34 | $b = 16$ |
| (d) | 54 | $a = 22$ | (i) | 38 | $b = 18$ |
| (e) | 62 | $a = 24$ | (j) | 40 | $b = 16$ |

*Suggestion*: Since $\angle A = \angle C$, what can be said of the relation between AB and BC? Use the formula:
$$A = \sqrt{s(s-a)(s-b)(s-c)}$$

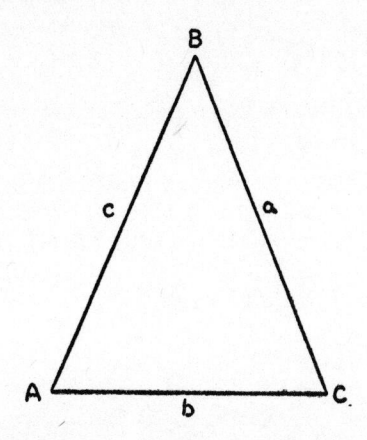

5. Find the areas to the nearest hundredth square inch of the triangles whose sides are:

| | Side | Side | Side | | Side | Side | Side |
|---|---|---|---|---|---|---|---|
| (a) | 7 | 8 | 9 | (f) | 9 | 11 | 16 |
| (b) | 6 | 4 | 8 | (g) | 5 | 14 | 17 |
| (c) | 10 | 8 | 14 | (h) | 6 | 11 | 15 |
| (d) | 5 | 6 | 9 | (i) | 8 | 10 | 16 |
| (e) | 8 | 7 | 13 | (j) | 13 | 15 | 22 |

6. Find the area of a rectangle with a perimeter of 64 inches, if one side is

(a) 14        (b) 13        (c) 12        (d) 11
(e) 10        (f) 9         (g) 8         (h) 7

*Suggestion*: Find the other side; opposite sides of a rectangle are equal. Area = product of two adjacent sides.

7. Find the area of a square if the diagonal is
(a) 24    (b) 25    (c) 26    (d) 27
(e) 28    (f) 29    (g) 30    (h) 32
(i) 34    (j) 36

8. In the ☐ above, $\angle A = 120°$. Find the area if

| | AD | AB | | AD | AB |
|---|---|---|---|---|---|
|(a)| 8 | 19 |(f)| 22 | 34 |
|(b)| 20 | 30 |(g)| 14 | 26 |
|(c)| 12 | 23 |(h)| 26 | 38 |
|(d)| 24 | 35 |(i)| 10 | 22 |
|(e)| 16 | 28 |(j)| 18 | 29 |

Suggestion: $\angle D$ is supplementary to $\angle A$. If a perpendicular is dropped from A to DC, what sort of △ is formed? The area = DC × the perpendicular.

9. Using $\frac{22}{7}$ as the value of $\pi$, find the area of the circle whose radius is
(a) 7       (b) 14      (c) 21      (d) 28
(e) 4.9     (f) 5.6     (g) 3.43    (h) 11.2
(i) 3.36    (j) 15.4    (k) 102.9   (l) 3.08

10. How many cubic feet of water will a well hold, if its depth is 20 feet, and its diameter is
(a) 6.16 ft.    (b) 6.72 ft.    (c) 6.86 ft.    (d) 6.3 ft.

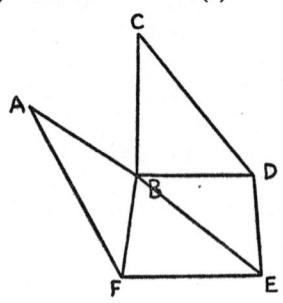

11. A farmer wishes to compute the area of a plot of land in the shape of the polygon above. He finds that AF is 100 yds.;

AB, 60 yds.; BF, 76 yds.; FE, 86 yds.; BE, 120 yds.; BD, 72 yds.; DE, 70 yds.; DC, 100 yds.; and CB, 70 yds. What is the area to the nearest hundredth of an acre of his land?

*Suggestion*: Find the area of each $\triangle$. The polygon's area = the sum of the four $\triangle$.

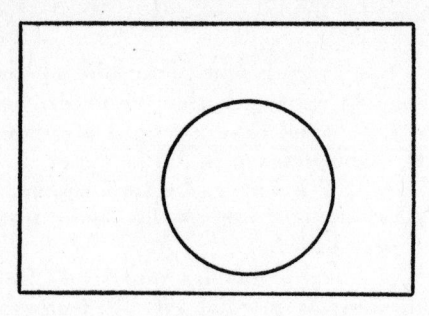

12. A farmer owns a plot of land in the shape of a rectangle. On the land is a circular pond with a diameter of 70 yds. If his land measures 180 yds. by 120 yds., how many acres of dry land does he own?

*Suggestion*: Find the area of the pond, letting $\pi = \frac{22}{7}$. Subtract from the area of the rectangle.

## EXERCISE 106

Solve the following problems:

1. The perimeter of a rectangle is 24 inches. The length is twice the width. Find its dimensions.

2. The perimeter of a kitchenette is 32 feet. The length is 2 feet less than twice the width. Find its dimensions.

3. A rectangle and a square have equal areas. The length of the rectangle is 4 inches more than that of the square, but the width is 3 inches less. How long is the side of the square?

4. If one side of a square is lengthened by 9 inches, and the other side is shortened by 6 inches, the area remains the same. How long is the side of the square?

5. A rectangle and a square have equal areas. The rectangle is 10 inches longer than the square, and its perimeter is 8 feet more than that of the square. What are the dimensions of each?

6. A rectangular field is 30 yards wide, and another is 20 yards wide. The first field is 10 yards longer than the second, and their combined area is 2300 square yards. What is the length of each field?

## 172 MATHEMATICS MADE EASY

7. A rectangular field is 12 yards longer than it is wide. If 15 yards is added to its length, and 6 yards taken from its width, the area remains the same. What are the dimensions of the field?

8. A rectangular field is three times as long as it is wide. If 20 yards is added to its width and the same amount taken from its length, the area is increased by 400 square yards. What are the dimensions of the field?

9. While trying to arrange his men in a solid square, an officer discovered that he had 45 more men than he needed for that purpose. With 26 more men, he could have arranged a square with one more man on each side. How many men did he have?

10. An officer arranged his men in a solid square, and noted that with 315 more men he could arrange five more men on each side. How many men did he have?

11. The length of a tennis doubles court is 42 feet more than its width. A singles court is marked off by decreasing the doubles court's width by $4\frac{1}{2}$ feet at each side. The area of the singles court is 702 square feet less than that of the doubles court. What are the dimensions of each court?

12. The perimeter of a kitchen is 44 feet, and its area is 202 square feet less than that of a living room. The length of the living room is 11 feet more than that of the kitchen, and the width of the living room is 4 feet more than that of the kitchen. What are the dimensions of each?

### ANSWERS
### EXERCISE 96

1. (a) 132°        (b) 117°        (c) 84°        (d) 77°
   (e) 90° 5′ 34″  (f) 36° 44′ 2″
2. (a) 19°         (b) 29°         (c) 3°         (d) 37°
   (e) 40° 24′ 42″ (f) 25° 33′ 17″
3. 30°    4. 18°    5. 15°    6. 18°
7. 10°    8. 80°    9. 84°    10. 165°
11. 40° and 50°
12. (a) 48° and 52°        (b) 51° and 39°
    (c) 58° and 32°        (d) 64° and 26°
    (e) 69° 30′ and 20° 30′ (f) 63° 30′ and 20° 30′
    (g) 54° 38′ and 35° 22′ (h) 64° 38′ 43″ and 25° 21′ 17″
13. (a) 94° and 86°        (b) 97° and 83°
    (c) 104° and 76°       (d) 113° and 67°
    (e) 115° 30′ and 64° 30′ (f) 114° 30′ and 65° 30′
    (g) 101° 39′ and 78° 21′ (h) 126° 37′ 51″ and 53° 22′ 9″

### EXERCISE 97

1. (a) ∠4    (b) ∠5    (c) ∠6    (d) ∠1    (e) ∠2    (f) ∠3
2. (a) ∠AOD  (b) ∠FOC  (c) ∠AOE  (d) ∠COB  (e) ∠EOD
   (f) ∠BOF

3. (a) 85°  (b) 48°  (c) 85°  (d) 47°
   (e) 133° (f) 132° (g) 95° (h) 133°
   (i) 132° (j) 95°

## EXERCISE 98

1. $\angle 1 = \angle 2$ — Hyp.
   $\angle 4 = \angle 3$ — Axiom 3
   $\angle 5 = \angle 6$ — Prop. I
   $AC = CD$ — Hyp.
   $\triangle BAC = \triangle CDE$ — a.s.a. = a.s.a.
   $\therefore AB = DE$ — Corresponding parts of equal $\triangle$ are =.

2. (a) 4 in.  (b) 5 in.  (c) 8 in.  (d) 137°  (e) 23°

## EXERCISE 99

1. $AB = AC$ — Hyp.
   $\angle B = \angle C$ — Prop. IV
   $\angle 1 = \angle 2$ — Hyp.
   $\angle 3 = \angle 4$ — Axiom 3
   $BC = BC$ — Identity
   $\triangle BCE = \triangle CBD$ — a.s.a. = a.s.a.
   $\therefore BE = CD$ — Corresponding parts of = $\triangle$.

2. (a) $AB = AC$ — Hyp.
   $BD = CE$ — Corresponding parts of = $\triangle$ (as proved in Problem 1).
   $\therefore AD = AE$ — Axiom 3

   2. (b) $\angle 1 = \angle 2$ — Hyp.
   $\angle 9 = \angle 10$ — Corresponding parts of = $\triangle$ (see Problem 1)
   $BD = CE$ — Corresponding parts of = $\triangle$ (see Problem 1)
   $\triangle BDF = \triangle CEF$ — a.s.a. = a.s.a.
   $\therefore FD = FE$ — Corresponding parts of = $\triangle$

3. (a) 20 in.  (b) $7\frac{1}{2}$ in.  (c) 17 in.  (d) $4\frac{1}{2}$ in.

4. (a) 63°  (b) 21°  (c) 42°  (d) 42°
   (e) 84°  (f) 96°  (g) 96°  (h) 75°
   (i) 105° (j) 105°

## EXERCISE 100

$\left.\begin{array}{l}\angle 1 = \angle 2 \\ AB = AC\end{array}\right\}$ — Hyp.
$\angle B = \angle C$ — Prop. IV
$\triangle ABD = \triangle ACD$ — a.s.a. = a.s.a.
$BD = DC$ — Corresponding parts of = $\triangle$
$\angle 3 = \angle 4$ — " " " "
But $\angle 3 + \angle 4 = 180°$ — Supplementary $\angle$s
$\therefore \angle 3 = 90°$ and $\angle 4 = 90°$ — Axiom 5.

## EXERCISE 101

1. (a) 132°  (b) 146°  (c) 82°  (d) 82°
   (e) 98°   (f) 98°   (g) 132° (h) 48°
   (i) 34°   (j) 146°  (k) 146° (l) 34°
   (m) 34°   (n) 146°  (o) 48°  (p) 132°
   (q) 132°  (r) 48°

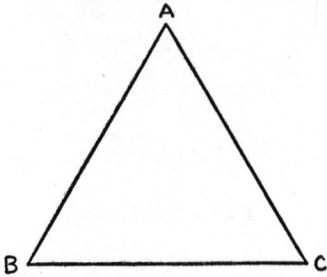

2. *Given:* △ABC with ∠A= ∠B= ∠C
   *To Prove:* AB=BC=CA

   *Proof*

   ∠B= ∠C — Hyp.
   Hence AB=AC — If the base ∠s of a △ are =, the arms opposite them are =.
   Similarly AB can be proved equal to BC
   ∴ AB=BC=CA — Axiom 1

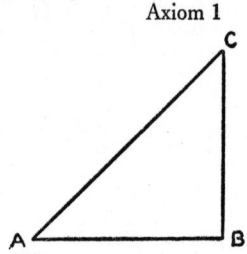

3. *Given:* ∠B=90°, ∠A=45°
   *To Prove:* AB=BC

   *Proof*

   ∠A+ ∠B+ ∠C=180° — The sum of the ∠s of a △=180°
   ∠A=45° and ∠B=90° — Hyp.
   Hence ∠C=45° — Axiom 3
   Or ∠A= ∠C — Axiom 1
   ∴ AB=BC — If two ∠s of a △ are =, the arms opposite them are =.

4. (a) *Given:* △BAC (diagram with problem) with ∠BCA=90° and ∠BAC=30°
   *To Prove:* BC=½ BA

   *Proof*

   Measure off CD=BC and join AD
   Then AC=AC — Identity
   ∠ACB= ∠ACD — All rt. ∠s are =.
   BC=CD — Construction.

## GEOMETRY

| | |
|---|---|
| △BCA = △CDA | s.a.s. = s.a.s. |
| ∠B = 60° | Hyp. |
| ∠D = 60° | Corresponding parts of = △ |
| And ∠BAD = 60° | The sum of the ∠s of a △ = 180° |
| Then BA = BD = DA | Proved in Problem 2 |
| BC = ½ BD | Construction |
| BC = ½ AB | Substitution |

(b) *Given:* △BAC with ∠BCA = 90° and BC = ½AB
*To Prove:* ∠BAC = 30°

*Proof*

| | |
|---|---|
| Prolong BC to D so that CD = BC and join AD | |
| BC = ½ BD | Construction |
| BC = ½ AB | Hyp. |
| BD = AB | Substitution |
| △BAC = △CAD | Proved in 4 (b) |
| Hence AB = AD | Corresponding parts of = △ |
| Or AB = AD = BD | Axiom 1 |
| Hence △BAD is equilateral and ∠B = 60° | Definition of equilateral △ |
| ∴ ∠A = 30° | The sum of the ∠s of a △(BAC) = 180° |

5. 100 ft. tall.    Proved in Problem 3.

6. (a) BE = BF = FC           Hyp.
    BE = ½ BF + FC            Axiom 5
    ∠CEB is a rt. ∠           Hyp.
    Hence ∠4 = 30°            Proven in Problem 4 (b)

| | |
|---|---|
| (b) ∠CBE = 60° | The sum of the ∠s of a △ = 180° |
| ∠FBE = ∠CBE | Identity |
| ∠FBE = 60° | Substitution |
| (c) BF = BE | Hyp. |
| ∠FBE = ∠BEF | Base ∠s of isosceles △ are =. |
| ∠FBE and ∠BEF each = 60° | Axiom 1 |
| ∠13 = 60° | The sum of the ∠s of a △ = 180° |
| (d) FE = FB | Arms of an equiangular △ are =. |
| FB = FC | Hyp. |
| Hence FE = FC | Axiom 1 |
| (e) CB = twice CF | Hyp. |
| FE = CF | Proven in (d) |
| CB = twice FE | Substitution |
| But AC = twice FE | Hyp. |
| ∴ AC = CB | Axiom 1 |
| (f) AC = CB | Proven in (e) |
| △ACB is isosceles | Definition of isosceles △ |
| ∠2 = ∠16 | Base ∠s of isosceles △ are =. |
| ∠4 = 30° | Proven in (a) |
| ∠3 = 150° | Definition of supplementary ∠s |
| ∠2 + ∠16 + ∠3 = 180° | The sum of the ∠s of a △ = 180° |
| ∠2 + ∠16 = 30° | Axiom 3 |
| ∠2 = ½ 30° or 15° | Axiom 5 |
| ∠1 = ∠2 | Vertical ∠s are =. |
| ∠1 = 15° | Substitution |

# MATHEMATICS MADE EASY

7. (a) 15°   (b) 150°   (c) 45°   (d) 30°
   (e) 60°   (f) 105°   (g) 75°   (h) 105°
   (i) 75°   (j) 120°   (k) 60°   (l) 45°
   (m) 15°   (n) 15°    (o) 135°  (p) 30°
8. 200 ft. $\angle C = 90°$ and $\angle A = 15°$, so $\angle ADB = 15°$. Hence $AB = BD = 400$ ft. $DC = \frac{1}{2} BD = \frac{1}{2} 400$ ft. $= 200$ ft.
9. 20 seconds. $BC = \frac{1}{2} AC$, so $AC = 880$ ft. At 30 miles per hour, an automobile travels 44 ft. per second. It therefore takes 20 seconds to travel 880 ft.
10. $\angle D$ and $\angle A$ are rt. $\angle s$     Construction.
    $\angle D = \angle A$     All rt. $\angle s$ are =.
    $DC = CA$     Construction.
    $\angle DCE = \angle BCA$     Vertical $\angle s$ are =.
    $\triangle BAC = \triangle EDC$     a.s.a. = a.s.a.
    $DE = AB$     Corresponding parts of = $\triangle$.

## EXERCISE 102

1. (a) 180°   (b) 360°   (c) 540°
   (d) 720°   (e) 900°   (f) 1080°
2. (a) 60°    (b) 90°    (c) 108°
   (d) 120°   (e) $128\frac{4}{7}°$   (f) 135°
3. (a) 20    (b) 10    (c) 4    (d) 12
   (e) 16    (f) 8     (g) 18   (h) 9
   (i) 5     (j) 15    (k) 6    (l) 24
4. 68°, 12°, and 10°.
5. 54°, 81°, 108°, 135°, and 162°
6. (a) $\angle A + \angle B + \angle C + \angle D + \angle E + \angle F = 720°$     The sum of the $\angle s$ of a polygon of n sides $= n - 2$ straight $\angle s$
   $\angle A = \angle B = \angle C = \angle D = \angle E = \angle F$     Definition of regular hexagon
   $\angle B = \frac{1}{6}$ of $720° = 120°$     Axiom 5
   $\angle 1 + \angle 4 + \angle B = 180°$     The sum of the $\angle s$ of a $\triangle = 180°$
   $BA = BC$     Def. of regular hexagon
   $\angle 1 = \angle 4$     Base $\angle s$ of an isosceles $\triangle$ are =.
   $\angle 1 + \angle 4 = 60°$     Axiom 3
   $\angle 1 = 30°$     Axiom 5
6. (b) $\angle A = 120°$     Proven in (a)
   $\angle 1 = 30°$     Proven in (a)
   $\angle FAG = 90°$     Axiom 3
   (c) $\angle FAG = 90°$     Proven in (b)
   Similarly, $\angle DCG = 90°$
   $\therefore DC \parallel AF$     $\perp s$ to the same line are $\parallel$
   (d) By a proof similar to (c) it can be shown that AC and FD are both $\perp$ to AF and $\therefore$ are $\parallel$
   (e) $\angle 6 = \angle 14$ and $\angle 7 = \angle 16$     Alternate interior $\angle s$ of $\parallel$ lines
   $CD = AF$     Hyp.
   $\triangle COD = \triangle AOF$     a.s.a. = a.s.a.
   $\therefore CO = OF$ and $AO = OD$     Corresponding parts of = $\triangle$.
   (f) In triangles FDC and FAD,
   $FD = FD$     Identity
   $AF = CD$     Hyp.
   $\angle AFD = \angle CDF$     All rt. $\angle s$ are =.
   $\triangle FDC = \triangle FAD$     s.a.s. = s.a.s.
   $\therefore AD = FC$     Corresponding parts of = $\triangle$.

# GEOMETRY

(g)    CO=OF and AO=OD      Proven in (e)
       CO=½CF and AO=½AD     Axiom 5
       But CF=AD                  Proven in (f)
       ∴ CO=AO                   Axiom 5

(h)    CO=AO                     Proven in (g)
       AB=BC                      Hyp.
       BO=BO                      Identity
       △ABO=△OBC           s.s.s.=s.s.s.
       ∴ ∠2=∠3                  Corresponding parts of=△ are =.

(i)     ∠2+∠3=∠B            Axiom 6
       ∠B=120°                  Proven in (a)
       ∠2=∠3                    Proven in (h)
       ∠2=½∠B=½120°=60°      Substitution
       ∠1=30°                    Proven in (a)
       ∠1+∠2+∠17=180°        The sum of the ∠s of a △=180°
       ∴ ∠17=90°                Axiom 3

(j)     OB⊥AC                    Proven in (i)
       FA⊥AC                    Proven in (b)
       ∴ OB ∥ AF                ⊥s to the same line are ∥.

(k)    In similar manner it can be shown that OE ∥ AF
       ∴ BOE is a straight line        Only one line can be drawn ∥ to a given line through a single point.

(l)     GHFA is a ▱             Definition of ▱
       ∴ GH=AF                 Opposite sides of ▱ are =.

(m)   ∠8=∠16                  Alternate interior ∠s of ∥ lines
       ∠25=∠22                 Vertical ∠s are =.
       DO=OA                     Proven in (e)
       △DOH=△AOG            a.s.a.=a.s.a.
       ∴ GO=OH                Corresponding parts of=△

(n)    ∠1=30°                    Proven in (a)
       ∠17=90°                  Proven in (i)
       ∴ BG=½AB               In a 30°60°90° △, the side opposite the 30° ∠ = ½ hypotenuse.

(o)    BG=½AB                 Proven in (n)
       AB=AF                    Hyp.
       BG=½AF                  Substitution
       GO=OH                   Proven in (m)
       GO=½GH                 Axiom 5
       GH=AF                    Proven in (l)
       GO=½AF                  Substitution
       ∴ GO=BG                Axiom 1
       ∠19=∠17                 All right ∠s are =
       AG=AG                    Identity
       △AGO=△AGB            s.a.s.=s.a.s.
       ∴ OA=AB                Corresponding parts of =△

(p)    ∠2=60°                    Proven in (i)
       OA=AB                   Proven in (o)
       Hence ∠22=60°           Base ∠s of an isosceles △ are =
       ∠25=60°                  Vertical ∠s are =
       Similarly ∠s 23, 25, 26, and 21 can be proved=to 60°

(q)    ∠2=60°                    Proven in (i)
       ∠23=60°                  Proven in (p)
       ∴ FC ∥ AB                If alternate interior ∠s are = the lines are ∥

## EXERCISE 103

1. (a) $\dfrac{a}{b} = \dfrac{c}{d}$     Hyp.

   Multiplying both sides by $\dfrac{b}{c}$     Axiom 4

   $\dfrac{a}{c} = \dfrac{b}{d}$

   (b) $\dfrac{a}{b} = \dfrac{c}{d}$     Hyp.

   $ad = bc$     Product of means = prod. of extremes

   Multiplying each side by $\dfrac{1}{ac}$     Axiom 4

   $\dfrac{d}{c} = \dfrac{b}{a}$

   (c) $\dfrac{a}{b} = \dfrac{c}{d}$     Hyp.

   $\dfrac{a}{b} + 1 = \dfrac{c}{d} + 1$     Axiom 2

   $\dfrac{a+b}{b} = \dfrac{c+d}{d}$

   or $a+b:b = c+d:d$

   (d) $\dfrac{a}{b} = \dfrac{c}{d}$     Hyp.

   $\dfrac{a}{b} - 1 = \dfrac{c}{d} - 1$     Axiom 3

   $\dfrac{a-b}{b} = \dfrac{c-d}{d}$

   or $a-b:b = c-d:d$

2. (a) 12    (b) 10    (c) 30    (d) 20
   (e) 7    (f) 6    (g) 25    (h) 12
   (i) 24    (j) 54    (k) 3    (l) 17
   (m) 4    (n) 25    (o) 7

3. $10\tfrac{2}{3}$ and $9\tfrac{1}{3}$

4. 14, 14, and 6 in.

5. (a) $66\tfrac{2}{3}$ mi.    (b) 200 mi.    (c) $266\tfrac{2}{3}$ mi.    (d) $166\tfrac{2}{3}$ mi.
   (e) $41\tfrac{2}{3}$ mi.    (f) $116\tfrac{2}{3}$ mi.    (g) $29\tfrac{1}{4}$ mi.    (h) $72\tfrac{11}{12}$ mi.
   (i) $45\tfrac{5}{8}$ mi.    (j) $85\tfrac{5}{12}$ mi.

6. (a) $1\tfrac{1}{2}$    (b) 2.4    (c) 1.35    (d) 3.6
   (e) 2.79    (f) 1.86    (g) 25.83    (h) 12.93
   (i) 22.26    (j) 29.52

7. (a) 2 hr. 6 min. 40 sec.    (b) 6 hr. 40 min.
   (c) 8 hr. 46 min. 40 sec.    (d) 5 hr. 33 min. 20 sec.
   (e) 1 hr. 23 min. 20 sec.    (f) 3 hr. 53 min. 20 sec.
   (g) 58 min. 20 sec.    (h) 2 hr. 25 min. 50 sec.
   (i) 1 hr. 31 min. 40 sec.    (j) 2 hr. 50 min. 50 sec.

8. (a) $1.67    (b) $5.00    (c) $6.67
   (d) $4.17    (e) $1.04    (f) $2.92
   (g) $.73    (h) $1.82    (i) $1.15
   (j) $2.14

9. 21 feet. If $x$ = height of the building, $x:7 = 6:2$.

# GEOMETRY

10. About 48 feet high. Your eye-level is about six feet from the ground, cutting off that amount from the height of both the steeple and the smokestack. The rest of the steeple (84 feet) is to the rest of the smokestack ($x-6$) as two blocks is to one block. Thus, $x-6=42$; and $x$, the smokestack, $=48$.
11. 10,000 feet (from a point directly below the summit). If $x=$ the distance, $6:5=12,000:x$.

## EXERCISE 104

1. (a) 10  (b) 13  (c) 14.87  (d) 17.20
   (e) 20.12  (f) 17.46  (g) 15  (h) 39
   (i) 16.55  (j) 18.36  (k) 20  (l) $\frac{7}{8}$
   (m) $\frac{1}{2}$  (n) 7.87  (o) 16.16  (p) 12.65
   (q) 48  (r) 103.23  (s) 26.87  (t) 17.89
2. (a) Parallel, because both ⊥ to AC
   (b) Parallel, because both ⊥ to AB
   (c) Equal and complementary  (d) same as (c)  (e) 45°
   (f) Equal  (g) Equal  (h) Equal  (i) Equal  (j) Equal
   (k) (1) 6 in.  (2) 8.49 in.  (3) 12 in.  (4) 16.97
3. (a) Parallel because both ⊥ to AC  (b) Parallel  (c) Equal
   (d) Equal
   (e) (1) 60°  (2) 30°  (3) 30°  (4) 60°
       (5) 30°  (6) 60°  (7) 30°  (8) 60°
   (f) $\frac{1}{2}$  (g) $\frac{1}{2}$  (h) $\frac{1}{2}$  (i) $\frac{1}{2}$  (j) $\frac{1}{2}$
   (k) (1) 12  (2) 10.39  (3) 20.78
       (4) 18  (5) 13.86  (6) 6.93
       (7) 16  (8) 8  (9) 27.71
       (10) 32  (11) 14  (12) 24
4. (a) 360°  (b) 240°  (c) 120°  (d) 90°
   (e) 30°  (f) 90°  (g) 60°  (h) 30°
   (i) $\frac{1}{2}$  (j) $\frac{1}{2}$
   (k) (1) 20  (2) 17.32  (3) 11.55  (4) 23.09
5. (a) 720°  (b) 150°  (c) 90°
   (d) 45° because FE=ED and the △ is isosceles  (e) 45°  (f) 135°
   (g) 90°  (h) Equal and parallel, because ABGF is a rectangle
   (i) Equal and parallel  (j) Equal, because FD=AF+AB=BG+AB=BG+FG; but FD=FG+GD; ∴ GD=BG  (k) 45°  (l) 45°
   (m) 150°  (n) 60°  (o) 30°  (p) $\frac{1}{2}$  (q) $\frac{1}{2}$  (r) 30°
   (s) 60°  (t) 30°  (u) 60°
   (v) (1) 32  (2) 27.71  (3) 19.60
       (4) 39.19  (5) 33.94  (6) 53.54
       (7) 37.59
   (w) 46.37

## EXERCISE 105

1. (a) 54  (b) 120  (c) 110.23  (d) 35.78
   (e) 46.43  (f) 96  (g) 244.61  (h) 280.59
   (i) 144  (j) 90.07
2. (a) 49  (b) 56.25  (c) 64  (d) 72.25
   (e) 81  (f) 90.25  (g) 100  (h) 110.25
   (i) 121  (j) 132.25
3. (a) 42.44  (b) 48.71  (c) 55.43  (d) 62.57
   (e) 93.53  (f) 208.43  (g) 115.47  (h) 190.96
   (i) 419.16  (j) 458.16  (k) 486.83  (e) 585.43

## MATHEMATICS MADE EASY

4. (a) 53.24  (b) 74.30  (c) 114.47
   (d) 107.12 (e) 160.69 (f) 31.75
   (g) 39.60  (h) 32.98  (i) 43.59  (j) 71.55
5. (a) 26.83  (b) 11.62  (c) 39.19
   (d) 14.14  (e) 24.25  (f) 46.98
   (g) 30.59  (h) 28.28  (i) 32.73  (j) 94.87
6. (a) 252    (b) 247    (c) 240    (d) 231
   (e) 220    (f) 207    (g) 192    (h) 175
7. (a) 288    (b) 312½   (c) 338    (d) 364½
   (e) 392    (f) 420½   (g) 450    (h) 512
   (i) 578    (j) 648
8. (a) 131.64 (b) 519.62 (c) 239.02
   (d) 727.46 (e) 387.98 (f) 647.79
   (g) 315.23 (h) 855.63 (i) 190.52 (j) 452.06
9. (a) 154    (b) 616    (c) 1386   (d) 2464
   (e) 75.46  (f) 98.56  (g) 36.98  (h) 384.24
   (i) 35.48  (j) 745.36 (k) 33,277.86 (l) 29.81
10. (a) 2385.15           (b) 2838.53
    (c) 2958.01           (d) 2494.8
11. 2.93 Acres  (14,157.239 sq. yds.)
12. 3.32 Acres (16,200 sq. yds.)

### EXERCISE 106

1. 8 in. by 4 in.    2. 10 ft. by 6 ft.    3. 12 in.    4. 18 in.
5. square, 15×15 in.; rectangle, 25×9 in.    6. 50 and 40 yards
7. 30 yards by 18 yards    8. 60 yd. by 20 yd.    9. 1270 men
10. 841 men    11. Doubles court, 78 ft. by 36 ft.; singles court, 78 ft. by 27 ft.
12. Kitchen, 12 ft. by 10 ft.; living room, 23 ft. by 14 ft.

PART II

The Practical Uses of Mathematics

# MATHEMATICS FOR BUSINESS

## CHAPTER XIV
## Trade Discounts

THIS SECTION deals with mathematics not as an abstract science but as a concrete guide to practical living. It contains the many answers to the question which, in various forms, arises again and again in our everyday life—how do you figure it out?

In this chapter we shall see how to figure it out when it comes to exchanging the desirable things of the world—that is, the buying and selling of goods.

In buying and selling goods, we use the following trade terms:

The *list price* of an article is the price at which it is listed and sold to the public.

The *trade discount* is the reduction from the list price of the article.

The *net price* is the price of the article after the discount has been made.

Examples:

1. The list price of an automobile is $1025. The dealer gets it at a discount of 20%. What is the net price to the dealer?

| List price | $1025 |
| Less 20% | 205 |
| Net price | $820 |

2. The discount on a radio is 40%. The net price is $126. What is the list price?

$126 is 60% (100% − 40%) of what number?

According to our percentage formula, the *base* equals the *percentage* divided by the *rate*. Translating this percentage formula into commercial language, we get the following merchandising formula: the *list price* equals the *net price* divided by the *rate* of the list price.

List price = $126 ÷ 60% = 126 ÷ $\frac{60}{100}$ = 126 ÷ $\frac{3}{5}$ = $210.

3. The real estate agent's discount on a house is 20%. He gets the house from the builder for $8800. What is the list price of the house to the customer?

$8800 \div 80\% = 8800 \div \frac{4}{5} = \$11000$.

## EXERCISE 107

Find the net price:

(a) $180 less 40%
(b) $270 less 33⅓%
(c) $648 less 25%
(d) $126 less 16⅔%
(e) $845 less 20%

(f) $193.20 less 40%
(g) $113.22 less 33⅓%
(h) $253.24 less 25%
(i) $233.22 less 16⅔%
(j) $146.35 less 20%

## EXERCISE 108

A. A manufacturer offers a trade discount of 40%. If he wishes the net prices to be those listed below, what must be the list price of each?

(a) $97.02
(b) $83.34
(c) $35.46
(d) $15.66
(e) $149.22
(f) $842.28
(g) $16.32
(h) $19.44
(i) $216.00
(j) $103.14

B. If his trade discount is only 33⅓%, what must be the list price of each?

## DISCOUNT SERIES

Sometimes a manufacturer, for various reasons, offers a discount in addition to a previous discount. Suppose he manufactures silk stockings to sell at a discount of 20%, and suppose he suddenly gets a shipment of silk at a very low price. He can now afford to allow an additional discount of 10%. On top of that, he may allow still another discount of 2% to some of his customers for prompt payments. In other words, he allows a *discount series*.

In a discount series, the first figure denotes the discount from the list price, the second denotes the discount from the remainder, and so on. If the stocking manufacturer lists his

# TRADE DISCOUNTS

stockings at $12 a dozen, he will compute his discount series as follows:

$12 less 20%, less 10%, less 2%.
$12 less 20% = $9.60
$9.60 less 10% = $8.64
$8.64 less 2% = $8.47

When there is a fraction of a cent in a remainder, the fraction may either be dropped or computed as a whole cent.

## EXERCISE 109

Find the net selling price for each of the following:

|     | List Price | Discounts |     | List Price | Discount |
| --- | --- | --- | --- | --- | --- |
| (a) | $ 120 | 20% and $16\frac{2}{3}$% | (k) | $ 225.15 | $33\frac{1}{3}$% and 20% |
| (b) | 3000 | 20% and $33\frac{1}{3}$% | (l) | 162.16 | 25% and $16\frac{2}{3}$% |
| (c) | 160 | 25% and 10% | (m) | 400.00 | 20% and 10% |
| (d) | 480 | $33\frac{1}{3}$% and 25% | (n) | 250.00 | 50% and $12\frac{1}{2}$% |
| (e) | 300 | 20% and 10% | (o) | 183.26 | $37\frac{1}{2}$% and 20% |
| (f) | 120 | 20% and $12\frac{1}{2}$% | (p) | 960.00 | $16\frac{2}{3}$% and $12\frac{1}{2}$% |
| (g) | 600 | 50% and 20% | (q) | 160.00 | 25% and 5% |
| (h) | 480 | 50% and 25% | (r) | 144.00 | $12\frac{1}{2}$% and 5% |
| (i) | 420 | 40% and $16\frac{2}{3}$% | (s) | 2600.00 | 15% and 10% |
| (j) | 1680 | $37\frac{1}{2}$% and 20% | (t) | 3000.00 | $22\frac{1}{2}$% and 10% |

## REDUCING A SERIES TO A SINGLE DISCOUNT

Instead of computing a series of discounts one by one, it is oftentimes more convenient to reduce the series to a single discount.

For example, reduce the series 20%, 10%, and 2% to an equivalent single discount.

| The list price | = 100 | % of the list price. |
| --- | --- | --- |
| Deducting | 20 | % of the list price, |
| we have left | 80 | % of the list price. |
| Deducting 10% of 80%, or | 8 | % of the list price, |
| we have left | 72 | % of the list price. |
| Deducting 2% of 72%, or | 1.44% | of the list price, |
| we have left | 70.56% | of the list price. |

Then 100% − 70.56% = 29.44%, the single discount.

## EXERCISE 110

Find the single rate of discount equivalent to:

(a) $2\frac{1}{2}\%$ and 10%
(b) $2\frac{1}{2}\%$ and 15%
(c) $2\frac{1}{2}\%$ and 20%
(d) $2\frac{1}{2}\%$ and $33\frac{1}{3}\%$
(e) 5% and 10%
(f) 5% and $12\frac{1}{2}\%$
(g) 5% and 15%
(h) 5% and $16\frac{2}{3}\%$
(i) 5% and 20%
(j) 5% and 25%
(k) 5% and $33\frac{1}{3}\%$
(l) 10% and 10%
(m) 10% and $12\frac{1}{2}\%$
(n) 10% and 15%
(o) 10% and $16\frac{2}{3}\%$
(p) 10% and 20%
(q) 10% and 25%
(r) 10% and $33\frac{1}{3}\%$
(s) $16\frac{2}{3}\%$ and $12\frac{1}{2}\%$
(t) $16\frac{2}{3}\%$ and 20%

(1) $16\frac{2}{3}\%$ and 25%
(2) 10%, 5%, and 10%
(3) 10%, 5%, and $12\frac{1}{2}\%$
(4) 10%, 5%, and 15%
(5) 10%, 5%, and $16\frac{2}{3}\%$
(6) 10%, 5%, and 20%
(7) 10%, 5%, and 25%
(8) 10%, 10%, and 10%
(9) 10%, 10%, and $16\frac{2}{3}\%$
(10) 10%, 10%, and $33\frac{1}{3}\%$
(11) 20%, 10%, and 10%
(12) 20%, 10%, and $12\frac{1}{2}\%$
(13) 20%, 10%, and $16\frac{2}{3}\%$
(14) 20%, 10%, and 25%
(15) 20%, 10%, and $33\frac{1}{3}\%$
(16) 25%, 10%, and 10%
(17) 25%, 10%, and 15%
(18) 25%, 10%, and 20%
(19) 25%, 10%, and 25%
(20) 25%, 10%, and $33\frac{1}{3}\%$

## EXERCISE 111

In the right-hand column below are the net selling prices of twenty products listed at $100.00. In the left-hand column are twenty series of trade discounts. Match the letter of the left-hand column with the correct number of the right-hand column.

(a) 25%, 10%, and 10%
(b) 20%, 10%, and 10%
(c) 20%, $16\frac{2}{3}\%$, and 10%
(d) 20% and $2\frac{1}{2}\%$
(e) 25%, 15%, and 10%
(f) $33\frac{1}{3}\%$, 10%, and 5%
(g) $16\frac{2}{3}\%$, 10%, and 5%
(h) 25%, $16\frac{2}{3}\%$, and 10%
(i) 20% and 10%
(j) 10% and 10%
(k) 10%, 10%, and 5%
(l) 20%, $12\frac{1}{2}\%$, and 10%

1. $61.20
2. 72.90
3. 63.00
4. 67.50
5. 56.25
6. 76.50
7. 72.00
8. 55.00
9. 60.75
10. 54.00
11. 52.00
12. 71.25

(m) 15% and 10%
(n) 25%, 20%, and 10%
(o) 10%, 10%, and 10%
(p) 16⅔%, 10%, and 10%
(q) 20%, 15%, and 10%
(r) 20%, 10%, and 10%
(s) 33⅓%, 25%, and 10%
(t) 33⅓%, 20%, and 10%

13. 57.37½
14. 40.00
15. 57.00
16. 57.60
17. 64.80
18. 78.00
19. 81.00
20. 76.95

### INVOICES

If an invoice or a bill is due at once, it bears the words "Terms cash." If due in 60 days, but with a special discount of 2% if paid in 30 days, or with a special discount of 3% if paid in 10 days, the invoice or bill may read "3/10, 2/30, n/60."

Example: An invoice amounting to $450 dated June 15, terms 3/10, 2/30, n/60, is paid July 12. How much is paid?

The account, as we see, is paid within 30 days, but not within 10 days. The special discount, therefore, is 2%. Then $450−2% = $441.

### EXERCISE 112
Practical Problems on Trade Discounts

1. An invoice amounting to $6400 dated May 15, terms 5/10, 3/30, n/60, is paid June 11. How much is paid?

2. An invoice amounting to $461.23 dated February 11, terms 4/30, 2/60, n/3mo. is paid on March 12. How much is paid?

3. If you could buy an automobile from one dealer at $900.00 less 33⅓% and 20%; and from another dealer at $1000.00 less 37½%, 20%, and 5%, which offer would you accept? How much better is it than the other?

4. The list price of a certain lamp is $15.00. If you buy a dozen at a discount of 25%, 10%, and 20% and sell them at a discount of 10% and 10%, what is your profit on the transaction?

5. A jobber buys merchandise at 25% and 20% less than list price and sells it at 20% less than list. What is his profit on merchandise listed at $10,000.00?

6. A jobber buys a suit of clothes at a discount of 33⅓%, 25%, and 10% and sells it to a retailer at a discount of 25% and 16⅔%. If the jobber's profit is $7.00, what is the list price of the suit?

## MATHEMATICS MADE EASY

### ANSWERS
#### EXERCISE 107

(a) $108    (b) $180    (c) $486    (d) $105    (e) $676
(f) $115.92    (g) $75.48    (h) $189.93    (i) $194.35    (j) $117.08

#### EXERCISE 108

|   | A | B |   | A | B |
|---|---|---|---|---|---|
| (a) | $161.70 | $145.53 | (f) | $1403.80 | $1263.42 |
| (b) | $138.90 | $125.01 | (g) | $27.20 | $24.48 |
| (c) | $59.10 | $53.19 | (h) | $32.40 | $29.16 |
| (d) | $26.10 | $23.49 | (i) | $360.00 | $324.00 |
| (e) | $248.70 | $223.83 | (j) | $171.90 | $155.71 |

#### EXERCISE 109

(a) $80    (b) $1600    (c) $144    (d) $480
(e) $216    (f) $84    (g) $240    (h) $180
(i) $210    (j) $840    (k) $120.08    (l) $101.35
(m) $288    (n) $109.38    (o) $91.63    (p) $700
(q) $108    (r) $119.70    (s) $1989    (t) $2092.50

#### EXERCISE 110

(a) $12\frac{1}{4}\%$    (1) $37\frac{1}{2}\%$
(b) $17\frac{1}{8}\%$    (2) $23.05\%$
(c) $22\%$    (3) $25.187\%$
(d) $35\%$    (4) $27.325\%$
(e) $14\frac{1}{2}\%$    (5) $28\frac{3}{4}\%$
(f) $16\frac{7}{8}\%$    (6) $31.6\%$
(g) $19\frac{1}{4}\%$    (7) $35\frac{7}{8}\%$
(h) $20\frac{5}{8}\%$    (8) $27.1\%$
(i) $24\%$    (9) $32\frac{1}{2}\%$
(j) $28\frac{3}{4}\%$    (10) $46\%$
(k) $36\frac{2}{3}\%$    (11) $35.2\%$
(l) $19\%$    (12) $37\%$
(m) $21\frac{1}{4}\%$    (13) $40\%$
(n) $23\frac{1}{2}\%$    (14) $46\%$
(o) $25\%$    (15) $52\%$
(p) $28\%$    (16) $39\frac{1}{4}\%$
(q) $32\frac{1}{2}\%$    (17) $42\frac{5}{8}\%$
(r) $40\%$    (18) $46\%$
(s) $27\frac{1}{12}\%$    (19) $49\frac{3}{8}\%$
(t) $33\frac{1}{8}\%$    (20) $55\%$

#### EXERCISE 111

(a) 9    (b) 17    (c) 14    (d) 18    (e) 13
(f) 15    (g) 12    (h) 5    (i) 7    (j) 19
(k) 20    (l) 3    (m) 6    (n) 10    (o) 2
(p) 4    (q) 1    (r) 16    (s) 8    (t) 11

#### EXERCISE 112

1. $6,208    2. $442.78    3. The second, by $5.00
4. $48.60    5. $2,000    6. $40.00

## CHAPTER XV
# Profit and Loss

IN COMPUTING the profit and loss on any transaction, we apply the principles as explained in our sections on Percentage and on Trade Discount.

For example:

1. A haberdasher buys a dozen shirts for $10.00 and makes a profit of 25%, as based on the cost. At what price does he sell these shirts?

   Profit made on transaction = 25% of $10.00 = $2.50
   Price at which shirts are sold = $10.00 + $2.50 = $12.50.

2. A bookseller buys 10 books for $18 and sells them for $30. What percent profit does he make, based on the cost?

   The amount of the profit = $30 − $18 = $12
   The percent of the profit, based on the cost = $12 \div 18 = \frac{12}{18} = \frac{2}{3} = 66\frac{2}{3}\%$

Note: To get the percent profit as based on the cost, divide the amount of the profit by the amount of the cost.

3. A retailer sells a number of shirts for $52 and makes $33\frac{1}{3}\%$ profit based on the cost. What is the cost?

   Cost + Profit = $52
   Profit = $33\frac{1}{3}\%$, or $\frac{1}{3}$ of cost
   Hence, Cost + $\frac{1}{3}$ of Cost = $52
   $\text{Cost} + \frac{\text{Cost}}{3} = \$52$
   3 × Cost + Cost = $156
   4 × Cost = $156
   Cost = $39.00

4. A retail clothier buys suits listed at $180 with trade discounts of 25% and 10%. He sells them at a profit of 60% based on the cost. At what price does he sell them?

| The list price ($140) | = 100% of the list price |
| Deducting 25% of the list price, we have left | 75% of the list price |
| Deducting 10% of 75%, we have left | 67.5% of the list price |
| That is, the cost | = 67½% of the list price |
| The cost = 67½% of $180 | = $121.50 |
| The clothier sells the goods at the cost price plus 60% of the cost | |
| That is, he sells the goods for $121.50 + 60% of $121.50 | = $194.40 |

Answer, $194.40

5. A grocer buys canned goods at a list price of $50 with trade discounts of 20% and 5%. He sells the goods for $60.80. What percent of profit based on the cost does he make?

$100\% - 20\% - 5\% = 76\%$
Cost = 76% of $50.00    = $38.00
Profit = $60.80 - $38.00    = $22.80
Percent profit = $\frac{22.80}{38.00} = .60$    = 60%

Answer, 60%

### EXERCISE 113

Find the selling price, given the net cost and the percent profit based on the cost:

| | Net Cost | % Profit | | Net Cost | % Profit |
|---|---|---|---|---|---|
| 1. | $10.00 | 20 | 6. | $ 84.00 | 37½ |
| 2. | 14.00 | 10 | 7. | 96.00 | 40 |
| 3. | 17.00 | 15 | 8. | 107.00 | 60 |
| 4. | 19.00 | 16⅔ | 9. | 38.00 | 50 |
| 5. | 23.00 | 33⅓ | 10. | 49.50 | 25 |

### EXERCISE 114

Find the percent profit based on the cost, given the net cost and the selling price:

| | Net Cost | Selling Price | | Net Cost | Selling Price |
|---|---|---|---|---|---|
| 1. | $20.00 | $25.00 | 6. | $ 81.00 | $108.00 |
| 2. | 29.00 | 43.50 | 7. | 114.00 | 133.00 |
| 3. | 27.00 | 43.20 | 8. | 127.00 | 146.05 |
| 4. | 34.00 | 47.60 | 9. | 68.00 | 74.80 |
| 5. | 36.00 | 49.50 | 10. | 89.50 | 107.40 |

# PROFIT AND LOSS

## EXERCISE 115

Find the net cost given the percent profit based on the cost and the selling price:

| | % Profit | Selling Price | | % Profit | Selling Price |
|---|---|---|---|---|---|
| 1. | $16\frac{2}{3}$ | $ 35.00 | 6. | 25 | $115.00 |
| 2. | 20 | 119.40 | 7. | $37\frac{1}{2}$ | 66.00 |
| 3. | $33\frac{1}{3}$ | 104.00 | 8. | $62\frac{1}{2}$ | 104.00 |
| 4. | 50 | 205.50 | 9. | $12\frac{1}{2}$ | 63.00 |
| 5. | 15 | 142.60 | 10. | 40 | 77.00 |

## EXERCISE 116

Solve the following problems:

1. A retailer buys a pair of shoes at a list price of $5.00 with trade discounts of 20% and 5%. He sells them at a profit of 60% based on the cost. What is the selling price of the pair of shoes?

2. A retailer buys shirts at $2.00 each with trade discounts of 20% and 10%. He sells them at a profit of 75% based on the cost. What is the selling price of each shirt?

3. A haberdasher buys neckties listed at $18.00 per dozen with trade discounts of 25% and 10%. He sells them at a profit of 60% based on the cost. For how much does he sell each tie?

4. A retailer buys suits listed at $35.00 with trade discounts of $33\frac{1}{3}$% and 10%. He sells them at $35.00 each. What percent profit based on the cost does he make?

5. A haberdasher buys socks listed at $9.60 per dozen pairs with trade discounts of $16\frac{2}{3}$%, 10% and 10%. He sells them at a profit at $62\frac{1}{2}$% based on the cost. At what price does he sell each pair?

6. A retailer buys dresses listed at $16.00 with trade discounts of $33\frac{1}{3}$%, 20% and 10%. He sells them for $14.40. What percent of profit based on the cost does he make?

7. A retailer buys sweaters listed at $8.00 with trade discounts of $33\frac{1}{3}$%, 10% and 10%. He sells them at a profit of $62\frac{1}{2}$% based on the cost. At what price does he sell each sweater?

8. A retailer buys a bookcase listed at $18.00 with trade discounts of $33\frac{1}{3}$%, 10% and 5%. He sells it for $15.39. What percent of profit based on the cost does he make?

9. A retailer buys a radio listed at $120.00 with trade discounts of 20%, $12\frac{1}{2}$% and 10%. He sells it at a profit of 60% based on the cost. At what price does he sell the radio?

10. A retailer buys a typewriter listed at $110.00 with trade dis-

counts of 25% and 10%. He sells it for $103.95. What percent of profit based on the cost does he make?

11. The owner of a furniture shop buys a living room suite listed at $240.00 with trade discounts of 20%, $16\frac{2}{3}$% and 10%. He sells it at a profit of $115.20. What percent of profit based on the cost does he make?

12. The owner of a furniture shop buys a bedroom suite listed at $180.00 with trade discounts of $33\frac{1}{3}$%, 10% and 10%. He sells it at a profit of 75% based on the cost. What is the selling price?

13. A retailer buys a lamp listed at $12.00 with trade discounts of $33\frac{1}{3}$% and 10%. He sells it at a profit of $4.32. What percent of profit based on the cost does this represent?

14. A department store buyer buys a bridge table and chairs for $25.00 with discounts of $33\frac{1}{3}$%, 10% and 10%. His mark-up is 50% of the cost. At what price does he sell the set?

15. The owner of a gift shop buys cigarette cases listed at $2.50 with trade discounts of $33\frac{1}{3}$%, 20% and 10%. He sells them at a profit of $62\frac{1}{2}$% based on the cost. What is the selling price of each cigarette case?

16. A cigar store owner buys ash trays listed at $1.00 with trade discounts of $16\frac{2}{3}$%, 10% and 10%. He sells them at a profit of 80% based on the cost. How much does he get for each ash tray?

17. A retailer buys a chess set listed at $5.00 and sells it for 15¢ less. His trade discounts are $33\frac{1}{3}$%, 10% and 5%. What percent profit based on the cost does he make?

18. A dealer buys a refrigerator listed at $150.00 with trade discounts of $16\frac{2}{3}$%, 10% and 10%. He sells it at a profit of 65% based on the cost. What is the selling price?

19. A dealer buys a rug listed at $200.00 with trade discounts of 20%, $16\frac{2}{3}$% and 10%. He sells it for $225.00. What percent of profit based on the cost does he make?

20. A dealer buys a piano listed at $800.00 with trade discounts of 25%, 20% and 10%. He sells it at a profit of 80% based on the cost. What is the selling price of the piano?

When the profit is based on the selling price, instead of the cost price, the procedure is as follows:

1. When the cost and the percent profit are given:

| Cost | Percent Profit Based on Selling Price | Selling Price | Amount of Profit | Percent Profit Based on Cost |
|------|---------------------------------------|---------------|------------------|------------------------------|
| $39  | 35%                                   | ?             | ?                | ?                            |

## PROFIT AND LOSS

Selling price = Cost plus amount of profit
But amount of profit = 35% of selling price
Hence selling price = Cost + 35% of selling price
That is, $S = 39 + \frac{35S}{100}$
$100S = 3900 + 35S$
$65S = 3900$

S, or selling price, = $60
Amount of profit = $60 − $39 = $21
% of profit
  based on cost = $\frac{21}{39}$ = 53.8%

Answer: $\begin{cases} \text{Selling price, \$60.} \\ \text{Amount of profit, \$21.} \\ \text{\% of profit based on cost, 53.8\%.} \end{cases}$

2. When the cost and the selling price are given:

| Cost | Selling Price | Amount of Profit | % Profit Based on Selling Price | % Profit Based on Cost |
|---|---|---|---|---|
| $22 | $33 | ? | ? | ? |

Amount of profit = $33 − $22 = $11
Percent of profit
  based on selling
  price = $\frac{11}{33} = \frac{1}{3} = 33\frac{1}{3}\%$
Percent of profit
  based on cost = $\frac{11}{22} = \frac{1}{2} = 50\%$

Answer: $\begin{cases} \text{Amount of profit, \$11.} \\ \text{Percent of profit based on selling price, } 33\frac{1}{3}\%. \\ \text{Percent of profit based on cost, 50\%.} \end{cases}$

3. When the selling price and the percent profit based on the selling price are given:

| Selling Price | % Profit Based on Selling Price | Cost | Amount of Profit | % Profit Based on Cost |
|---|---|---|---|---|
| $125 | 44% | ? | ? | ? |

Cost = $125 − 44% of $125 = $70
Amount of profit = $125 − $70 = $55
% profit based on cost = $\frac{55}{70}$ = 78.6%

Answer: $\begin{cases} \text{Cost, \$70.} \\ \text{Amount of profit, \$55.} \\ \text{\% profit based on cost, 78.6\%.} \end{cases}$

## EXERCISE 117

In each of the following problems find (a) the selling price, (b) the amount of the profit and (c) the percent of profit based on the cost.

| | Cost | % Profit Based on Selling Price | | Cost | % Profit Based on Selling Price |
|---|---|---|---|---|---|
| 1. | $ 6.00 | 40 | 6. | $30.24 | 28 |
| 2. | 12.00 | $33\frac{1}{3}$ | 7. | 57.60 | 36 |
| 3. | 13.00 | 35 | 8. | 53.55 | 37 |
| 4. | 13.20 | 45 | 9. | 99.36 | 31 |
| 5. | 105.00 | 30 | 10. | 96.00 | 32 |

## EXERCISE 118

In each of the following problems, given the cost and the selling price, find (a) the percent profit based on the selling price, (b) the percent profit based on the cost and (c) the amount of the profit.

| | Cost | Selling Price | | Cost | Selling Price |
|---|---|---|---|---|---|
| 1. | $ 8.00 | $10.00 | 6. | $45.00 | $ 72.00 |
| 2. | 33.00 | 55.00 | 7. | 16.00 | 25.00 |
| 3. | 11.00 | 15.00 | 8. | 60.00 | 150.00 |
| 4. | 44.00 | 66.00 | 9. | 24.00 | 50.00 |
| 5. | 12.00 | 16.00 | 10. | 72.00 | 125.00 |

## EXERCISE 119

In the following problems, given the selling price and the percent profit based on the selling price, find (a) the cost, (b) the amount of the profit and (c) the percent profit based on the cost.

| | Selling Price | % Profit Based on Selling Price | | Selling Price | % Profit Based on Selling Price |
|---|---|---|---|---|---|
| 1. | $15.00 | 40 | 6. | $54.00 | $44\frac{4}{9}$ |
| 2. | 40.00 | $37\frac{1}{2}$ | 7. | 25.00 | 36 |
| 3. | 18.00 | $44\frac{4}{9}$ | 8. | 60.00 | $41\frac{2}{3}$ |
| 4. | 50.00 | 44 | 9. | 40.00 | $52\frac{1}{2}$ |
| 5. | 20.00 | 40 | 10. | 45.00 | $53\frac{1}{3}$ |

## GROSS PROFIT AND NET PROFIT

In the computation of the foregoing examples, we have omitted an important item—the cost of doing business. Let us now consider this item:

# PROFIT AND LOSS

Suppose an automobile dealer buys a car from the manufacturer at a net cost of $777.60. His cost of doing business is 32%, based on the selling price; and his net profit, also based on the selling price, is 14%. (a) What is the percent of his gross profit? (b) At what price does he sell the car? (c) What is his net profit?

(a) Gross profit $= 32\% + 14\% = 46\%$
(b) S (selling price) $= 777.60 + \frac{46S}{100}$
    100S $= 77760 + 46S$
    54S $= 77760$
    S $= \$1440$
(c) Net profit $= 14\%$ of $\$1440 = \$201.60$

Answer: (a) 46%; (b) $1440.00; (c) $201.60.

## MARKING GOODS

Suppose the automobile dealer employs a salesman to sell the car. How is the salesman to know the price at which the dealer wants to sell the car, without at the same time allowing the customer to know the price? The answer is—by means of a code, or cipher.

A code that marks the price of an article generally consists of a word or a phrase containing ten different letters, spelled either forwards or backwards.

Thus, the code may consist of the phrase GO FETCH JIM.

Spelled forwards, the key would be:

  1  2  3  4  5  6  7  8  9  0
  G  O  F  E  T  C  H  J  I  M

Spelled backwards, the key would be:

  1  2  3  4  5  6  7  8  9  0
  M  I  J  H  C  T  E  F  O  G

When a figure is repeated, an extra letter, say X, is generally used. Thus, $255 = icx$.

When a figure appears three times in succession, two extra letters, like X and Y, are used. Thus, $2555 = icxy$.

And now, using the above code, still spelled backwards, we can mark the cost price ($777.60) and the selling price ($1440) in the foregoing example:

exy.tg/mhxg.

## EXERCISE 120

In each of the following problems profit and the cost of doing business are expressed as percentages of the selling price. In marking prices use the code word "farsighted" spelled backwards with "x" and "y" as repeaters. Thus the code is

| 1 | 2 | 3 | 4 | 5 | 6 | 7 | 8 | 9 | 0 |
|---|---|---|---|---|---|---|---|---|---|
| D | E | T | H | G | I | S | R | A | F |

1. A retailer buys a lamp at a net cost of $36.00. His cost of doing business is 31% and his profit is 9%. At what price does he sell the lamp, (b) what is his net profit and (c) how does he mark the lamp in code with the price of the cost and selling price?

2. A furniture dealer buys a bookcase at a net cost of $25.20. His cost of doing business is 26% and his profit is 11%. At what price does he sell the lamp, (b) what is his net profit and (c) how does he mark the lamp in code with the price of the cost and selling price?

3. A department store buyer buys a suit of clothes at a net cost of $38.88. His cost of doing business is 32% and his profit is 14%. (a) At what price does he sell the suit, (b) what is his net profit and (c) how does he mark the suit in code to show the cost price and the selling price?

4. The owner of a gift shop buys a bridge table and chairs at a net cost of $17.50. His cost of doing business is 18% and his profit is 12%. (a) At what price does he sell the set, (b) what is his net profit and (c) how does he mark the set in code to show the cost price and the selling price?

5. A hardware dealer buys a set of dishes for a net cost of $21.24. His cost of doing business is 27% and his profit is 14%. (a) At what price does he sell the set, (b) what is his net profit and (c) how does he mark the set in code to show the cost price and the selling price?

6. A haberdasher buys a hat at a net cost of $3.35. His cost of doing business is 23% and his profit is 12%. (a) At what price does he sell the hat, (b) what is his net profit and (c) how does he mark the hat in code to show the cost price and the selling price?

7. An electrical goods retailer buys a vacuum cleaner at a net cost of $27.84. His cost of doing business is 29% and his profit is 13%. (a) At what price does he sell the cleaner, (b) what is his net profit and (c) how does he mark the cleaner in code to show the cost price and the selling price?

8. A department store buyer buys a radio at a net cost of $47.25. His cost of doing business is 30% and his profit is 7%. (a) At what

## PROFIT AND LOSS

price does he sell the radio, (b) what is his net profit and (c) how does he mark the radio in code to show the cost price and the selling price?

9. A hardware dealer buys a set of dishes at a net cost of $8.04. His cost of doing business is 24% and his profit is 9%. (a) At what price does he sell the set, (b) what is his net profit and (c) how does he mark the set in code to show the cost price and the selling price?

10. An electrical goods retailer buys a vacuum cleaner at a net cost of $46.40. His cost of doing business is 31% and his profit is 11%. (a) At what price does he sell the cleaner, (b) what is his net profit and (c) how does he mark the cleaner in code to show the cost price and the selling price?

### COMPUTING LOSSES

1. A retailer bought 500 shirts at $1.00 each, expecting to sell them at $1.50 each. Owing to a protracted period of unemployment in his town, he was obliged to sell them at 85 cents each. His operating expenses in handling those shirts were $55. (a) What was his loss on the sales? (b) What was his net loss?

    (a) Cost of goods sold          = $500
        Amount realized from sales  =  425
        Loss on sales               =  $75

    (b) Loss on sales            = $75
        Operating expenses     =  55
        Net loss                  = $130
        Answer: (a) $75; (b) $130.

2. Mr. Jones bought a number of dresses for $7920 and sold them for $8078. His operating expenses were $375. (a) What was the profit on sales? (b) What was the net loss?

    (a) Amount realized from sales  = $8070
        Cost of goods sold         =  7920
        Profit on sales            =  $158

    (b) Operating expenses       = $375
        Profit on sales           =  158
        Net loss                 = $217
        Answer: (a) $158; (b) $217.

## EXERCISE 121

Compute (a) the profit or loss on sales, and (b) the net profit or loss, in the following examples:

| | Cost of Sales | Sales | Overhead |
|---|---|---|---|
| 1. | $1243.50 | $1425 | $175 |
| 2. | $2567.75 | $3124.50 | $425.18 |
| 3. | $3250 | $3175 | $315.25 |
| 4. | $2400 | $2527.80 | $127.80 |
| 5. | $1565.24 | $1824.50 | $249.26 |
| 6. | $23,450.61 | $28,379.45 | $6241.56 |
| 7. | $39,724.56 | $39,825.46 | $245.64 |
| 8. | $43,543.50 | $42,924.75 | $2459.50 |
| 9. | $125,342.56 | $130,425.50 | $16,250 |
| 10. | $250,452.12 | $284,352.12 | $26,150.38 |
| 11. | $42,450 | $45,300 | 20% of cost |
| 12. | $12,356.20 | $28,475 | 40% of cost |
| 13. | $24,345.56 | $30,144 | 25% of sales |
| 14. | $25,349 | $26,135 | 30% of cost |
| 15. | $49,342.12 | $58,543.28 | 24% of cost price |

## ANSWERS

### EXERCISE 113

1. $12.00    2. $15.40    3. $19.55    4. $22.17
5. $30.67    6. $115.50    7. $134.40    8. $171.20
9. $57.00    10. $61.88

### EXERCISE 114

1. 25%    2. 50%    3. 60%    4. 40%
5. 37½%    6. 33⅓%    7. 16⅔%    8. 15%
9. 10%    10. 20%

### EXERCISE 115

1. $30.00    2. $99.50    3. $78.00    4. $137.00
5. $124.00    6. $92.00    7. $48.00    8. $64.00
9. $56.00    10. $55.00

### EXERCISE 116

1. $6.08    2. $2.52    3. $1.62    4. 66⅔%
5. $.88    6. 87½%    7. $7.02    8. 50%
9. $120.96    10. 40%    11. 80%    12. $170.10
13. 60%    14. $20.25    15. $1.95    16. $1.22
17. 70%    18. $167.06    19. 87½%    20. $777.60

# PROFIT AND LOSS

### EXERCISE 117

|    | (a)       | (b)     | (c)    |     | (a)      | (b)     | (c)   |
|----|-----------|---------|--------|-----|----------|---------|-------|
| 1. | $ 10.00   | $ 4.00  | 66.7%  | 6.  | $ 42.00  | $11.76  | 45.1% |
| 2. | 18.00     | 6.00    | 50%    | 7.  | 90.00    | 32.40   | 56.3% |
| 3. | 20.00     | 7.00    | 53.8%  | 8.  | 85.00    | 31.45   | 58.7% |
| 4. | 24.00     | 10.80   | 81.8%  | 9.  | 144.00   | 44.64   | 44.9% |
| 5. | 150.00    | 45.00   | 42.8%  | 10. | 141.18   | 45.18   | 47.1% |

### EXERCISE 118

1. (a) 20% (b) 33.3% (c) $2.00   2. (a) 40% (b) 66.7% (c) $22.00   3. (a) $25\frac{2}{3}$% (b) 36.4% (c) $4.00
4. (a) $33\frac{1}{3}$% (b) 50% (c) $22.00   5. (a) 25% (b) 33.3% (c) $4.00   6. (a) $37\frac{1}{2}$% (b) 60% (c) $27.00   7. (a) 36%
(b) 56.3% (c) $9.00   8. (a) 60% (b) 150% (c) $90.00
9. (a) 52% (b) 108.3% (c) $26.00   10. (a) $42\frac{2}{5}$%
(b) 73% (c) $53.00

### EXERCISE 119

1.  (a) $9.00    (b) $6.00    (c) 66.7%
2.  (a) $25.00   (b) $15.00   (c) 60%
3.  (a) $10.00   (b) $8.00    (c) 80%
4.  (a) $28.00   (b) $22.00   (c) 78.6%
5.  (a) $12.00   (b) $8.00    (c) 66.7%
6.  (a) $30.00   (b) $24.00   (c) 80%
7.  (a) $16.00   (b) $9.00    (c) 56.3%
8.  (a) $35.00   (b) $25.00   (c) 71.4%
9.  (a) $19.00   (b) $21.00   (c) 110.5%
10. (a) $21.00   (b) $24.00   (c) 114.3%

### EXERCISE 120

1.  (a) $60.00   (b) $5.40    (c) ti/if
2.  (a) $40.00   (b) $4.40    (c) eg.ef/hf
3.  (a) $72.00   (b) $10.08   (c) tr.xy/se
4.  (a) $25.00   (b) $3.00    (c) ds.gf/eg
5.  (a) $36.00   (b) $5.04    (c) ed.eh/ti
6.  (a) $5.00    (b) $.60     (c) t.xg/g
7.  (a) $48.00   (b) $6.24    (c) es.rh/hr
8.  (a) $75.00   (b) $5.25    (c) hs.eg/sg
9.  (a) $12.00   (b) $1.08    (c) r.fh/de
10. (a) $80.00   (b) $8.80    (c) hi.hf/rf

### EXERCISE 121

|    | (a)                | (b)                 |
|----|--------------------|---------------------|
| 1. | Profit, $181.65    | Profit, $6.65       |
| 2. | Profit, $556.75    | Profit, $131.57     |
| 3. | Loss, $75          | Loss, $390.25       |
| 4. | Profit, $127.80    | No profit, no loss  |
| 5. | Profit, $259.26    | Profit, $10         |
| 6. | Profit, $4928.84   | Loss, $1312.72      |
| 7. | Profit, $100.90    | Loss, $144.74       |

8. Loss, $1618.75
9. Profit, $5082.94
10. Profit, $33,906
11. Profit, $2850
12. Profit, $16,118.80
13. Profit, $5797.44
14. Profit, $786
15. Profit, $9201.16

Loss, $4078.25
Loss, $11,167.06
Profit, $7756
Loss, $5640
Profit, $11,176.32
Loss, $1737.56
Loss, $6818.70
Loss, $2640.95

## CHAPTER XVI
# Commission and Brokerage

### DEFINITIONS

MANUFACTURERS OF GOODS, farmers, and owners of real estate or of other property frequently find it convenient to sell their goods or their property through agents. An agent who buys or who sells goods or who transacts any other kind of business for another person is called a *commission merchant*, or *broker*.

The person for whom the agent sells the goods or transacts the business is called the *principal*.

The compensation paid by the principal to the broker for his service in transacting the business is called *commission* or *brokerage*.

A shipment of goods that is sold on commission is called a *consignment*. The person who ships the goods is the *consignor*. The person to whom the goods are shipped—that is, the commission merchant—is the *consignee*.

The total amount received by the commission merchant for the goods sold by him is called the *gross proceeds*.

The amount remaining after all the necessary expenses, such as commission, freight, storage, insurance, etc. are paid, is called the *net proceeds*.

The first cost of a purchase—that is, the amount actually paid for the merchandise—is the *prime cost* of the purchase.

The prime cost plus the expenses of the purchase, such as commission, freight, storage, insurance, etc., all add up to what is called the *gross cost*.

The itemized statement of the sales made by the commission merchant for the principal is called an *account sales*.

The itemized statement of the merchandise purchased by the commission merchant from the principal is called the *account purchase*.

A commission merchant sometimes guarantees the payment

for goods that he sells or the quality of the goods that he buys. The charge which he makes for this service is called a *guaranty*.

And now let us see how some of these definitions apply in actual practice.

## COMPUTING A BROKERAGE TRANSACTION

1. Find the net proceeds, and supply the missing information in the following example:

| Gross Proceeds | Freight | Guaranty | Commission | Other Charges | Total Charges | Net Proceeds |
|---|---|---|---|---|---|---|
| $4500 | $150 | 2% | 3% | $17.75 | | |

Gross proceeds........................................$4500.00
  Less the following charges:
Freight.............................................$150
Guaranty..............2% of $4500...........  90
Commission...........3% of $4500........... 135
Other charges...................................  17.75
Total charges....................................... 392.75
  Net proceeds.....................................$4107.25

Answer

| Guaranty | Commission | Total Charges | Net Proceeds |
|---|---|---|---|
| $90 | $135 | $392.75 | $4107.25 |

2. Find the gross cost, and supply the missing information in the following example:

| Prime Cost | Guaranty | Commission | Freight | Other Charges | Total Charges | Gross Cost |
|---|---|---|---|---|---|---|
| $575 | 3% | 4% | $27.50 | $5.75 | | |

Prime cost.............................................$575
  Plus the following charges:
Guaranty..............3% of $575.............$17.25
Commission...........4% of $575............. 23.00
Freight............................................. 27.50
Other charges...................................  5.75
Total charges.......................................  73.50
  Gross cost.........................................$648.50

Answer

| Guaranty | Commission | Total Charges | Gross Cost |
|---|---|---|---|
| $17.25 | $23.00 | $73.50 | $648.50 |

# COMMISSION AND BROKERAGE

## EXERCISE 122

Find the net proceeds, and supply the missing information as indicated by the top line:

| | Gross Proceeds | Freight and Cartage | Collection and Guaranty | | Commission | | Other Charges | Total Charges | Net Proceeds |
|---|---|---|---|---|---|---|---|---|---|
| 1. | $ 400 | $ 15.20 | 2% | $8.00 | 3½% | $14.00 | $ 8.65 | $45.85 | $354.15 |
| 2. | 240 | 25.00 | 2½% | | 3% | | 4.55 | | |
| 3. | 3000 | 86.30 | 2% | | 3% | | 21.33 | | |
| 4. | 640 | 11.93 | 2½% | | 2½% | | 5.83 | | |
| 5. | 2600 | 73.20 | 1½% | | 2½% | | 19.25 | | |
| 6. | 3750 | 97.25 | 2% | | 3% | | 31.40 | | |
| 7. | 176 | 7.33 | 2% | | 3% | | 3.20 | | |
| 8. | 4780 | 124.00 | 2% | | 2½% | | 26.35 | | |
| 9. | 1936 | 47.20 | 1½% | | 5% | | 39.40 | | |
| 10. | 1875 | 42.33 | 2% | | 6% | | 13.00 | | |
| 11. | 965 | 21.20 | 3% | | 3½% | | 9.13 | | |
| 12. | 564 | 8.35 | 2½% | | 3½% | | 7.18 | | |
| 13. | 4400 | 169.50 | 3% | | 7½% | | 5.63 | | |
| 14. | 2250 | 39.50 | 2% | | 2½% | | 9.43 | | |
| 15. | 1985 | 42.65 | 1½% | | 3½% | | 11.43 | | |
| 16. | 895 | 33.20 | 1½% | | 4% | | 27.93 | | |
| 17. | 3200 | 93.45 | 2% | | 5% | | 11.20 | | |
| 18. | 2435 | 38.63 | 1½% | | 3% | | 15.93 | | |
| 19. | 5890 | 132.50 | 2% | | 3½% | | 24.80 | | |
| 20. | 1009 | 48.90 | 1½% | | 2% | | 10.45 | | |
| Totals* | $.... | $..... | $... | | $.... | | $.... | $.... | $..... |

## EXERCISE 123

Solve the following problems, preparing an account sales for each: (Use your own name as the agent; any name you please for the principal.)

1. You receive from a fruit grower a consignment of 620 barrels of apples to be sold on a commission of 3½%. You sell 300 barrels at $4.50 per bbl.; 200 at $4.60; and 120 at $4.65. Freight and cartage amount to $78.40. You charge 2½% for guaranty and collection. Find the net proceeds.

2. You sell 1200 barrels of pork at $17.25 a barrel on a commission of 2½%. Your expenses are: freight, $82.30; storage, $30; insurance $8. You charge 2% for collection. Find the net proceeds.

---

*The totals of Freight, Collection, Commission, and other Charges should equal the grand total of Total Charges. Net Proceeds added to Total Charges should equal the grand total of Gross Proceeds.

3. You receive from a mill a consignment of 960 barrels of flour. You pay freight charges of $278; trucking, 7½¢ per barrel; cooperage, $18.90. You sell 300 barrels at $9.10; 240 barrels at $8.90; 160 barrels at $9.60; 100 barrels at $9.80; and the rest at $9.90. You charge a commission of 2½%; and 2½% for collection and guaranty. Find the net proceeds.

4. You receive a consignment of 4200 bunches of bananas. You pay freight charges of $1193.20; dock labor, $149; advertising $12. You sell 700 bunches at $2.05; 900 bunches at $1.90; 1200 bunches at $1.95; 1400 bunches at $1.75. You charge 7% for commission and 1½% for collection. Find the net proceeds.

5. You receive a consignment of 4000 bushels of corn. You pay freight charges of $80; cartage of 2½¢ per bushel; insurance $9; storage $21. You sell 900 bu. at 59¢; 1600 bu. at 56¢; and the rest at 54¢. You charge 3% for commission and 2% for collection and guaranty. Find the net proceeds.

6. You receive from a farmer a consignment of 540 crates of strawberries, 190 crates of raspberries, and 700 sacks of white potatoes. You pay freight charges of $51.75; storage, $17; insurance $3. You sell the strawberries at $1.80 per crate; the raspberries at $2.35 per crate; and the potatoes at $1.40 per sack. You charge a commission of 3%, and 2% for collection. Find the net proceeds.

7. You receive a consignment of 72 cwt. of hogs and 456 cwt. of beef cattle. You pay $51 for storage and feed. You sell the hogs for 9¢ per pound and the beef cattle for 7¢ per pound. You charge 4% commission and 1½% guaranty. Find the net proceeds.

8. You receive from a farmer a consignment of 19 cwt. of wool, 700 bu. of corn, 500 bu. of oats, and 300 bu. of barley. You pay $39.60 freight and cartage; $15, storage; and $6.50 insurance. You sell the wool at 32¢ per pound; the corn at 94¢ per bushel; the oats at 54¢ per bushel; and the barley at 91¢ per bushel. You charge a commission of 3%; and 2% for collection and guaranty. Find the net proceeds.

9. You receive a consignment of 3600 boxes of oranges. You pay freight charges of 65¢ per box; dock labor $40; cartage 12½¢ per box; insurance, $15. You sell 860 boxes at $3.60; 940 boxes at $3.75; and the rest at $3.50. Your commission is 4½%. You charge 2% for collection and guaranty. Find the net proceeds.

10. You sell 1400 sacks of white potatoes at $1.35 per sack. You pay $148.30 for freight and cartage; storage $21; insurance $3.50. You charge 4% for commission; 1½% for collection and guaranty. Find the net proceeds.

## COMMISSION AND BROKERAGE

### EXERCISE 124

Find the gross cost of each of the following:

|     | Prime Cost | Guaranty | | Commission | | Freight and Cartage | Other Charges | Total Charges | Gross Cost |
|-----|-----------|----------|--------|-----------|--------|-----------|---------|---------|---------|
| 1.  | $1040 | 2%    | $20.80 | 4%     | $41.60 | $59.60 | $11.20 | $133.20 | $1173.20 |
| 2.  | 8160  | 2½%   |        | 3½%    |        | 48.30  | 10.45  |         |          |
| 3.  | 9020  | 1½%   |        | 3%     |        | 83.40  | 15.42  |         |          |
| 4.  | 2300  | 2%    |        | 3%     |        | 15.40  | 4.30   |         |          |
| 5.  | 1175  | 1%    |        | 3½%    |        | 5.98   | 2.35   |         |          |
| 6.  | 1600  | —     |        | 4%     |        | 11.25  | —      |         |          |
| 7.  | 1298  | 1½%   |        | 3%     |        | 14.54  | 9.60   |         |          |
| 8.  | 6100  | 2%    |        | 4½%    |        | 46.50  | 8.33   |         |          |
| 9.  | 8921  | 1½%   |        | 4%     |        | 87.50  | 18.55  |         |          |
| 10. | 5710  | 2½%   |        | 5%     |        | 62.50  | 10.00  |         |          |
| 11. | 3200  | 1½%   |        | 4½%    |        | 45.20  | 11.60  |         |          |
| 12. | 6180  | 2½%   |        | 4%     |        | —      | 5.00   |         |          |
| 13. | 8298  | 2%    |        | 6%     |        | 75.36  | 14.35  |         |          |
| 14. | 376   | 1%    |        | 4%     |        | 11.50  | 2.45   |         |          |
| 15. | 948   | 2%    |        | 3½%    |        | 22.47  | 3.65   |         |          |
| 16. | 1240  | 1½%   |        | 4½%    |        | 15.38  | 6.57   |         |          |
| 17. | 1440  | 2%    |        | 5%     |        | 26.30  | 3.50   |         |          |
| 18. | 2700  | 1½%   |        | 4%     |        | 52.11  | 7.33   |         |          |
| 19. | 1680  | 2%    |        | 6%     |        | 12.25  | 3.25   |         |          |
| 20. | 6900  | 1½%   |        | 5%     |        | 77.50  | 10.45  |         |          |
|     | $....  | $....  |        | $....  |        | $....  | $....  | $....   | $......  |

### EXERCISE 125

Prepare an account purchase from each of the following sets of facts: (Use your own name as the agent; any name you please for the principal.)

1. You buy 500 pounds of coffee at 18¢ and 320 pounds of tea at 33¢. Your commission is 4%; guaranty fee, 1%. Cartage is $6.30. Storage is $3.50.

2. You purchase for a customer 5900 bushels of corn at 95¢ per bushel. Freight and cartage come to $740; your commission is 5%; guaranty fee, ½%.

3. You buy for a customer 25,000 pounds of wool at 35¢ per pound, and 750 bales of cotton (500 pounds to a bale) at 21¢ per pound. Freight and cartage on both purchases come to $89.00. Guaranty fee on the cotton is 2%; inspection fee for the wool is 2¢ per pound (this is not counted in determining the commission). Your commission is 3½%.

4. You buy for a customer 140 barrels of sugar (250 pounds to a

barrel) at 4¢ per pound. Cartage and other expenses come to $124.40. Your commission is 3%; fee for guaranty is 1%.

5. You buy 750 pounds of tea at 43¢ per pound and 1500 pounds of coffee at 28¢ per pound. Cartage comes to $18.00; commission is 3%; guaranty fee is $\frac{1}{2}$%.

### MISCELLANEOUS PROBLEMS IN COMMISSION AND BROKERAGE

**1.** A lawyer remits $650 to his client after deducting 20% for his services in collecting a claim. A. How much did he collect? B. How much did he retain as his fee?

| | |
|---|---|
| Amount he collected | = 100% of itself |
| Less percentage of his fee | 20% |
| Amount remitted to client = $650 = | 80% of amount collected. |
| Amount he collected | = $650 ÷ 80% |
| | = $812.50 |

Amount retained as fee
= $812.50 − $650      = $162.50

Answer: A, $812.50; B, $162.50.

**2.** A salesman sells a certain amount of merchandise at a 10% commission during the first week of the month; an equal amount at a 15% commission during the second week; an equal amount at a 15% commission during the third week; and twice as much at a 20% commission during the last week. His total commissions for the month equal $1000. How much does he sell altogether?

Let S = the amount of his sales during each of the first three weeks.
Let 2S = the amount of his sales during the last week.

10% of S = $\frac{10S}{100} = \frac{S}{10}$ = his commission for the first week
15% of S = $\frac{15S}{100} = \frac{3S}{20}$ = "     "     "   "   second week
15% of S = $\frac{15S}{100} = \frac{3S}{20}$ = "     "     "   "   third week
20% of 2S = $\frac{40S}{100} = \frac{2S}{5}$ = "     "     "   "   last week

$\frac{S}{10} + \frac{3S}{20} + \frac{3S}{20} + \frac{2S}{5} = 1000$
2S + 3S + 3S + 8S = 20,000
16S = 20,000
S = $1250 = the sales during the first week.
S + S + S + 2S = the total sales for the month.
1250 + 1250 + 1250 + 2500 = $6250

Answer, $6250.

# COMMISSION AND BROKERAGE

### EXERCISE 126

Solve the following problems:

1. A lawyer received for collection a claim of $240.00. He collected 80% of the claim and charged 15% for his services. How much did he pay his client?

2. A book agent sold 140 books at $3.00 each. His commission was $37\frac{1}{2}\%$. How much did he earn?

3. An auctioneer sold $5200.00 worth of merchandise. His commission was $4\frac{1}{2}\%$. How much did he earn?

4. A lawyer remits $765.00 to his client after deducting 15% for his services in collecting a claim. What amount was collected?

5. A salesman earns $300 at a commission of 6%. How much did he sell?

6. A salesman sells a certain amount of merchandise at a commission of 10% in the first two weeks of a month. His commission is then raised to 15%, and he sells an equal amount of merchandise in the rest of the month. If his total earnings for the month were $1,000.00, how much did he sell altogether?

7. A commission merchant charged $42.75 for selling 1500 bushels of corn, at 3% commission. At what price per bushel did he sell the corn?

8. A commission merchant charged $42.72 at a rate of 3% for selling wheat at 89¢ per bushel. How many bushels did he sell? If his expenses were $189.20, what were the net proceeds?

9. How many pounds of coffee at 33¢ per pound can be bought for $800? Commission is 4%, and other charges come to $9.00.

10. A salesman sells twice as much in February as he did in January. During those two months he draws $400 against commissions. That amount is deducted from his earnings, and a check for $170.00 is sent to him. If his commission was 10%, how much did he sell in January?

### ANSWERS
### EXERCISE 122

|    | Collection and Guaranty | Commission | Total Charges | Net Proceeds |
|----|----|----|----|----|
| 1. | $ 8.00  | $ 14.00 | $ 45.85 | $ 354.15 |
| 2. |   6.00  |   7.20  |   42.75 |   197.25 |
| 3. |  60.00  |  90.00  |  257.63 |  2742.37 |
| 4. |  16.00  |  16.00  |   49.76 |   590.24 |
| 5. |  39.00  |  65.00  |  196.45 |  2403.55 |
| 6. |  75.00  | 112.50  |  316.15 |  3433.85 |

|     | Collection and Guaranty | Commission | Total Charges | Net Proceeds |
|-----|-------------------------|------------|---------------|--------------|
| 7.  | $ 3.52                  | $ 5.28     | $ 19.33       | $ 156.67     |
| 8.  | 95.60                   | 119.50     | 365.45        | 4414.55      |
| 9.  | 29.04                   | 96.80      | 212.44        | 1723.56      |
| 10. | 37.50                   | 112.50     | 205.33        | 1669.67      |
| 11. | 28.95                   | 33.78      | 93.06         | 871.94       |
| 12. | 14.10                   | 19.74      | 49.37         | 514.63       |
| 13. | 132.00                  | 330.00     | 637.13        | 3762.87      |
| 14. | 45.00                   | 56.25      | 150.18        | 2099.82      |
| 15. | 29.78                   | 69.48      | 153.34        | 1831.66      |
| 16. | 13.43                   | 35.80      | 110.36        | 784.64       |
| 17. | 64.00                   | 160.00     | 328.65        | 2871.35      |
| 18. | 36.53                   | 73.05      | 164.14        | 2270.86      |
| 19. | 117.80                  | 412.30     | 687.40        | 5202.60      |
| 20. | 15.14                   | 20.18      | 94.67         | 914.33       |

Totals: Gross Proceeds—$42,990.00; Freight—$1157.62; Guaranty—$866.39; Commission—$1849.36; Other Charges—$306.07; Total Charges—$4,179.44; Net Proceeds: $38,810.56.

## EXERCISE 123

This form should be:

---

**ACCOUNT SALES**

New York City, *January* 10,193—

John Doe
Commission Merchant

Sold for Account of:
*Richard Roe*
*Matteawan, N. Y.*

| 193– | | | | | |
|------|---|---|---|---|---|
| Jan. | 4 | 300 bbl. apples at $4.50 | $1350 | 00 | |
|      | 5 | 200  "    "    "  4.60   | 920   | 00 | |
|      | 6 | 120  "    "    "  4.65   | 558   | 00 | |
|      |   | Gross proceeds           |       |    | $2828 | 00 |
|      |   | Charges:                 |       |    |       |    |
|      |   | Freight and cartage      | 78    | 40 |       |    |
|      |   | Commission, 3½% of $2828 | 98    | 98 |       |    |
|      |   | Guaranty and collection, 2½% | 70 | 70 |      |    |
|      |   |                          |       |    | 246   | 08 |
|      |   | Net proceeds             |       |    | 2581  | 92 |

## COMMISSION AND BROKERAGE

2. Gross proceeds: $20,700. Commission: $517.50. Collection: $414.00. Total charges: $1051.80. *Net Proceeds:* $19,648.20

3. Sales: $2730, $2136, $1536, $980, and $1584. Gross Proceeds: $8966.00. Commission: $224.15. Collection and guaranty: $224.15. Total Charges: $817.20. *Net Proceeds:* $8148.80

4. Sales: $1435, $1710, $2340, and $2450. Gross Proceeds: $7935.00. Commission: $555.45. Collection: $119.03. Total Charges: $2028.68. *Net Proceeds:* $5906.32.

5. Sales: $531, $896, and $810. Gross Proceeds: $2237.00. Commission: $67.11. Collection and guaranty: $44.74. Total Charges: $321.85. *Net Proceeds:* $1915.15.

6. Sales: Strawberries, $972; Raspberries, $446.50; Potatoes, $980. Gross Proceeds: $2398.50. Commission: $71.96. Collection: $47.97. Total Charges: $191.68. *Net Proceeds:* $2206.82.

7. Sales: Hogs, $648; Cattle, $3192. Gross Proceeds: $3840.00. Commission: $153.60. Guaranty: $57.60. Total Charges: $262.20. *Net Proceeds:* $3577.80.

8. Sales: Wool, $608; Corn, $658; Oats, $270; Barley, $273. Gross Proceeds: $1809.00. Commission: $54.27. Collection and Guaranty: $36.18. Total Charges: $151.55. *Net Proceeds:* $1657.45.

9. Sales: $3096, $3525, and $6300. Gross Proceeds: $12,921.00. Commission: $581.45. Collection and Guaranty: $258.42. Total Charges: $3684.87. *Net Proceeds:* $9236.13.

10. Gross Proceeds: $1890.00. Commission: $75.60. Collection and Guaranty: $28.35. Total Charges: $276.75. *Net Proceeds:* $1613.25.

### EXERCISE 124

|     | Guaranty | Commission | Total Charges | Gross Cost |
| --- | --- | --- | --- | --- |
| 1.  | $ 20.80  | $ 41.60    | $133.20       | $1173.20   |
| 2.  | 204.00   | 285.60     | 548.35        | 8708.35    |
| 3.  | 135.30   | 270.60     | 504.72        | 9524.72    |
| 4.  | 46.00    | 69.00      | 134.70        | 2434.70    |
| 5.  | 11.75    | 41.13      | 61.21         | 1236.21    |
| 6.  | —        | 64.00      | 75.25         | 1675.25    |
| 7.  | 19.47    | 38.94      | 82.55         | 1380.55    |
| 8.  | 122.00   | 274.50     | 451.33        | 6551.33    |
| 9.  | 133.82   | 356.84     | 596.81        | 9517.71    |
| 10. | 142.75   | 285.50     | 500.75        | 6210.75    |
| 11. | 48.00    | 144.00     | 248.80        | 3448.80    |
| 12. | 154.50   | 247.20     | 406.70        | 6586.70    |
| 13. | 165.96   | 497.88     | 753.55        | 9051.55    |
| 14. | 3.76     | 15.04      | 32.75         | 408.75     |
| 15. | 18.96    | 33.18      | 78.26         | 1026.26    |
| 16. | 18.60    | 55.80      | 96.35         | 1336.35    |
| 17. | 28.80    | 72.00      | 130.60        | 1570.60    |
| 18. | 40.50    | 108.00     | 207.94        | 2907.94    |
| 19. | 33.60    | 100.80     | 149.90        | 1829.90    |
| 20. | 103.50   | 345.00     | 536.45        | 7436.45    |

Totals: Prime Cost, $78,286; Guaranty, $1452.07; Commission, $3346.61; Freight and Cartage, $773.04; Other Charges, $158.35; Total Charges, $5730.07; Gross Cost, $84,016.07.

## EXERCISE 125

**1.** The form:

JOHN DOE<br>Commission Merchant

January 10, 193–

Purchased for account of:
Richard Roe
Matteawan, N. Y.

| 19– | | |
|---|---|---|
| Jan. 5 | 500 lb. coffee at 18¢ | $ 90 00 |
| Jan. 7 | 320 lb. tea  " 33¢ | 105 60 |
| | Charges: | |
| | Cartage | 6 30 |
| | Storage | 3 50 |
| | Guaranty 1% | 1 96 |
| | Commission 4% | 7 82 |
| | Total charged to your account | $215 18 |

**2.** Prime cost: $5905. Commission: $295.25. Guaranty: $29.53. Gross Cost: $6969.78.

**3.** Prime cost: Wool, $8750; Cotton, $78,750. Guaranty: $1575. Inspection: $500. Commission: $3062.50. Gross cost: $92,726.50.

**4.** Prime cost: $1400. Commission: $42. Guaranty $14. Gross Cost: $1580.40.

**5.** Prime cost: Tea, $322.50; Coffee, $420. Commission: $22.28. Guaranty: $3.71. Gross Cost: $786.49.

## EXERCISE 126

**1.** $163.20   **2.** $157.50   **3.** $234   **4.** $900   **5.** $5000   **6.** $8000
**7.** 95¢ per bushel   **8.** 1600 bushels; net proceeds were $1192.08
**9.** 2300 pounds   **10.** $1900

## CHAPTER XVII
# Transportation

THE COST OF TRANSPORTATION is an important item in the exchange of goods. There are three general ways of shipping goods—by *parcel post*, by *freight*, and by *express*.

### PARCEL POST
The schedule of parcel post rates is as follows:

| Zones | Miles | First Pound | Additional Pounds |
| --- | --- | --- | --- |
| Local |  | 7¢ | 1.0¢ for each 2 pounds |
| 1 | Up to 50 | 8¢ | 1.1¢ for each pound |
| 2 | 50 to 150 | 8¢ | 1.1¢ for each pound |
| 3 | 150 to 300 | 9¢ | 2.0¢ for each pound |
| 4 | 300 to 600 | 10¢ | 3.5¢ for each pound |
| 5 | 600 to 1000 | 11¢ | 5.3¢ for each pound |
| 6 | 1000 to 1400 | 12¢ | 7.0¢ for each pound |
| 7 | 1400 to 1800 | 14¢ | 9.0¢ for each pound |
| 8 | Over 1800 | 15¢ | 11.0¢ for each pound |

The above rates do not apply to books, for which there is a flat rate of 1.5¢ per pound to all zones.

### PARCEL POST ZONES FROM NEW YORK CITY

1. Birmingham, Ala. 5
2. Los Angeles, Calif. 8
3. San Francisco, Calif. 8
4. Denver, Colo. 7
5. Bridgeport, Conn. 1
6. New Haven, Conn. 2
7. Washington, D. C. 3
8. Miami, Fla. 6
9. Jacksonville, Fla. 5
10. Wichita, Kans. 6
11. Louisville, Ky. 5
12. New Orleans, La. 6
13. Bar Harbor, Me. 4
14. Baltimore, Md. 3
15. Boston, Mass. 2
16. New Bedford, Mass. 3
17. Kalamazoo, Mich. 5
18. Detroit, Mich. 4
19. Minneapolis, Minn. 6
20. Cleveland, Ohio 4

## EXAMPLES

1. If a package weighing 22 pounds is shipped by uninsured parcel post from New York City to Minneapolis, what is the cost of the shipment?

> Minneapolis is in the 6th zone from New York City.
> Shipping cost for 22 pounds = $.12 + (21 × $.07) = $1.59

2. What is the cost of shipping from New York City to Louisville, Kentucky, by uninsured parcel post, a package weighing 17 pounds?

> Louisville is in the 5th zone from New York City.
> Shipping cost for 17 pounds = $.11 + (16 × $.053) = $.96

### EXERCISE 127

Find the cost of each of the following uninsured parcel post shipments from New York City:

| | Pounds | Destination | Cost |
|---|---|---|---|
| 1. | 21 | Birmingham, Ala. | .......... |
| 2. | 34 | Los Angeles, Calif. | .......... |
| 3. | 45 | San Francisco, Calif. | .......... |
| 4. | 67 | Denver, Colo. | .......... |
| 5. | 22 | Bridgeport, Conn. | .......... |
| 6. | 36 | New Haven, Conn. | .......... |
| 7. | 47 | Washington, D. C. | .......... |
| 8. | 65 | Miami, Fla. | .......... |
| 9. | 43 | Jacksonville, Fla. | .......... |
| 10. | 25 | Wichita, Kans. | .......... |
| 11. | 37 | Louisville, Ky. | .......... |
| 12. | 49 | New Orleans, La. | .......... |
| 13. | 27 | Bar Harbor, Me. | .......... |
| 14. | 39 | Baltimore, Md. | .......... |
| 15. | 51 | Boston, Mass. | .......... |
| 16. | 29 | New Bedford, Mass. | .......... |
| 17. | 41 | Kalamazoo, Mich. | .......... |
| 18. | 56 | Detroit, Mich. | .......... |
| 19. | 32 | Minneapolis, Minn. | .......... |
| 20. | 62 | Cleveland, Ohio | .......... |

TRANSPORTATION

Note: If you want to insure your shipment, add to the cost of the shipment the cost of the insurance, in accordance with the following schedule:

| Valuation | Cost |
|---|---|
| Up to $5 | 5¢ |
| Up to $25 | 10¢ |
| Up to $50 | 15¢ |
| Up to $100 | 25¢ |
| Up to $150 | 30¢ |
| Up to $200 | 35¢ |

## FREIGHT AND EXPRESS

The cost of the shipment of goods by freight or by express is generally computed in terms of 100 pounds, or Cwt.

For example:

1. Find the freight charges on a shipment of goods weighing 344,000 pounds, at the rate of $.27 per Cwt.

    344,000 pounds = 3440 Cwt. (344,000 ÷ 100)
    3440 × $.27 = $928.80
                Answer, $928.80

2. Find the express charges on a shipment of goods weighing 437 pounds, at the rate of $6.50 per Cwt.

    437 pounds = 4.37 Cwt. (437 ÷ 100)
    4.37 × $6.52 = $28.49
            Answer, $28.49

### EXERCISE 128

A. Find the cost of sending the following shipments by freight:

| Pounds | Rate per Cwt. | Pounds | Rate per Cwt. |
|---|---|---|---|
| 1. 152,800 | $ .56 | 6. 135,700 | $2.80 |
| 2. 326,400 | .28 | 7. 246,800 | .67 |
| 3. 89,700 | 1.32 | 8. 147,600 | .74 |
| 4. 62,300 | .41 | 9. 138,600 | 1.17 |
| 5. 894,200 | .86 | 10. 121,500 | .53 |

B. Find the cost of sending the following shipments by express:

| | Pounds | Rate per Cwt. | | Pounds | Rate per Cwt. |
|---|---|---|---|---|---|
| 1. | 130 | $ 5.82 | 6. | 147 | $ 7.72 |
| 2. | 141 | 3.55 | 7. | 196 | 1.74 |
| 3. | 152 | 2.64 | 8. | 207 | 10.76 |
| 4. | 211 | 12.49 | 9. | 157 | 8.59 |
| 5. | 163 | 5.37 | 10. | 161 | 4.92 |

## ANSWERS
### EXERCISE 127

1. $1.17   2. $3.78   3. $4.99   4. $6.08
5. $0.32   6. $0.47   7. $1.01   8. $4.60
9. $2.34   10. $1.80  11. $2.02  12. $3.48
13. $1.01  14. $0.85  15. $0.63  16. $0.65
17. $2.23  18. $2.03  19. $2.29  20. $2.24

### EXERCISE 128A

1. $855.68   2. $913.92   3. $1184.04   4. $255.43
5. $7690.12  6. $3799.60  7. $1653.56   8. $1092.24
9. $1621.62  10. $643.95

### EXERCISE 128B

1. $7.57   2. $5.01    3. $4.02   4. $26.35
5. $8.75   6. $11.35   7. $3.41   8. $22.27
9. $13.49  10. $7.92

## CHAPTER XVIII
# Hours and Wages

THERE are two systems generally employed in computing wages—(1) the hour-rate system, and (2) the piece-work system.

### 1. THE HOUR-RATE SYSTEM

When the wages of an employee are based upon the actual number of hours spent at work, the employer generally uses a time-clock to keep the records. Each employee has his time-card, which he punches when he begins his work in the morning, when he goes out for lunch, when he returns after lunch, and when he goes home in the evening. On the basis of this time-card the employer prepares his pay-roll, showing (a) the total number of hours the employee has worked; (b) the rate per hour; and (c) the pay due the employee for the week's work, this pay being equal to the product of the total hours of work times the rate per hour.

In computing the time-cards as given in the following exercises, please note that when an employee is a few minutes late on any day, he must make up the time either on that day or on some other day. Hours are computed in round figures. That is, if a man works from 7:58 to 12:01 and from 12:57 to 5:03, he is credited with 8 hours' work. If he works from 7:57 to 12:01 and from 12:57 to 5:18, he is credited with $8\frac{1}{4}$ hours. If he works from 7:58 to 12:02 and from 12:57 to 5:32, he is credited with $8\frac{1}{2}$ hours. And so on.

### EXERCISE 129A

Compute the time for each day and the total for the week on the following time-cards:

1.

|  | In | Out | In | Out | Hours |
|---|---|---|---|---|---|
| Monday | 7:57 | 12:01 | 12:59 | 5:05 | |
| Tuesday | 8:01 | 12:02 | 12:57 | 6:03 | |
| Wednesday | 8:16 | 12:04 | 1:02 | 5:01 | |
| Thursday | 8:01 | 12:05 | 12:57 | 5:05 | |
| Friday | 9:05 | 12:03 | 1:02 | 5:10 | |
| Saturday | 7:59 | 12:03 | .... | .... | |
| Total | | | | | |

2.

| | | | | | |
|---|---|---|---|---|---|
| Monday | 7:58 | 12:02 | 12:58 | 5:17 | |
| Tuesday | 7:59 | 12:03 | 12:58 | 5:03 | |
| Wednesday | 8:01 | 12:02 | 1:03 | 5:33 | |
| Thursday | 8:00 | 12:04 | 12:59 | 6:17 | |
| Friday | 7:56 | 12:05 | 12:56 | 5:06 | |
| Saturday | 8:01 | 1:02 | .... | .... | |
| Total | | | | | |

In some industries, time after 5 P.M. is computed at one and a half times the regular rate. This may be indicated on the time-card. For example, on the first time-card above, the hours on Tuesday would be marked $9\frac{1}{2}$ instead of only 9. (8 hours of regular work plus 1 hour at $1\frac{1}{2}$ times the regular rate. 8 plus $1\frac{1}{2}$ equals $9\frac{1}{2}$.)

### EXERCISE 129B

Compute the time for each day and the total for the week on this basis.

### EXERCISE 130

Prepare the following pay-roll sheets:

#### A

| Employee's No. | M. | T. | W. | Th. | F. | S. | Total Time | Wages per hour | Total Wages |
|---|---|---|---|---|---|---|---|---|---|
| 1. | $8\frac{3}{4}$ | $8\frac{1}{4}$ | $8\frac{1}{2}$ | 8 | $8\frac{1}{4}$ | 4 | $45\frac{3}{4}$ | 40¢ | $18.30 |
| 2. | 8 | 9 | 9 | 8 | $7\frac{1}{2}$ | 5 | | 42 | |
| 3. | $8\frac{1}{4}$ | $8\frac{1}{2}$ | 8 | 9 | $8\frac{1}{2}$ | $5\frac{1}{4}$ | | 42 | |
| 4. | 9 | 8 | 9 | 9 | 8 | 4 | | 45 | |

## HOURS AND WAGES

| | | | | | | | |
|---|---|---|---|---|---|---|---|
| 5. | 8 | 8½ | 8 | 9 | 8 | 4 | 46 |
| 6. | 8¼ | 8½ | 8¾ | 8 | 9 | 4½ | 48 |
| 7. | 8 | 8 | 9 | 9 | 8 | 4 | 50 |
| 8. | 7½ | 7½ | 8 | 8 | 8½ | 4 | 54 |
| 9. | 9 | 9 | 9 | 8 | 8 | 5 | 46 |
| 10. | 8 | 8½ | 8½ | 8½ | 8 | 6 | 52 |
| 11. | 8 | 9 | 9 | 8 | 8½ | 6 | 60 |
| 12. | 8½ | 8½ | 8½ | 9 | 8 | 5 | 64 |

### B

| | | | | | | | |
|---|---|---|---|---|---|---|---|
| 1. | 8 | 9 | 7½ | 8½ | 8¼ | 5¼ | 52 |
| 2. | 9 | 9 | 8½ | 8 | 8½ | 4 | 53 |
| 3. | 8 | 9 | 8½ | 8½ | 8¾ | 5 | 48 |
| 4. | 9 | 9 | 8 | 8 | 8½ | 5 | 52½ |
| 5. | 8 | 9 | 8 | 8 | 8 | 4 | 55 |
| 6. | 8½ | 9 | 8½ | 8½ | 8¾ | 5 | 56 |
| 7. | 8 | 9 | 8 | 8 | 8 | 4 | 64 |
| 8. | 8½ | 9 | 8½ | 8½ | 8½ | 4½ | 54 |
| 9. | 8 | 9 | 8½ | 9 | 9 | 5 | 50 |
| 10. | 9 | 9 | 8 | 8 | 8½ | 4¼ | 56 |
| 11. | 8 | 9 | 9 | 9 | 7 | 5 | 52 |
| 12. | 8½ | 9 | 8¼ | 8 | 8½ | 5¼ | 48 |

### C

In some industries, employees are paid on an 8-hour day basis. Fill out the pay-roll which follows, using the top line as a guide:

| Employee's No. | M. | T. | W. | Th. | F. | S. | Rate per Day | Rate per Hour | Total Hours | Total Wages |
|---|---|---|---|---|---|---|---|---|---|---|
| 1. | 8¾ | 9¼ | 8 | 8 | 8½ | 4 | $5.60 | $.70 | 46½ | $32.55 |
| 2. | 8½ | 7½ | 9 | 8¼ | 9¼ | 5 | 6.40 | | | |
| 3. | 8¼ | 8¼ | 9¼ | 8½ | 8¼ | 4¾ | 6.72 | | | |
| 4. | 8 | 8 | 9 | 8 | 9 | 5 | 6.16 | | | |
| 5. | 9 | 9 | 9 | 8 | 8½ | 4½ | 6.04 | | | |
| 6. | 8 | 8½ | 8½ | 8½ | 9 | 5 | 5.92 | | | |
| 7. | 8 | 8½ | 9 | 8½ | 0 | 4 | 7.12 | | | |
| 8. | 8½ | 8½ | 8½ | 8½ | 8½ | 5 | 7.04 | | | |
| 9. | 9 | 9 | 9 | 9 | 9 | 4 | 5.84 | | | |
| 10. | 8¾ | 8½ | 8½ | 8¾ | 9 | 4½ | 6.48 | | | |
| 11. | 8 | 8 | 7 | 9 | 9 | 4½ | 6.32 | | | |
| 12. | 9 | 8 | 9 | 9 | 8½ | 5 | 7.00 | | | |

## D

In computing the wages due each worker, it is necessary to deduct 2% of the total wages for Social Security Tax. Show the amount due each worker in the three payrolls just completed:

## EXERCISE 131

### A

Compute the following payroll, using the top line as a guide: (Hint—Overtime is paid at the rate of time and a quarter.)

| Employee's No. | M. | T. | W. | Th. | F. | S. | Rate per Hour | Hours Regular | Hours Overtime | Wages Regular | Wages Overtime | Total Wages |
|---|---|---|---|---|---|---|---|---|---|---|---|---|
| 1. | 8 | 9 | 10 | 8½ | 6 | 6 | 60¢ | 42 | 5½ | $25.20 | $4.13 | $29.33 |
| 2. | 9 | 8½ | 8 | 8 | 8 | 5 | 58 | | | | | |
| 3. | 9 | 8½ | 9 | 9 | 7½ | 6 | 62 | | | | | |
| 4. | 8 | 9 | 8½ | 8½ | 9 | 4 | 64 | | | | | |
| 5. | 8½ | 8½ | 9½ | 9½ | 8 | 6 | 70 | | | | | |
| 6. | 8 | 8½ | 8½ | 0 | 8 | 5 | 58 | | | | | |
| 7. | 9 | 9 | 9 | 0 | 9 | 6 | 64 | | | | | |
| 8. | 8½ | 8½ | 8½ | 8½ | 8½ | 6 | 62 | | | | | |
| 9. | 9 | 9 | 9 | 8½ | 7½ | 4½ | 72 | | | | | |
| 10. | 8½ | 8 | 8 | 8½ | 7½ | 5 | 54 | | | | | |
| 11. | 8 | 8 | 8 | 8 | 8½ | 4 | 60 | | | | | |
| 12. | 9½ | 9½ | 8½ | 8 | 7½ | 5 | 72 | | | | | |

### B

Deduct 2% for Social Security from each of the salaries in the above exercise and show the amount actually paid to each worker:

## 2. THE PIECE-WORK SYSTEM

The preparation of a piece-work payroll is similar to that of the hour-rate payroll. The amount of the wages in the piece-work system is equal to the total number of pieces times the rate per piece.

# HOURS AND WAGES

### EXERCISE 132

Fill out the following piece-work payroll, using the top line as a guide:

| Employee's No. | Type of Article | \multicolumn{6}{c}{Articles Produced} | Total Articles | Rate per Article | Wages |
|---|---|---|---|---|---|---|---|---|---|---|
| | | M. | T. | W. | Th. | F. | S. | | | |
| 1. | B–17 | 26 | 28 | 24 | 24 | 26 | 14 | 142 | $.35 | $49.70 |
| 2. | B–18 | 22 | 25 | 26 | 24 | 22 | 12 | | .38 | |
| 3. | B–19 | 18 | 16 | 19 | 17 | 19 | 9 | | .42 | |
| 4. | Z–19 | 7 | 8 | 6 | 8 | 8 | 4 | | .65 | |
| 5. | Q–34 | 11 | 12 | 11 | 13 | 15 | 6 | | .60 | |
| 6. | Q–38 | 14 | 16 | 16 | 15 | 15 | 7 | | .54 | |
| 7. | J–13 | 13 | 16 | 16 | 14 | 18 | 8 | | .52 | |
| 8. | B–37 | 38 | 39 | 42 | 41 | 40 | 21 | | .20 | |
| 9. | B–41 | 36 | 33 | 35 | 38 | 38 | 18 | | .22½ | |
| 10. | B–42 | 34 | 32 | 32 | 31 | 34 | 16 | | .25 | |
| 11. | Z–17 | 9 | 9 | 9 | 10 | 11 | 5 | | .60 | |
| 12. | J–15 | 16 | 17 | 19 | 2 | 21 | 12 | | .50 | |

### THE DIFFERENTIAL PIECE-WORK SYSTEM

In certain industries the rate per article is sometimes arranged on a sliding scale, called the *differential piece-work wage system*. Thus, if a worker in a certain factory can produce only from 1 to 12 pieces of work a day, he gets paid for them all at the rate of let us say $.20 per piece. If he can produce from 13 to 14 pieces, he gets paid for them all at the rate of $.22 per piece. If he can produce from 15 to 16 pieces, he gets paid for them all at the rate of $.24 per piece. And so on—the more pieces he can produce, the higher pay he gets for each piece. This system is based on the theory that the employee will produce more work if the scale of his pay is graduated in accordance with the amount of work he produces.

### EXERCISE 133

Prepare a pay-roll, using the following differential schedule of rates:

| Articles per day | Rate per Article |
|---|---|
| 1–12 | $ .25 |
| 13–14 | .27 |
| 15–16 | .29 |

220   MATHEMATICS MADE EASY

| Articles per day | Rate per Article |
|---|---|
| 17–18 | .32 |
| 19–20 | .35 |
| 21–22 | .38 |
| 23–24 | .41 |
| 25–26 | .44 |
| 27 or more | .47 |

| Employee's No. | Monday Art. | Wage | Tuesday Art. | Wage | Wednesday Art. | Wage | Thursday Art. | Wage | Friday Art. | Wage | Saturday* Art. | Wage | Total Wages |
|---|---|---|---|---|---|---|---|---|---|---|---|---|---|
| 1. | 21 | $7.98 | 19 | $6.65 | 20 | $7.00 | 18 | $5.76 | 21 | $7.98 | 11 | $4.18 | $39.55 |
| 2. | 18 | | 19 | | 19 | | 17 | | 18 | | 8 | | |
| 3. | 20 | | 20 | | 20 | | 19 | | 22 | | 11 | | |
| 4. | 13 | | 15 | | 15 | | 17 | | 18 | | 9 | | |
| 5. | 23 | | 23 | | 25 | | 25 | | 26 | | 14 | | |
| 6. | 22 | | 24 | | 23 | | 25 | | 24 | | 13 | | |
| 7. | 19 | | 21 | | 20 | | 19 | | 18 | | 10 | | |
| 8. | 17 | | 18 | | 18 | | 20 | | 19 | | 10 | | |
| 9. | 18 | | 19 | | 21 | | 24 | | 23 | | 11 | | |
| 10. | 15 | | 15 | | 14 | | 16 | | 14 | | 8 | | |
| 11. | 19 | | 18 | | 17 | | 20 | | 21 | | 10 | | |
| 12. | 24 | | 25 | | 27 | | 28 | | 27 | | 15 | | |
| Totals | | $ | | $ | | $ | | $ | | $ | | $ | $ |

## CURRENCY BREAKDOWN

In preparing his pay-roll, the employer tries to "break down" the wages of each employee, and the total sum of wages for all the employees, into the smallest possible number of bills and coins.

For example:

Suppose Mr. A's pay-roll is as follows:

| Employee's Number | |
|---|---|
| 1. | $43.24 |
| 2. | 52.45 |
| 3. | 27.65 |
| 4. | 45.80 |
| 5. | 48.38 |

He will instruct his bookkeeper to prepare the following currency breakdown for his pay-roll:

---

*Since Saturday is a half-day, compute according to the schedule of double the actual production. In the top line although employee No. 1 produced only 11 articles, he is paid for those 11 articles in accordance with the schedule for 22 articles.

# HOURS AND WAGES

| Employee's Number | Total Wages | $20 | Bills $10 | $5 | $2 | $1 | 50¢ | Coins 25¢ | 10¢ | 5¢ | 1¢ |
|---|---|---|---|---|---|---|---|---|---|---|---|
| 1. | $43.24 | 2 | | | 1 | 1 | | | 2 | | 4 |
| 2. | 52.45 | 2 | 1 | | | 1 | | | 4 | 1 | |
| 3. | 27.65 | 1 | | 1 | 1 | | 1 | | 1 | 1 | |
| 4. | 45.80 | 2 | | 1 | | | | 1 | 1 | 1 | |
| 5. | 48.38 | 2 | | | 1 | 1 | 1 | | 1 | 1 | 3 |
| Total | $217.52 | 9 | 1 | 3 | 4 | 2 | 2 | 2 | 8 | 3 | 7 |

His currency memorandum, prepared for the bank teller, will be as follows:

|  | Numbers | Amount |
|---|---|---|
| Pennies | 7 | .07 |
| Nickels | 3 | .15 |
| Dimes | 8 | .80 |
| Quarters | 2 | .50 |
| Halves | 2 | 1.00 |
| Ones | 2 | 2.00 |
| Twos | 4 | 8.00 |
| Fives | 3 | 15.00 |
| Tens | 1 | 10.00 |
| Twenties | 9 | 180.00 |
| Total | | $217.52 |

## EXERCISE 134
### A

Prepare the currency breakdown for the following payroll:

| Employee's No. | Total Wages | $20 | Bills $10 | $5 | $2 | $1 | 50¢ | Coins 25¢ | 10¢ | 5¢ | 1¢ |
|---|---|---|---|---|---|---|---|---|---|---|---|
| 1. | $49.70 | 2 | | 1 | 2 | | 1 | | 2 | | |
| 2. | 49.78 | | | | | | | | | | |
| 3. | 41.16 | | | | | | | | | | |
| 4. | 26.65 | | | | | | | | | | |
| 5. | 40.80 | | | | | | | | | | |
| 6. | 44.82 | | | | | | | | | | |
| 7. | 44.20 | | | | | | | | | | |
| 8. | 44.20 | | | | | | | | | | |
| 9. | 44.55 | | | | | | | | | | |
| 10. | 44.75 | | | | | | | | | | |
| 11. | 31.80 | | | | | | | | | | |
| 12. | 43.50 | | | | | | | | | | |
| Totals | | $ | $ | $ | $ | $ | $ | $ | $ | $ | $ |

### B

Prepare a currency memorandum (for the bank teller) for the currency breakdown above.

## ANSWERS

### EXERCISE 129A

1. Hours are: 8, 9, $7\frac{3}{4}$, 8, 7, and 4. Total is $43\frac{3}{4}$.
2. Hours are: $8\frac{1}{4}$, 8, $8\frac{1}{2}$, $9\frac{1}{4}$, 8, and 5. Total is 47.

### EXERCISE 129B

1. 8, $9\frac{1}{2}$, $7\frac{3}{4}$, 8, 7, and 4. Total is $44\frac{1}{4}$.
2. $8\frac{3}{8}$, 8, $8\frac{3}{4}$, $9\frac{7}{8}$, 8, and $5\frac{1}{2}$. Total is $48\frac{1}{2}$.

### EXERCISE 130A

Total time: $45\frac{3}{4}$, $46\frac{1}{2}$, $47\frac{1}{2}$, 47, $45\frac{1}{2}$, 47, 46, $43\frac{1}{2}$, 48, $47\frac{1}{2}$, $48\frac{1}{2}$, and $47\frac{1}{2}$. Total wages: \$18.30, \$19.53, \$19.95, \$21.15, \$20.93, \$22.56, \$23.00, \$23.49, \$22.08, \$24.70, \$29.10, and \$30.40.

### EXERCISE 130B

Total time: $46\frac{1}{2}$, 47, $47\frac{3}{4}$, $47\frac{1}{2}$, 45, $48\frac{1}{4}$, 45, $47\frac{1}{2}$, $48\frac{1}{2}$, $46\frac{3}{4}$, 47, $47\frac{1}{2}$. Total wages: \$24.18, \$24.91, \$22.92, \$24.94, \$24.75, \$27.02, \$28.80, \$25.65, \$24.25, \$26.18, \$24.44, \$22.80.

### EXERCISE 130C

Rates per hour: \$.70, \$.80, \$.84, \$.77, \$.75½, \$.74, \$.89, \$.88, \$.73, \$.81, \$.79, \$.87½.
Total hours: $46\frac{1}{2}$, $47\frac{1}{2}$, $47\frac{1}{4}$, 47, 48, $47\frac{1}{2}$, 38, $47\frac{1}{2}$, 49, 48, $45\frac{1}{2}$, $48\frac{1}{2}$.
Total Wages: \$32.55, \$39, \$39.69, \$36.19, \$36.24, \$35.15, \$33.82, \$41.80, \$35.77, \$38.88, \$35.95, \$42.44.

### EXERCISE 130D

(a) \$17.93, \$19.14, \$19.55, \$20.73, \$20.51, \$22.11, \$22.54, \$23.02, \$21.64, \$24.21, \$28.52, \$29.79.

(b) \$23.82, \$24.51, \$22.46, \$24.54, \$24.25, \$26.48, \$28.22, \$25.14, \$23.76, \$25.66, \$23.95, \$22.32.

(c) \$31.90, \$38.22, \$38.90, \$35.47, \$35.52, \$34.45, \$33.14, \$40.96, \$35.05, \$38.10, \$35.23, \$41.79.

### EXERCISE 131A

| | Hours | | Wages | | Total |
|---|---|---|---|---|---|
| | Regular | Overtime | Regular | Overtime | Wages |
| 1. | 42 | $5\frac{1}{2}$ | \$25.20 | \$4.13 | \$29.33 |
| 2. | 44 | $2\frac{1}{2}$ | 25.52 | 1.81 | 27.33 |
| 3. | $43\frac{1}{2}$ | $5\frac{1}{2}$ | 26.97 | 4.26 | 31.23 |
| 4. | 44 | 3 | 28.16 | 2.40 | 30.56 |
| 5. | 44 | 6 | 30.80 | 5.25 | 36.05 |
| 6. | 36 | 2 | 20.88 | 1.45 | 22.33 |
| 7. | 36 | 6 | 23.04 | 4.80 | 27.84 |
| 8. | 44 | $4\frac{1}{2}$ | 27.28 | 3.49 | 30.77 |
| 9. | $43\frac{1}{2}$ | 4 | 31.32 | 3.60 | 34.92 |
| 10. | $43\frac{1}{2}$ | 2 | 23.49 | 1.35 | 24.84 |
| 11. | 44 | $\frac{1}{2}$ | 26.40 | .38 | 26.78 |
| 12. | $43\frac{1}{2}$ | $4\frac{1}{2}$ | 31.32 | 4.05 | 35.37 |

### EXERCISE 131B

\$28.74, \$26.78, \$20.71, \$29.95, \$35.33, \$21.88, \$27.28, \$30.15, \$34.22, \$24.34, \$26.24, \$34.66.

# HOURS AND WAGES

### EXERCISE 132

Totals of articles: 142, 131, 98, 41, 68, 83, 85, 221, 198, 179, 53, 87.
Wages: $49.70, $49.78, $41.16, $26.65, $40.80, $44.82, $44.20, $44.20, $44.55, $44.75, $31.80, $43.50.

### EXERCISE 133

|     | M Wage  | T Wage  | W Wage  | Th Wage | F Wage  | S Wage  | Total    |
|-----|---------|---------|---------|---------|---------|---------|----------|
| 1.  | $ 7.98  | $ 6.65  | $ 7.00  | $ 5.76  | $ 7.98  | $ 4.18  | $ 39.55  |
| 2.  | 5.76    | 6.65    | 6.65    | 5.44    | 5.76    | 2.32    | 32.58    |
| 3.  | 7.00    | 7.00    | 7.00    | 6.65    | 8.36    | 4.18    | 40.19    |
| 4.  | 3.51    | 4.35    | 4.35    | 5.44    | 5.76    | 2.88    | 26.29    |
| 5.  | 9.43    | 9.43    | 11.00   | 11.00   | 11.44   | 6.58    | 58.88    |
| 6.  | 8.36    | 9.84    | 9.43    | 11.00   | 9.84    | 5.72    | 54.19    |
| 7.  | 6.65    | 7.98    | 7.00    | 6.65    | 5.76    | 3.50    | 37.54    |
| 8.  | 5.44    | 5.76    | 5.76    | 7.00    | 6.65    | 3.50    | 34.11    |
| 9.  | 5.76    | 6.65    | 7.98    | 9.84    | 9.43    | 4.18    | 43.84    |
| 10. | 4.35    | 4.35    | 3.78    | 4.64    | 3.78    | 2.32    | 23.22    |
| 11. | 6.65    | 5.76    | 5.44    | 7.00    | 7.98    | 3.50    | 36.33    |
| 12. | 9.84    | 11.00   | 12.69   | 13.16   | 12.69   | 7.05    | 66.43    |
| Totals | $80.73 | $85.42 | $88.08 | $93.58 | $95.43 | $49.91 | $493.15 |

### EXERCISE 134A

|     |          | $20 | $10 | $5 | $2 | $1 | 50¢  | 25¢ | 10¢ | 5¢   | 1¢   |
|-----|----------|-----|-----|----|----|----|------|-----|-----|------|------|
| 1.  | $ 49.70  | 2   |     | 1  | 2  |    | 1    |     | 2   |      |      |
| 2.  | 49.78    | 2   |     | 1  | 2  |    | 1    |     | 2   | 1    | 3    |
| 3.  | 41.16    | 2   |     |    |    | 1  |      |     | 1   | 1    | 1    |
| 4.  | 26.65    | 1   |     | 1  |    |    | 1    | 1   | 1   | 1    |      |
| 5.  | 40.80    | 2   |     |    |    |    | 1    | 1   |     | 1    |      |
| 6.  | 44.82    | 2   |     |    | 2  |    |      | 1   |     | 1    | 2    |
| 7.  | 44.20    | 2   |     |    | 2  |    |      |     | 2   |      |      |
| 8.  | 44.20    | 2   |     |    | 2  |    |      |     | 2   |      |      |
| 9.  | 44.55    | 2   |     |    | 2  |    | 1    |     |     | 1    |      |
| 10. | 44.75    | 2   |     |    | 2  |    | 1    | 1   |     |      |      |
| 11. | 31.80    | 1   | 1   |    |    | 1  | 1    | 1   |     | 1    |      |
| 12. | 43.50    | 2   |     |    | 1  | 1  | 1    |     |     |      |      |
|     | $505.91  | $440| $10 | $15| $30| $4 | $4.50| $1  | $1  | $.35 | $.06 |

### EXERCISE 134B

|          | Number | Amount  |
|----------|--------|---------|
| Pennies  | 6      | .06     |
| Nickels  | 7      | .35     |
| Dimes    | 10     | 1.00    |
| Quarters | 4      | 1.00    |
| Halves   | 9      | 4.50    |
| Ones     | 4      | 4.00    |
| Twos     | 15     | 30.00   |
| Fives    | 3      | 15.00   |
| Tens     | 1      | 10.00   |
| Twenties | 22     | 440.00  |
| Total    |        | 505.91  |

## CHAPTER XIX
## Interest

*Interest* is money paid for the use of money.

The *principal* is the money on which interest is paid.

The *rate of interest* is the percentage rate of the principal paid in interest for one year.

The *time* is the period for which interest is paid.

Example:

Find the interest on $725 at 6% for 2 yr.

$$\text{Interest for 1 yr.} = 6\% \text{ of } \$725 = \$43.50$$
$$\text{Interest for 2 yr.} = 2 \times \$43.50 = \$87.00$$

From this we get the following formula:

*To find the interest, given the principal, rate, and time,* multiply the principal by the rate, and the product by the time.

$$I = P \times R \times T$$

### INTEREST COMPUTED BY DAYS

In the above example, the interest is computed by years. If the time for which interest is paid happens to include days, we reduce the days to a fraction and proceed as above.

It is the general custom, in computing interest, to take 30 days to the month, which means 360 days to the year. For example:

1. Find the interest on $480 for 2 yr. 3 mo. 10 da. at 6%, counting 360 da. to the yr.

10 da. = $\frac{1}{3}$ of a month.

$3\frac{1}{3}$ mo. = $\frac{10}{3}$ of $\frac{1}{12}$ yr. = $\frac{10}{36}$ yr. = $\frac{5}{18}$ yr.

$2\frac{5}{18}$ yr. $\times 6\% \times 480 = \frac{41}{18} \times \frac{6}{100} \times \frac{480}{1}$

Cancelling this, we get $65.60

Answer, $65.60

2. Find the interest on $2400 for 10 months at 6%, counting 360 da. to the yr.

# INTEREST

10 mo. = 300 da. = $\frac{5}{6}$ of a yr.

$$\frac{\cancel{\$} \times \cancel{6} \times \cancel{2400}^{120}}{\cancel{\$} \times \cancel{100} \times 1} = \$120.$$

Answer, $120.

## EXERCISE 135

Solve by cancellation, counting 360 days to the year:

| No. | Principal | Time | 2% | 3% | 4% | 5% | 6% |
|---|---|---|---|---|---|---|---|
| 1. | $10,800 | 10 days | | | | | |
| 2. | 9600 | 15 " | | | | | |
| 3. | 6000 | 30 " | | | | | |
| 4. | 4800 | 45 " | | | | | |
| 5. | 4200 | 60 " | | | | | |
| 6. | 7200 | 75 " | | | | | |
| 7. | 3600 | 90 " | | | | | |
| 8. | 5400 | 120 " | | | | | |
| 9. | 2000 | 180 " | | | | | |
| 10. | 6000 | 3½ years | | | | | |

## THE 60-DAY, 6% METHOD

This is a very easy method to compute interest at 6%, since it is based upon the fact that if the rate for one year is 6%, then the rate for 60 days, or 2 months, is $\frac{1}{6}$ of 6%, or 1%.

Examples:

1. Find the interest on $360 for 5 mo. 17 da. at 6%.

| | |
|---|---|
| The interest for 2 mo. is 1% of $360 | = $3.60 |
| The interest for 2 mo. more | = 3.60 |
| The interest for 1 mo. is ½ of $3.60 | = 1.80 |
| The interest for 15 da. is ½ of $1.80 | = .90 |
| The interest for 1 da. is $\frac{1}{15}$ of $.90 | = .06 |
| The interest for 1 da. more | = .06 |
| The interest for 5 mo. 17 da. | = $10.02 |

2. Find the interest on $480 for 3 mo. 21 da. at 6%.

| | |
|---|---|
| The interest for 2 mo. | = $4.80 |
| The interest for 1 mo. | = 2.40 |
| The interest for 15 da. | = 1.20 |
| The interest for 6 da. is $\frac{1}{5}$ of $2.40 | = .48 |
| The interest for 3 mo. 21 da. | = $8.88 |

This 60-day method is especially convenient for practical purposes, since most bank notes run for 30 days, 60 days, or 90 days.

## EXERCISE 136

Using the 60-day method, find the interest at 6% on the following:

| No. | Principal | Time | No. | Principal | Time |
|-----|-----------|------|-----|-----------|------|
| 1.  | $ 593 | 60 days | 11. | $ 945 | 40 days |
| 2.  | 840   | 5 "  | 12. | 960   | 55 " |
| 3.  | 800   | 48 " | 13. | 870   | 114 " |
| 4.  | 630   | 20 " | 14. | 480   | 12 " |
| 5.  | 420   | 1 "  | 15. | 2400  | 3 " |
| 6.  | 324   | 50 " | 16. | 750   | 45 " |
| 7.  | 916   | 30 " | 17. | 694   | 120 " |
| 8.  | 880   | 6 "  | 18. | 820   | 15 " |
| 9.  | 1030  | 54 " | 19. | 135   | 4 " |
| 10. | 900   | 2 "  | 20. | 390   | 200 " |

## THE 60-DAY METHOD APPLIED TO OTHER RATES

The 60-day method can be easily applied to compute the interest at the other rates in common use.

Thus, since 1 is $\frac{1}{6}$ of 6, the interest at 1% is $\frac{1}{6}$ of the interest at 6%.

In like manner, since 5 is $\frac{1}{6}$ less than 6, the interest at 5% is $\frac{1}{6}$ less than the interest at 6%. The interest at $4\frac{1}{2}$% is $\frac{1}{4}$ less than the interest at 6%, the interest at 4% is $\frac{1}{3}$ less than the interest at 6%, the interest at 7% is $\frac{1}{6}$ *more* than the interest at 6%, and so on.

Examples:

1. Find the interest on $2480 for 3 mo. 3 da. at 5%.

    Interest for 2 mo. at 6% = $24.80
    Interest for 1 mo. at 6% = 12.40
    Interest for 3 da. at 6% =   1.24
    Total interest at 6% = $38.44
    Deduct $\frac{1}{6}$           6.40
    Interest at 5% = $32.04

2. Find the interest on $2480 for 3 mo. 3 da. at 7%.
    Proceed as above, and then *add* $6.40 to $38.44.

# INTEREST

3. Find the interest on $2480 for 3 mo. 3 da. at $4\frac{1}{2}\%$.

Proceed as in Example 1, and then deduct $9.61 from $38.44. And so on.

## EXERCISE 137

Find the interest in the following, using the 60-day method for 6% and then adjusting to the given interest rate:

| No. | Principal | Rate | Time | No. | Principal | Rate | Time |
|---|---|---|---|---|---|---|---|
| 1. | $9648 | 1% | 120 days | 11. | $ 216 | 3% | 40 days |
| 2. | 817 | $7\frac{1}{2}\%$ | 144 " | 12. | 672 | $1\frac{1}{2}\%$ | 80 " |
| 3. | 859 | $1\frac{1}{2}\%$ | 240 " | 13. | 336 | 4% | 45 " |
| 4. | 926 | 8% | 135 " | 14. | 500 | 2% | 270 " |
| 5. | 1972 | 5% | 36 " | 15. | 8917 | $2\frac{1}{2}\%$ | 72 " |
| 6. | 764 | 2% | 90 " | 16. | 734 | $4\frac{1}{2}\%$ | 160 " |
| 7. | 333 | $4\frac{1}{2}\%$ | 40 " | 17. | 763 | 3% | 240 " |
| 8. | 295 | $2\frac{1}{2}\%$ | 288 " | 18. | 1971 | 5% | 216 " |
| 9. | 5931 | 4% | 270 " | 19. | 897 | $7\frac{1}{2}\%$ | 96 " |
| 10. | 3814 | 1% | 180 " | 20. | 976 | 8% | 225 " |

## COMPUTING THE TIME BY THE COMPOUND SUBTRACTION METHOD

Find the number of years, months, and days from April 15, 1937, to February 4, 1939.

Note: Allow 30 days to the month, 360 days to the year.

| yr. | mo. | da. |
|---|---|---|
| 1939 | 2 | 4 |
| 1937 | 4 | 15 |
| 1 | 9 | 19 |

Since we can't subtract 15 days from 4 days, we borrow 1 month from the 2 months. Allowing 30 days to the month, we now subtract 15 days from 34 days, leaving 19 days. In the same way, we proceed with the rest of the subtraction and we get 1 yr. 9 mo. 19 da.

Find the number of years, months, and days from August 19, 1933, to January 6, 1938.

| yr. | mo. | da. |
|---|---|---|
| 1938 | 1 | 6 |
| 1933 | 8 | 19 |
| 4 | 4 | 17 |

## EXERCISE 138

### A

Find the number of years, months, and days between each of the following dates by the compound subtraction method:

1. April 4, 1939 to January 10, 1940
2. May 9, 1939 to December 5, 1940
3. March 11, 1940 to November 10, 1940
4. April 18, 1938 to March 16, 1941
5. June 19, 1937 to February 2, 1941
6. August 26, 1936 to March 19, 1940
7. February 27, 1938 to January 26, 1941
8. September 15, 1935 to June 14, 1940
9. July 29, 1910 to June 30, 1939
10. May 4, 1936 to April 2, 1939

### B

Find the interest in the following problems, using the compound subtraction method of determining the time:

| No. | Principal | Rate | From | To |
| --- | --- | --- | --- | --- |
| 1. | $ 238 | 2% | June 15, 1939 | September 15, 1939 |
| 2. | 1269 | 7½% | August 28, 1939 | December 4, 1939 |
| 3. | 1848 | 2½% | September 24, 1939 | December 6, 1939 |
| 4. | 1963 | 8% | June 14, 1939 | March 14, 1940 |
| 5. | 8940 | 6% | March 13, 1939 | May 7, 1939 |
| 6. | 9964 | 3% | May 19, 1939 | January 19, 1940 |
| 7. | 2168 | 5% | October 28, 1939 | December 4, 1939 |
| 8. | 1894 | 1% | September 25, 1939 | March 25, 1940 |
| 9. | 874 | 2% | November 27, 1939 | May 27, 1940 |
| 10. | 964 | 4% | September 19, 1939 | February 4, 1940 |
| 11. | 1971 | 2½% | August 14, 1939 | June 2, 1940 |
| 12. | 8952 | 6% | July 19, 1939 | October 9, 1939 |
| 13. | 8840 | 5% | September 25, 1939 | May 1, 1940 |
| 14. | 6987 | 4½% | November 23, 1939 | May 3, 1940 |
| 15. | 1827 | 6% | September 27, 1939 | November 7, 1939 |
| 16. | 9960 | 3% | January 15, 1940 | January 27, 1940 |
| 17. | 893 | 7½% | March 19, 1939 | August 13, 1939 |
| 18. | 9640 | 4½% | December 28, 1939 | January 6, 1940 |
| 19. | 8341 | 8% | September 28, 1939 | August 13, 1940 |
| 20. | 2816 | 6% | August 18, 1939 | March 3, 1940 |

## BANKERS' TABLE OF THE DIFFERENCE OF TIME

Bankers generally use tables in order to compute the difference in time between any two dates, and also the accumulated interest on any sum. The following is a convenient table which shows at a glance the difference in time between the date of the loan and the date on which it is to be repaid with interest:

|           | Jan. | Feb. | Mar. | Apr. | May | June | July | Aug. | Sept. | Oct. | Nov. | Dec. |
|-----------|------|------|------|------|-----|------|------|------|-------|------|------|------|
| January   | 365  | 31   | 59   | 90   | 120 | 151  | 181  | 212  | 243   | 273  | 304  | 334  |
| February  | 334  | 365  | 28   | 59   | 89  | 120  | 150  | 181  | 212   | 242  | 273  | 303  |
| March     | 306  | 337  | 365  | 31   | 61  | 92   | 122  | 153  | 184   | 214  | 245  | 275  |
| April     | 275  | 306  | 334  | 365  | 30  | 61   | 91   | 122  | 153   | 183  | 214  | 244  |
| May       | 245  | 276  | 304  | 335  | 365 | 31   | 61   | 92   | 123   | 153  | 184  | 214  |
| June      | 214  | 245  | 273  | 304  | 334 | 365  | 30   | 61   | 92    | 122  | 153  | 183  |
| July      | 184  | 215  | 243  | 274  | 304 | 335  | 365  | 31   | 62    | 92   | 123  | 153  |
| August    | 153  | 184  | 212  | 243  | 273 | 304  | 334  | 365  | 31    | 61   | 92   | 122  |
| September | 122  | 153  | 181  | 212  | 242 | 273  | 303  | 334  | 365   | 30   | 61   | 91   |
| October   | 92   | 123  | 151  | 182  | 212 | 243  | 273  | 304  | 335   | 365  | 31   | 61   |
| November  | 61   | 92   | 120  | 151  | 181 | 212  | 242  | 273  | 304   | 334  | 365  | 30   |
| December  | 31   | 62   | 90   | 121  | 151 | 182  | 212  | 243  | 274   | 304  | 335  | 365  |

The exact number of days from any day of any month to the corresponding day of any month within a year is found *opposite* the *first* month and *under* the second. For example, the number of days from April 6 to October 6 is 183. The number of days from April 6 to October 15 is 183+9, or 192 days. The number of days from October 22 to March 25 is 151+3, or 154 days.

Note: We get the 9 by subtracting 6 from 15, and the 3 by subtracting 22 from 25.

## EXACT INTEREST

Interest is generally based upon a 30-day month and a 360-day year. But the government, and some of the bankers, prefer to base their interest upon a 365-day year. When the interest is thus computed for the exact number of days, it is called *exact interest*.

Example:

Find the exact interest on $2482 from December 21, 1938, to February 9, 1939, at 5%.

Referring to the Bankers' Table on page 229, we find that the exact time from December 21, 1938 to February 9, 1939, is 62 minus 12, or 50 days. The interest required is

$$\frac{50}{365} \times \frac{5}{100} \times \frac{2482}{1}$$

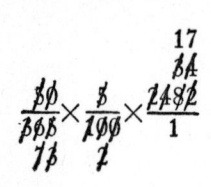

Answer, $17.00

## EXERCISE 139

Find the *exact* time between the following dates.

| No. | From | To |
|---|---|---|
| 1. | February 17, 1939 | July 15, 1939 |
| 2. | June 10, 1939 | April 9, 1940 |
| 3. | November 18, 1939 | August 17, 1940 |
| 4. | January 14, 1939 | September 12, 1939 |
| 5. | October 30, 1939 | June 24, 1940 |
| 6. | August 11, 1939 | December 5, 1939 |
| 7. | March 20, 1939 | June 17, 1939 |
| 8. | July 28, 1939 | March 25, 1940 |
| 9. | September 12, 1939 | December 10, 1939 |
| 10. | July 12, 1939 | November 15, 1939 |
| 11. | December 14, 1939 | October 10, 1940 |
| 12. | April 8, 1939 | September 12, 1939 |
| 13. | January 18, 1939 | November 5, 1939 |
| 14. | November 13, 1939 | June 11, 1940 |
| 15. | December 8, 1939 | May 7, 1940 |
| 16. | October 14, 1939 | December 19, 1939 |
| 17. | August 17, 1939 | June 16, 1940 |
| 18. | February 6, 1939 | October 11, 1939 |
| 19. | May 19, 1939 | December 5, 1939 |
| 20. | September 15, 1939 | April 23, 1940 |

# INTEREST

## GENERAL PROBLEMS IN SIMPLE INTEREST

The formula for interest, as you will recall, is as follows:

$$I = P \times R \times T$$

With this formula in mind, find the missing quantity (on a 360-day per year basis) in each of the following problems:

1. Principal    Rate    Time    Interest
   $860         ?       72 days $8.60

   $8.60 = 860 \times R \times \frac{1}{5}$ of a year
   $8.60 = 152R$
   $R = 8.60 \div 152 = .05 = 5\%$
   
   Answer, 5%

2. Principal    Rate    Time    Interest
   ?           5%      96 days $10.40

   $10.40 = P \times \frac{5}{100} \times \frac{4}{15}$ of a year
   $10.40 = \frac{P}{75}$
   $P = 10.40 \times 75 = 780$
   
   Answer, $780.

3. Principal    Rate    Time    Interest
   $540        6%      ?       $9.00

   $9 = 540 \times \frac{6}{100} \times T$
   $9 = \frac{3240T}{100}$
   $900 = 3240T$
   $T = 900 \div 3240 = \frac{5}{18}$
   $\frac{5}{18}$ of a year = 100 days.
   
   Answer, 100 days.

## EXERCISE 140

Find the missing quantity (on a 360-day basis) in each of the following problems:

| No. | Principal | Rate | Time | Interest |
|---|---|---|---|---|
| 1. | $1084 | ? | 18 days | $ 2.71 |
| 2. | ? | $2\frac{1}{2}\%$ | 288 days | 78.84 |
| 3. | 20,961 | $4\frac{1}{2}\%$ | ? days | 418.22 |
| 4. | ? | 4% | 90 days | 2.38 |
| 5. | 1786 | ? | 144 days | 53.58 |

## MATHEMATICS MADE EASY

| No. | Principal | Rate | Time | Interest |
|---|---|---|---|---|
| 6. | 3788 | 1% | ? days | 18.94 |
| 7. | ? | 2½% | 96 days | 25.38 |
| 8. | 4476 | 6% | ? days | 59.68 |
| 9. | 2410 | ? | 16 days | 4.82 |
| 10. | 5481 | 6% | ? days | 109.62 |
| 11. | 3696 | ? | 18 days | 9.24 |
| 12. | 1748 | 2% | ? days | 17.48 |
| 13. | ? | 8% | 315 days | 1167.74 |
| 14. | 3926 | ? | 135 days | 53.89 |
| 15. | 1928 | 4% | ? days | 28.92 |
| 16. | 2210 | ? | 216 days | 66.30 |
| 17. | 2235 | ? | 108 days | 40.23 |
| 18. | ? | 6% | 195 days | 273.48 |
| 19. | 4980 | 3% | ? days | 9.96 |
| 20. | ? | 3% | 240 days | 99.64 |

## COMPOUND INTEREST

When interest is added to the principal and becomes a part of that principal, the total interest on that increased principal is called *compound interest*.

Interest is compounded annually, semiannually, or quarterly, according to agreement.

In order to compute *compound interest*, all you need to do is to compute *simple interest* on the new principal at the various periods mutually agreed upon.

For example:

Find (a) the amount, and (b) the interest, for 3 years at 5%, the interest being compounded annually.

Interest for 1st year = 5% of $120 = $6.   Amount = $126.
Interest for 2nd year = 5% of $126 = $6.30.   Amount = $132.30
Interest for 3d year = 5% of $132.30 = $6.62.   Amount = $138.92
                    Answer: Amount = $138.92; Interest = $18.92.

Note 1. If the interest in the above example is compounded for 3½ years, we add to $138.92 the interest upon this sum for 6 months.

Note 2. If the interest at 5% is compounded semiannually for 3 years, it amounts to the same as interest at 2½% compounded annually for 6 years.

# INTEREST

## COMPOUND INTEREST TABLE
(Based on $1.00)

The following Compound Interest Table will save you a great deal of time and labor and computation:

| Year | 2 Per Cent | 2½ Per Cent | 3 Per Cent | 3½ Per Cent | 4 Per Cent |
|---|---|---|---|---|---|
| 1 | 1.02000 | 1.02500 | 1.03000 | 1.03500 | 1.04000 |
| 2 | 1.04040 | 1.05063 | 1.06090 | 1.07123 | 1.08160 |
| 3 | 1.06121 | 1.07689 | 1.09273 | 1.10872 | 1.12486 |
| 4 | 1.08243 | 1.10381 | 1.12551 | 1.14752 | 1.16986 |
| 5 | 1.10408 | 1.13141 | 1.15927 | 1.18769 | 1.21665 |
| 6 | 1.12616 | 1.15969 | 1.19405 | 1.22926 | 1.26532 |
| 7 | 1.14869 | 1.18869 | 1.22987 | 1.27228 | 1.31593 |
| 8 | 1.17166 | 1.21840 | 1.26677 | 1.31681 | 1.36857 |
| 9 | 1.19509 | 1.24886 | 1.30477 | 1.36290 | 1.42331 |
| 10 | 1.21899 | 1.28099 | 1.34392 | 1.41060 | 1.48024 |
| 11 | 1.24337 | 1.31209 | 1.38423 | 1.45997 | 1.53945 |
| 12 | 1.26824 | 1.34489 | 1.42576 | 1.51107 | 1.60103 |
| 13 | 1.29361 | 1.37851 | 1.46853 | 1.56396 | 1.66507 |
| 14 | 1.31948 | 1.41297 | 1.51259 | 1.61870 | 1.73168 |
| 15 | 1.34587 | 1.44830 | 1.55797 | 1.67535 | 1.80094 |
| 16 | 1.37279 | 1.48451 | 1.60471 | 1.73399 | 1.87298 |
| 17 | 1.40024 | 1.52162 | 1.65285 | 1.79468 | 1.94790 |
| 18 | 1.42825 | 1.55966 | 1.70243 | 1.85749 | 2.02582 |
| 19 | 1.45681 | 1.59865 | 1.75351 | 1.92250 | 2.10685 |
| 20 | 1.48595 | 1.63862 | 1.80611 | 1.98979 | 2.19112 |

| Year | 4½ Per Cent | 5 Per Cent | 5½ Per Cent | 6 Per Cent | 7 Per Cent |
|---|---|---|---|---|---|
| 1 | 1.04500 | 1.05000 | 1.05500 | 1.06000 | 1.07000 |
| 2 | 1.09203 | 1.10250 | 1.11303 | 1.12360 | 1.14490 |
| 3 | 1.14117 | 1.15763 | 1.17424 | 1.19102 | 1.22504 |
| 4 | 1.19252 | 1.21551 | 1.23882 | 1.26248 | 1.31080 |
| 5 | 1.24618 | 1.27628 | 1.30696 | 1.33823 | 1.40255 |
| 6 | 1.30226 | 1.34010 | 1.37884 | 1.41852 | 1.50073 |
| 7 | 1.36086 | 1.40710 | 1.45468 | 1.50363 | 1.60578 |
| 8 | 1.42210 | 1.47646 | 1.53469 | 1.59385 | 1.71819 |
| 9 | 1.48610 | 1.55133 | 1.61909 | 1.68948 | 1.83846 |
| 10 | 1.55297 | 1.62889 | 1.70814 | 1.79085 | 1.96715 |
| 11 | 1.62285 | 1.71034 | 1.80209 | 1.89830 | 2.10485 |
| 12 | 1.69588 | 1.79586 | 1.90121 | 2.01220 | 2.25219 |
| 13 | 1.77220 | 1.88565 | 2.00577 | 2.13293 | 2.40985 |
| 14 | 1.85194 | 1.97993 | 2.11609 | 2.26090 | 2.57853 |
| 15 | 1.93528 | 2.07893 | 2.23248 | 2.39656 | 2.75903 |
| 16 | 2.02237 | 2.18287 | 2.35526 | 2.54035 | 2.95216 |
| 17 | 2.11338 | 2.29202 | 2.48480 | 2.69277 | 3.15882 |
| 18 | 2.20848 | 2.40662 | 2.62147 | 2.85434 | 3.37993 |
| 19 | 2.30786 | 2.52695 | 2.76565 | 3.02560 | 3.61653 |
| 20 | 2.41171 | 2.65330 | 2.91776 | 3.20714 | 3.86968 |

## GENERAL PROBLEMS IN COMPOUND INTEREST

Using the Compound Interest Table, find the amount and the interest in the following cases:

1. Principal      Rate      Time
   $574      6%      5 years

Multiplying the amount of $1 at 6% for 5 years (1.33823) by $574, we get $768.14.

Subtracting $574 from $768.14, we get $194.14.

         Answer: Amount = $768.14; Interest = $194.14.

2. Principal      Rate      Time
   $250      2%      16 years

250 × 1.37279 = $343.20
$343.20 − $250 = $93.20

         Answer: Amount = $348.20; Interest = $93.20.

### EXERCISE 141

Using the Compound Interest Table, find the amount and the interest in the following problems:

| No. | Principal | Rate | Time | No. | Principal | Rate | Time |
|---|---|---|---|---|---|---|---|
| 1. | $300 | 4% | 6 years | 11. | $110 | 5% | 9 years |
| 2. | 160 | 2% | 12 " | 12. | 900 | 2% | 4 " |
| 3. | 200 | 5% | 11 " | 13. | 875 | 5% | 17 " |
| 4. | 80 | 3% | 15 " | 14. | 125 | 6% | 10 " |
| 5. | 400 | 4% | 7 " | 15. | 120 | 3% | 19 " |
| 6. | 90 | 5% | 3 " | 16. | 20 | 6% | 18 " |
| 7. | 500 | 2% | 16 " | 17. | 70 | 4% | 14 " |
| 8. | 250 | 3% | 8 " | 18. | 444 | 2% | 15 " |
| 9. | 375 | 4% | 12 " | 19. | 842 | 6% | 11 " |
| 10. | 625 | 6% | 13 " | 20. | 630 | 3% | 5 " |

### EXERCISE 142

Solve the following problems:

1. The parents of a 14-year-old boy deposit $500 in a savings bank for him. The bank pays 4% interest, compounded semi-annually. What amount will there be in the boy's name when he is 21 years old, provided there were neither withdrawals nor further deposits up to that time?

2. Upon a girl's graduation from elementary school, her parents decide to deposit for her in a savings bank enough to provide for her

expenses at college four years later. If the bank pays 5% compounded semi-annually, how much must the parents deposit to amount to $3000 in four years?

3. A man deposits $500 in a savings bank at 6% interest, compounded semi-annually. He leaves the money there, without withdrawals or further deposits, until the first time it amounts to more than $1000. He then withdraws $1000 in order to buy a bond. How long did he wait to buy the bond and how much did he then have left in the bank?

4. A man deposits a certain sum of money in a savings bank at 4% interest, compounded annually. At the end of twelve years his interest is $2283.80. How much did he deposit?

5. A man deposits $5600 in a savings bank which compounds interest annually. At the end of 15 years the interest amounts to $3124.80. What was the rate of interest?

6. A man deposits $875 in a savings bank at 5% interest, compounded semi-annually. How long will it take for the interest to amount to $631.40?

## EXERCISE 143

Solve the following problems:

1. How much will $5, deposited annually for five years, amount to if it is invested at 5% interest, compounded annually?

2. How much will $800, deposited semi-annually for ten years, amount to if it is invested at 6% interest, compounded semi-annually?

3. A man buys an automobile for $1000 and estimates that at the end of 4 years it will be worth only $200. How much must he deposit every six months at 4% interest, compounded semi-annually, to be able to buy a new car at the end of four years? (Assume that the price of the car remains the same and that he trades in his old car in part payment.)

4. A man buys a house for $25,000, paying $10,000 in cash. He contracts to pay the rest, with interest at 4%, compounded annually, in ten equal installments. How much does he pay each year?

5. A man deposits $50 each year in his bank at 4% interest, compounded annually. A neighbor deposits the same sum in a bank which pays 4% *simple* interest. How much more will the first man have at the end of twenty years?

6. A corporation issues bonds amounting to $50,000. In order to redeem them at the end of twenty years, how much must the corporation put into its sinking fund each year for investment at $4\frac{1}{2}$% compounded annually?

## ANSWERS
### EXERCISE 135

| No. | Principal | Time | 2% | 3% | 4% | 5% | 6% |
|---|---|---|---|---|---|---|---|
| 1. | $10,800 | 10 days | $6 | $9 | $12 | $15 | $18 |
| 2. | 9,600 | 15 " | 8 | 12 | 16 | 20 | 24 |
| 3. | 6,000 | 30 " | 10 | 15 | 20 | 25 | 30 |
| 4. | 4,800 | 45 " | 12 | 18 | 24 | 30 | 36 |
| 5. | 4,200 | 60 " | 14 | 21 | 28 | 35 | 42 |
| 6. | 7,200 | 75 " | 30 | 45 | 60 | 75 | 90 |
| 7. | 3,600 | 90 " | 18 | 27 | 36 | 45 | 54 |
| 8. | 5,400 | 120 " | 36 | 54 | 72 | 90 | 108 |
| 9. | 2,000 | 180 " | 20 | 30 | 40 | 50 | 60 |
| 10. | 6,000 | 3½ years | $420 | $630 | $840 | $1050 | $1260 |

### EXERCISE 136

1. $5.93  2. $.70  3. $6.40  4. $2.10  5. $.07
6. $2.70  7. $4.58  8. $.88  9. $9.27  10. $.30
11. $6.30  12. $8.80  13. $16.53  14. $.96  15. $1.20
16. $5  17. $13.88  18. $2.05  19. $.07  20. $13

### EXERCISE 137

1. $32.16  2. $24.51  3. $8.59  4. $22.78  5. $9.86
6. $3.92  7. $166.50  8. $5.90  9. $177.93  10. $19.07
11. $.72  12. $2.24  13. $1.68  14. $7.50  15. $44.59
16. $14.68  17. $15.26  18. $59.13  19. $17.94  20. $48.80

### EXERCISE 138A

1. 9 months, 6 days
2. 1 year, 6 months, 26 days
3. 7 months, 29 days
4. 2 years, 10 months, 28 days
5. 3 years, 7 months, 13 days
6. 3 years, 6 months, 23 days
7. 2 years, 10 months, 29 days
8. 4 years, 8 months, 29 days
9. 28 years, 11 months, 1 day
10. 2 years, 10 months, 28 days

### EXERCISE 138B

1. $1.19  2. $25.38  3. $9.24  4. $107.78
5. $80.46  6. $199.28  7. $10.84  8. $9.47
9. $8.74  10. $14.46  11. $39.42  12. $119.36
13. $265.20  14. $139.74  15. $12.18  16. $9.96
17. $26.79  18. $9.64  19. $583.87  20. $91.16

### EXERCISE 139

1. 148 days  2. 303 days  3. 272 days  4. 241 days
5. 237 days  6. 117 days  7. 89 days  8. 240 days
9. 89 days  10. 126 days  11. 300 days  12. 157 days
13. 291 days  14. 210 days  15. 150 days  16. 66 days
17. 303 days  18. 247 days  19. 200 days  20. 220 days

### EXERCISE 140

1. 5%  2. $3842  3. 160 days  4. $238
5. 7½%  6. 180 days  7. $3807  8. 80 days
9. 4½%  10. 120 days  11. 5%  12. 180 days
13. $16,682  14. 4%  15. 135 days  16. 5%
17. 6%  18. $8848  19. 24 days  20. $4982

# INTEREST

### EXERCISE 141

| No. | Amount | Interest | No. | Amount | Interest |
|---|---|---|---|---|---|
| 1. | $379.59 | $79.59 | 11. | $170.64 | $60.64 |
| 2. | 202.91 | 42.91 | 12. | 974.16 | 74.16 |
| 3. | 342.06 | 142.06 | 13. | 2005.50 | 1130.50 |
| 4. | 124.64 | 44.64 | 14. | 223.85 | 98.85 |
| 5. | 526.36 | 126.36 | 15. | 210.42 | 90.42 |
| 6. | 104.18 | 14.18 | 16. | 57.09 | 37.09 |
| 7. | 686.40 | 186.40 | 17. | 121.22 | 41.22 |
| 8. | 316.70 | 66.70 | 18. | 597.58 | 153.58 |
| 9. | 600.38 | 225.38 | 19. | 1598.37 | 756.37 |
| 10. | 1338.06 | 713.06 | 20. | 730.38 | 100.38 |

### EXERCISE 142

1. $659.75   2. $2461.42 (plus a small fraction of a cent)
3. 12 years; $16.40 left in the bank.   4. $3800   5. 3%   6. 11 years.

### EXERCISE 143

1. $29.01   2. $23,415.60   3. $91.38   4. $177.82   5. $128.46   6. $1524.88

## CHAPTER XX
# Payments and Collections

WHEN A MAN BORROWS MONEY at a certain rate of interest and makes partial payments on the note at various intervals, one of two methods may be used to calculate the balance. The first method is based on the *United States Rule*, a rule adopted as the result of a decision handed down by the Supreme Court. The second method is the *Merchants' Rule*, a rule which is still in common use among many business men.

Let us examine these two methods:

### THE UNITED STATES RULE

In accordance with the United States Rule, interest and payment of principal are handled as they occur in calendar order.

For example:

A man borrowed $1200 on April 1, 1935, and signed a note for 4 years at 6%. He made the following payments on account:

June 1, 1936—$200.
December 1, 1936—$200.
August 1, 1937—$200.
December 1, 1937—$200.

Using the United States Rule, how much is due at maturity?

In solving this problem, let us count 30 days to the month, 360 days to the year.

Note due............................................April 1, 1939
Face of note........................................$1200.00

Interest on $1200 from April 1, 1935, to June 1, 1936,
   $1\frac{1}{6}$ yr., at 6%........................................ 84.00
Amount due on note, June 1, 1936......................$1284.00
Payment, June 1, 1936............................... 200.00
Balance............................................$1084.00

# PAYMENTS AND COLLECTIONS

Interest on $1084 from June 1, 1936, to December 1, 1936,
  $\frac{1}{2}$ yr., at 6%.................................... $32.52
Amount due on note, December 1, 1936................. $1116.52
Payment, December 1, 1936........................... 200.00
Balance.............................................. $916.52

Interest on $916.52 from December 1, 1936, to August 1,
  1937, $\frac{2}{3}$ yr., at 6%.................................. 36.66
Amount due on note, August 1, 1937.................. $953.18
Payment, August 1, 1937............................. 200.00
Balance.............................................. $753.18

Interest on $753.18 from August 1, 1937, to December 1,
  1937, $\frac{1}{3}$ yr., at 6%.................................. 15.06
Amount due on note, December 1, 1937................ $768.24
Payment............................................. 200.00
Balance.............................................. $568.24

Interest on $568.24 from December 1, 1937, to
  April 1, 1939, $1\frac{1}{3}$ yr., at 6%....................... 45.46
Amount due at maturity.............................. $613.70

Answer, $613.70

## THE MERCHANTS' RULE

In accordance with the Merchants' Rule, the entire face of the note bears interest until the date of the settlement, and each payment on the note bears interest from the date of the payment until the date of the settlement. On the date of the settlement the total of all the payments is deducted from the face value of the note.

For example:

A man borrowed $15000 and signed a note on April 15, 1938, for 1 year at 6%. He made the following payments on account:

May 19, 1938—$2000.
October 21, 1938—$3000.
February 7, 1939—$2400.
Using the Merchants' Rule, how much was due at maturity?

In doing this problem, let us count 30 days to the month and 360 days to the year, and let us use the compound subtraction method to determine the number of days for which interest is to be computed in each case.

Note due..........................................April 15, 1939

Face of note......................................$15,000.00
Interest for 1 year at 6%..........................    900.00
Value of note, April 15, 1939......................$15,900.00

1st. payment, May 19, 1938................$2000.00
Interest from May 19, 1938, to April 15,
    1939, 326 days, at 6%...................  108.67
Value of 1st. payment on April 15, 1939.......$2108.67

2nd. payment, October 21, 1938..............$3000.00
Interest from October 21, 1938, to
    April 15, 1939, 174 days, at 6% ...........  87.00
Value of 2nd. payment on April 15, 1939......$3087.00

3rd. payment, February 7, 1939..............$2400.00
Interest from February 7, 1939, to
    April 15, 1939, 68 days, at 6%.............  27.20
Value of 3rd. payment on April 15, 1939......$2427.20

Total value of all three payments
    on April 15, 1939..................................$7622.87
Balance due, April 15, 1939...........................$8277.13

Answer, $8277.13

## EXERCISE 144

Solve the following problems:

1. A man borrows $6000 on January 1, 1936 and makes out a note with a time of four years and interest at 6%. He makes the following payments on account: March 1, 1937—$1000; September 1, 1937—$1000; May 1, 1938—$1000; September 1, 1938—$1000. Using the United States Rule, how much is due at maturity?

2. A man borrows $7200 and makes out a note on March 10, 1937 with interest at 5% and a time of three years. He makes the following payments on account: August 25, 1937—$1200; December 13, 1937—$1200; October 1, 1938—$1500; May 7, 1939—$2400; December 13, 1939—$1000. Using the United States Rule, how much is due at maturity?

3. A man borrowed $2400 and made out a note on June 1, 1939 with a time of 10 months and interest at 6%. He made the following

# PAYMENTS AND COLLECTIONS 241

payments on account: August 4, 1939—$600; October 9, 1939—$420; December 12, 1939—$540; January 16, 1940—$660. Using the Merchants' Rule, how much is due at maturity?

4. A man borrowed $7200 on July 15, 1939. He made out an eight-month note with interest at 5% and made the following payments on account: September 12, 1939—$216; October 15, 1939—$648; December 18, 1939—$864; January 2, 1940—$3240. Using the Merchants' Rule, how much was due at maturity?

## INSTALLMENT BUYING

Does it pay to buy on the installment plan? Does the convenience of easy and regular payments justify the cost of such payments? Just how much do you spend for the privilege of buying an article on the installment plan? And what rate of interest do you pay for this privilege?

Let us see.

Suppose you decide to buy a typewriter on the installment plan. The terms are as follows: A down payment of $30 and 11 monthly installments of $6 each. The cash price of the typewriter is $85. (a) What is the difference between the cash price and the installment price? (b) What rate of interest do you pay for the convenience of the installment plan on this purchase?

(a) Installment price of typewriter $= \$30 + (11 \times \$6) = \$96$
  Cash price of typewriter $= \$85$
  Difference in cost $= \$11$

(b) The additional $11 may be regarded as the amount of the interest charged you for a series of 11 loans amounting to $66. These 11 loans are for $6 each, but the time that they are on interest varies.

Thus: The 1st. loan of $6 is for 1 month.
" 2nd. " " " " " 2 months.
" 3rd. " " " " " 3 months.
" 4th. " " " " " 4 months.

The 5th loan of $6 is for 5 months. And so on, until you reach the final payment of $6, which is a loan for 11 months.

In other words, these successive loans of $6 each are equivalent to a single loan of $6 for $(1+2+3+4+5+6+7+8+9+10+11)$ months $= \$6$ for 66 months.

Hence, the principal on which you pay the interest is $6, and the time is 66 months.

And the interest, as we have seen, is $11.

The formula for interest, as you will recall, is

$$I = P \times R \times T$$
$$\$11 = \$6 \times R \times \tfrac{66}{12} = \$33R$$
$$R = \$\tfrac{11}{33} = \tfrac{1}{3} = 33\tfrac{1}{3}\%$$

Answer: (a) $11.00; (b) $33\tfrac{1}{3}\%$

## EXERCISE 145

Solve the following problems:

1. A man bought a radio on the installment plan for a down payment of $50 and nine monthly installments of $20 each. The cash price of the radio was $200. How much did he pay for the nine-months extension of time?

2. A man bought a bedroom suite on the installment plan for a down payment of $38 and eighteen monthly installments of $14 each. The cash price was $250. What was the difference between the installment price and the cash price?

3. A man bought a piano on the installment plan for a down-payment of $100 and twelve monthly installments of $40 each. The cash price was $500. What was the difference between the installment price and the cash price?

4. A man bought a typewriter on the installment plan for a down-payment of $10 and fifteen monthly installments of $5.41 each. The cash price was $78. What was the difference between the installment price and the cash price?

5. A man bought a refrigerator on the installment plan for a down-payment of $36. and eighteen monthly installments of $8.95 each. The cash price was $175. What was the difference between the installment price and the cash price?

6. A man bought an automobile on the installment plan for a down payment of $64 and fifteen monthly installments of $42.96. The cash price of the automobile was $630. What was the difference between the installment price and the cash price?

7. A man bought a vacuum cleaner on the installment plan for a down payment of $14 and ten monthly installments of $6.24 each. The cash price of the vacuum cleaner was $65. What was the difference between the installment price and the cash price?

8. A man bought a rug on the installment plan for a down-payment of $35 and eight monthly installments of $7.08 each. The cash price

# PAYMENTS AND COLLECTIONS

of the rug was $81. What was the difference between the installment price and the cash price?

9. A woman bought a fur coat on the installment plan for a down-payment of $350 and twelve monthly installments of $61.50 each. The cash price of the coat was $1020. What was the difference between the installment price and the cash price?

10. A man bought a camera on the installment plan for a down-payment of $19 and eighteen monthly installments of $6.80 each. The cash price of the camera was $125. What was the difference between the installment price and the cash price?

## EXERCISE 146

Solve the following problems:

1. A man bought some chairs on the installment plan for a down-payment of $50 and twelve monthly installments of $5 each. The cash price of the chairs was $95. (a) What was the difference between the cash price and the installment price? (b) What rate of interest did the purchaser pay?

2. A woman bought a set of dishes on the installment plan, for a down-payment of $10 and seven monthly installments of $4 each. The cash price of the dishes was $32. (a) What was the difference between the cash price and the installment price? (b) What rate of interest did the purchaser pay?

3. A man bought a radio-phonograph combination on the installment plan for a down-payment of $60 and eleven monthly installments of $12. The cash price of the combination was $170. (a) What was the difference between the cash price and the installment price? (b) What rate of interest did the purchaser pay?

4. A man bought a typewriter on the installment plan for a down-payment of $25 and ten monthly installments of $10 each. The cash price of the typewriter was $105. (a) What was the difference between the cash price and the installment price? (b) What rate of interest did the purchaser pay?

5. A couple bought a living room suite on the installment plan for a down-payment of $70 and ten monthly installments of $15 each. The cash price of the suite was $195. (a) What was the difference between the cash price and the installment price? (b) What rate of interest did the purchaser pay?

6. A couple bought a dining room set on the installment plan for a down-payment of $35 and eighteen monthly installments of $8 each. The cash price of the set was $160. (a) What was the difference be-

tween the cash price and the installment price? (b) What rate of interest did the purchaser pay?

7. A couple bought a bedroom suite on the installment plan for a down-payment of $100 and 12 monthly installments of $20 each. The cash price of the suite was $305. (a) What was the difference between the cash price and the installment price? (b) What rate of interest did the purchaser pay?

8. A man bought a radio on the installment plan for a down-payment of $80 and nine monthly installments of $15 each. The cash price of the radio was $195. (a) What was the difference between the cash price and the installment price? (b) What rate of interest did the purchaser pay?

9. A man bought a radio on the installment plan for a down-payment of $45 and fourteen monthly installments of $10 each. The cash price of the radio was $170. (a) What was the difference between the cash price and the installment price? (b) What rate of interest did the purchaser pay?

10. A man bought a radio on the installment plan for a down-payment of $90 and eight monthly installments of $15 each. The cash price of the radio was $190. (a) What was the difference between the cash price and the installment price? (b) What rate of interest did the purchaser pay?

## ANSWERS
### EXERCISE 144

1. $3068.52   2. $522.99   3. $246.20   4. $2455.48

### EXERCISE 145

1. $30   2. $40   3. $80   4. $13.15   5. $22.10
6. $78.40   7. $11.40   8. $10.64   9. $68   10. $16.40

### EXERCISE 146

1. (a) $15  (b) 46.2%        6. (a) $19  (b) 16.7%
2. (a) $6   (b) 85.7%        7. (a) $35  (b) 26.9%
3. (a) $22  (b) 33.3%        8. (a) $20  (b) 35.6%
4. (a) $20  (b) 43.6%        9. (a) $15  (b) 17.1%
5. (a) $25  (b) 36.4%       10. (a) $20  (b) 44.4%

## CHAPTER XXI
# Banking and Loans

A *bank* is an institution authorized by law to receive and loan money and to perform certain other financial operations.

A *savings bank* is a bank in which people keep their savings and from which they receive a low rate of interest.

### INTEREST IN SAVINGS BANKS

Many people would like to know just how the interest is computed on their savings. Here is how it is done:

As a general rule, savings banks pay interest semiannually, on January 1st and July 1st, adding this interest to the principal on deposit. The interest paid to the depositor, therefore, is *compound* interest. It is computed on the basis of the *smallest balance* on deposit during the preceding six months. The interest is computed on the dollars only. No interest is paid on the cents.

Let us, for example, look at a specimen bank account which pays 4% annually, or 2% semiannually:

| Date | | Deposits | | Interest | | Payments | Balance | |
|---|---|---|---|---|---|---|---|---|
| Jan. | 1 | $1200 | 50 | | | | $1200 | 50 |
| Feb. | 1 | 150 | | | | | 1350 | 50 |
| Apr. | 5 | | | | | $240 | 1110 | 50 |
| June | 8 | 120 | | | | | 1230 | 50 |
| June | 15 | | | | | 130 | 1100 | 50 |
| July | 1 | | | $22 | | | 1122 | 50 |
| Sept. | 12 | 400 | | | | | 1522 | 50 |
| Jan. | 1 | | | 22 | 44 | | 1544 | 94 |

Explanation: The interest on July 1 is computed on $1100, the smallest amount on deposit from Jan. 1 to July 1. The interest on Jan. 1 is computed on $1122, the smallest amount on deposit from July 1 to Jan. 1.

## MATHEMATICS MADE EASY

### EXERCISE 147

In the following problems, find the balance due after each deposit, payment, or addition of interest. Interest is at the rate of 2% every six months (4% per annum) on the smallest balance on deposit during the six-month period preceding Jan. 1 or July 1.

1.
| Date | Deposits | Interest | Payments | Balance |
|---|---|---|---|---|
| Jan. 1 | $865.00 | | | |
| Feb. 2 | | | 185.00 | |
| Feb. 19 | 235.00 | | | |
| Mar. 5 | 476.00 | | | |
| Mar. 7 | | | 237.00 | |
| Apr. 18 | | | 20.75 | |
| Apr. 19 | 105.00 | | | |
| July 1 | | ? | | |
| Aug. 16 | | | 118.45 | |
| Sept. 24 | 49.50 | | | |
| Nov. 7 | | | 93.75 | |
| Jan. 1 | | ? | | |

2.
| Date | Deposits | Interest | Payments | Balance |
|---|---|---|---|---|
| Jan. 1 | $195.40 | | | |
| Feb. 26 | 397.50 | | | |
| Mar. 3 | | | $167.49 | |
| Apr. 11 | 42.23 | | | |
| May 16 | | | 437.50 | |
| June 11 | 187.49 | | | |
| July 1 | | ? | | |
| Aug. 9 | 96.50 | | | |
| Aug. 10 | | | 87.88 | |
| Sept. 18 | 433.10 | | | |
| Oct. 17 | | | 350.00 | |
| Nov. 10 | 51.19 | | | |
| Dec. 4 | | | 325.00 | |
| Jan. 1 | | ? | | |

### CHECK ACCOUNTS IN COMMERCIAL BANKS

On check accounts in commercial banks, no interest is allowed. In order to get the balance at the end of any month, add to the balance at the beginning of the month the sum of the deposits made during the month, and deduct from this the sum of the checks drawn during the month.

# BANKING AND LOANS

## EXERCISE 148

Solve the following problems:

1. A man had a balance of $334.92 at the beginning of a month. He made deposits of $50.00, $74.25, $584.25, $60.00, $74.25, and $74.25. He drew checks for $55.00, $25.00, $3.37, $25.00, $11.02, $19.12, $8.32, $8.00, $699.92, $35.00, $.45, $3.51, $9.64, $8.00, $5.76, $6.43, $9.22, $3.00, $6.14, $35.00 What is his balance?

2. A man had a balance of $273.65 at the beginning of a month. He made deposits of $100.00 and $145.00. He drew checks for $25.00, $15.00, $20.00, $.28, $14.35, $20.00, $55.00, $10.00, $4.50, $18.60, $5.66, $4.56, $10.54. What is his balance?

3. A man had a balance of $256.73 at the beginning of a month. He made deposits of $100.00, $30.00, $33.00, $17.60. He drew checks for $10.00, $3.00, $4.92, $5.79, $15.30, $12.61, $5.90, $10.00, $3.00, $2.23, $10.00, $3.00, $10.00, $55.00, $2.50, $5.00, $10.00, and $1.80. What is his balance?

4. A man had a balance of $279.99 at the beginning of a month. He made deposits of $28.00, $41.00, $44.00, $16.00, and $64.00. He drew checks for $16.91, $12.50, $10.00, $10.00, $16.50, $27.50, $5.00, $3.16, $10.80, $31.00, $7.53, $9.22, and $15.00. What is his balance?

## BORROWING MONEY

If you borrow money, either from a bank or from an individual, you are generally required to give a promissory note as evidence of your debt. Such a note is made secure in one of the three following ways:

1. The note is endorsed by some responsible person, who signs his name across the back and who thus obligates himself to pay the debt if you do not pay it yourself.

2. The note is endorsed by two or more persons, who thus render themselves collectively and individually liable. The lender of the money can compel them all together, or any one of them separately, to pay the required sum.

3. The note is secured by the deposit of stocks, bonds, or other valuable securities. These are called *collateral securities*.

## THE DATE OF MATURITY

Notes are generally issued for 30, 60, or 90 days, or for 1, 2, or 3 months. The day on which a note falls due—that is, the

248    MATHEMATICS MADE EASY

day on which the payment must be made—is called the *date of maturity*.

## NON-INTEREST-BEARING NOTES

When you borrow money from a bank, the banker generally requires the interest to be paid in advance.

A note on which the interest is thus paid in advance, or *discounted*, is called a *non-interest-bearing note*.

The period for which the discount is made is called the *term of discount*.

The balance received by the borrower, after the discount has been deducted from the face of the note, is called the *proceeds*.

Find the discount and the proceeds on the following non-interest-bearing notes:

1.  Face of Note     Term of Discount     Interest
         $625                60 days                 6%

    Face of note..................................$625
    Discount of $625, 60 da. @ 6%...............  6.25
    Proceeds....................................$618.75
                      Answer: $6.25; $618.75

2.  Face of Note     Term of Discount     Interest
         $4500               30 days                 5%

    Face of note..................................$4500
    Discount of $4500, 30 da. @ 5%.............   18.75
    Proceeds....................................$4481.25
                      Answer: $18.75; $4481.25

## EXERCISE 149

Find the discount and the proceeds of the following non-interest-bearing notes:

| No. | Face of Note | Term of Discount | Interest | No. | Face of Note | Term of Discount | Interest |
|---|---|---|---|---|---|---|---|
| 1. | $ 500 | 30 da. | 6% | 6. | $1962 | 40 da. | $4\frac{1}{2}$% |
| 2. | $ 525 | 60 da. | 6% | 7. | $ 600 | 58 da. | 6% |
| 3. | $1350 | 90 da. | 6% | 8. | $6000 | 43 da. | 6% |
| 4. | $1875 | 72 da. | 5% | 9. | $1500 | 68 da. | 6% |
| 5. | $1842 | 108 da. | 5% | 10. | $ 300 | 19 da. | 6% |

BANKING AND LOANS 249

## DISCOUNTING NOTES BEFORE MATURITY

It often happens that a manufacturer or a wholesaler or a retail dealer holds a note on a customer and wants to get the money on it before maturity—that is, before the note falls due. In that case, he endorses the note and sells it to a bank for the amount due at maturity, less the discount charged by the bank for the service.

For example:

1. A shoe manufacturer receives a 60-day note for $1600 from a jobber. The note is dated April 16. On May 11 he discounts it at his bank, which charges him $4\frac{1}{2}\%$. What are the proceeds?

The 60-day note falls due on June 16.
The term of discount is the time from May 11 to June 15, or 35 days.
Our procedure, then, is as follows:
Face of note..................................$1600.
Discount, 35 days, @ $4\frac{1}{2}\%$..................... 7.
Proceeds....................................$1593.
Answer, $1593.

2. A 60-day note for $6000 was discounted July 18 at 6%. If the proceeds were $5970, what was the date of the note? What was the date of maturity?

The discount on the note = $6000 − $5970 = $30.
Using the formula, $I = P \times R \times T$, or $D = F \times R \times T$ (Discount = Face of Note × Rate × Term of Discount), we have
$30 = 6000 \times \frac{6}{100} \times T$
$30 = 360\ T$
$T = \frac{1}{12}$ of a year, or 30 days.

The date of maturity was 30 days *after* July 18, or August 17.
The date of the note was 30 days *before* August 17, or June 18.
Answer: June 18; August 17.

### EXERCISE 150

Find the date of maturity and the term of discount of each of the following notes:

| No. | Date of Note | Time | Discount Date |
| --- | --- | --- | --- |
| 1. | Apr. 27 | 90 days | June 14 |
| 2. | Nov. 10 | 3 months | Dec. 1 |
| 3. | Mar. 11 | 60 days | Mar. 21 |
| 4. | Oct. 30 | 4 months | Nov. 15 |
| 5. | June 22 | 2 months | July 5 |

## EXERCISE 151

Solve the following problems:

1. A man receives a 60-day note for $800, dated September 15. On October 10 he discounts it at his bank, which charges $4\frac{1}{2}\%$. What are the proceeds?

2. A 90-day note for $300, dated February 12, was discounted on March 6 at 6%. Find the proceeds.

3. A three-month note for $968, dated May 19, was discounted July 5 at 4%. What were the proceeds?

4. A 90-day note for $900, dated August 5, was discounted September 2 at 6%. What were the proceeds?

5. A 30-day note for $288, dated June 15, was discounted June 24 at 5%. What were the proceeds?

6. A six-month note for $4000, dated January 11, was discounted February 2 at 6%. What were the proceeds?

7. A two-month note for $270, dated March 18, was discounted April 11 at 4%. What were the proceeds?

8. A 90-day note for $420, dated July 11, was discounted September 1 at 6%. What were the proceeds?

9. A one-month note for $216, dated October 19, was discounted at 5%. What were the proceeds?

10. A 120-day note for $6600, dated April 25, was discounted June 23 at 6%. What were the proceeds?

11. A 30-day note dated November 19 was discounted on December 2 at 6%. If the proceeds were $1196.60, what was the face of the note?

12. A note for $576 dated October 18 was discounted November 6 at 5%. If the proceeds were $572.64, what was the time of the note? What was the discount term?

13. A 60-day note for $12,000 was discounted July 21 at 6%. If the proceeds were $11,894, what was the date of the note? What was the date of maturity?

14. A 90-day note for $400 dated January 3 was discounted at $4\frac{1}{2}\%$. If the proceeds were $396.50, what was the discount date?

15. A 30-day note for $840 was discounted August 30 at 6%. If the proceeds were $837.34, what was the date of maturity? What was the date of the note?

16. A six-month note for $810 dated January 7 was discounted at 4%. If the proceeds were $800.01, what was the term of discount? What was the date of discount?

# BANKING AND LOANS

17. A four-month note for $3300 dated May 9 was discounted May 10. If the proceeds were $3232.90, what was the rate of discount?

18. A three-month note for $1836 dated May 5 was discounted at 4%. If the proceeds were $1817.64, what was the discount term? What was the date of discount?

19. A two-month note for $532 was discounted September 23 at 5%. If the proceeds were $529.84, what was the date of maturity? The date of the note?

20. A 60-day note dated April 14 was discounted May 13 at 6%. If the proceeds of the note were $1790.70, what was the face of the note?

## GENERAL PROBLEMS IN BANKING AND LOANS

1. Find the amount at maturity of the following interest-bearing note:

| Face Amount | Time to Run | Rate |
|---|---|---|
| $1200 | 90 days | 6% |

$1200 \times \frac{6}{100} \times \frac{1}{4}$ (of a year) $= \$18$
$\$1200 + \$18 = \$1218$

Answer, $1218.

2. Find the time to run on the following interest-bearing note:

| Face Amount | Rate | Amount at Maturity |
|---|---|---|
| $1200 | 6% | $1218 |

$\$1218 - \$1200 = \$18 =$ Interest.
$I = F \times R \times T$
$\$18 = 1200 \times \frac{6}{100} \times T$
$\$18 = 72T$
$T = \frac{1}{4}$ of a year $= 90$ days.

Answer, 90 days.

3. Find the rate of interest on the following note:

| Face Amount | Time to Run | Amount at Maturity |
|---|---|---|
| $1200 | 90 days | $1218 |

$18 = 1200 \times R \times \frac{1}{4}$
$18 = 300R$
$R = \frac{6}{100} = 6\%$

4. Find the face amount of the following interest-bearing note:

| Time to Run | Rate | Amount at Maturity |
|---|---|---|
| 90 days | 6% | $1218 |

$F = \$1218 - I$
Therefore $I = (1218 - I) \times R \times T$
$I = (1218 - I) \times \frac{6}{100} \times \frac{1}{4}$
$I = \frac{7308 - 6I}{100 \times 4}$
$400I = 7308 - 6I$
$400I + 6I = 7308$
$406I = 7308$
$I = 18$
$1218 - 18 = 1200$

Answer, $1200

## EXERCISE 152

Find the amount at maturity of the following interest-bearing notes:

| No. | Face Amount | Time to Run | Rate |
|---|---|---|---|
| 1. | $1848 | 60 days | 4% |
| 2. | 648 | 30 days | 5% |
| 3. | 1644 | 90 days | 6% |
| 4. | 9623 | 120 days | 3% |
| 5. | 640 | 30 days | $4\frac{1}{2}$% |

## EXERCISE 153

Find the time to run of each of the following interest-bearing notes:

| No. | Face Amount | Rate | Amount at Maturity |
|---|---|---|---|
| 1. | $1764 | 3% | $1777.23 |
| 2. | 2343 | 4% | 2358.62 |
| 3. | 194 | $4\frac{1}{2}$% | 196.81 |
| 4. | 3672 | 5% | 3687.30 |
| 5. | 794 | 6% | 801.94 |

## EXERCISE 154

Find the rate of interest on each of the following notes:

| No. | Face Amount | Time to Run | Amount at Maturity |
|---|---|---|---|
| 1. | $ 874 | 30 days | $ 878.37 |
| 2. | 1008 | 90 days | 1020.60 |
| 3. | 2320 | 60 days | 2337.40 |
| 4. | 861 | 120 days | 872.48 |
| 5. | 17,280 | 90 days | 17,409.60 |

## EXERCISE 155

Find the face amount of the following interest-bearing notes:

| No. | Time to Run | Rate | Amount at Maturity |
|---|---|---|---|
| 1. | 120 days | $4\frac{1}{2}\%$ | $ 308.56 |
| 2. | 60 days  | 3% | 1236.15 |
| 3. | 30 days  | 5% | 1156.80 |
| 4. | 90 days  | 6% | 340.54 |
| 5. | 120 days | 4% | 7533.12 |

## DRAFTS

A *draft* is a written order by which one person directs another person to pay a certain sum of money.

A *commercial draft* is a draft made by one business house on another business house to secure the payment of a debt.

Suppose John Smith, a clothing manufacturer, has sold $1800 worth of clothes, on April 10, 1939, to William Brown, the owner of a department store, on 30 days' credit. When Mr. Smith sends the bill to Mr. Brown, he also sends him a draft. Mr. Brown accepts the draft on April 12, by writing "Accepted, April 12, 1939, William Brown" across the face. He then returns the draft to Mr. Smith. Mr. Smith may now discount this draft at a bank, just as he would discount a promissory note. Suppose Mr. Smith discounts the draft on April 16, and the bank charges him 6%, plus $\frac{1}{10}\%$ for collecting the money from Mr. Brown. What are the proceeds? In other words, how much money does Mr. Smith get from the bank?

The draft is due 30 days after April 12, the day of its acceptance. It is discounted on April 16. Hence the term of discount is 26 days (30 days − 4 days).

The interest on this note equals the face amount × the rate × the term of discount ($I = F \times R \times T$):

$1800 \times \frac{6}{100} \times \frac{26}{360}$

Cancelling this, we get $7.80

The collection charge $= \frac{1}{10}$ of 1% of $1800, or $\frac{1}{1000}$ of $1800 = $1.80

The total charge on the draft $= $7.80 + $1.80 = $9.60

Hence the proceeds $= $1800 − $9.60 = $1790.40

Answer, $1790.40

## 254 MATHEMATICS MADE EASY

Using the same formula, $I = F \times R \times T$, you can find any of its four terms if the other three terms are given or can be figured out.

Let us, for example, look at the above problem from a different angle:

A draft maturing 30 days after sight is dated April 10, accepted April 12, and discounted April 16 at 6%. The bank charges $\frac{1}{10}\%$ for collection, and the proceeds are $1790.40. What is the face amount of the draft?

$$F(\text{Face Amount}) = \$1790.40 + (F \times \tfrac{6}{100} \times \tfrac{26}{360}) + (F \times \tfrac{1}{1000})$$
$$F = 1790.40 + \tfrac{13F}{3000} + \tfrac{F}{1000}$$
$$3000F = 5{,}371{,}200 + 13F + 3F$$
$$2976F = 5{,}371{,}200$$
$$F = 1800$$

Answer, $1800.

A draft that matures 30 days, or 60 days, or 90 days, or at any other specified time *after it is accepted*, is regarded as a draft maturing $T$ days after sight. Sometimes, however, a draft is made out to mature at a specified time *after it is issued*, and not after it is seen or accepted. Such a draft is regarded as a draft maturing $T$ days after date.

Let us, for instance, consider the following example:

A draft for $2160 maturing 60 days after date is dated March 20, accepted March 25 and discounted March 30 at 5%. The bank charges $\frac{1}{8}\%$ for collection. What are the proceeds?

This draft is due 60 days after March 20, the date on which it is issued. It is discounted on March 30. Hence the term of discount is 50 days.

$$\text{Int.} = 2160 \times \tfrac{5}{100} \times \tfrac{50}{360} = \$15$$
Collection charge $2160 \times \tfrac{1}{800} = \$2.70$
Total charge $= \$15 + \$2.70 = \$17.70$
Proceeds $= \$2160 - \$17.70 = \$2142.30$

Answer, $2142.30.

# BANKING AND LOANS

## EXERCISE 156

Find the date of maturity and the term of discount of the following drafts:

| No. | Date of Draft | When Payable | Date Accepted | Date Discounted |
|---|---|---|---|---|
| 1. | Jan. 26 | 60 days after sight | Feb. 1 | Feb. 10 |
| 2. | Mar. 23 | 90 " " date | Mar. 27 | Mar. 30 |
| 3. | May 4 | 4 months after sight | May 10 | May 12 |
| 4. | June 29 | 60 days after date | July 2 | July 5 |
| 5. | Sept. 15 | 30 " " sight | Sept. 19 | Sept. 25 |
| 6. | Dec. 9 | 2 months after date | Dec. 15 | Dec. 19 |
| 7. | Feb. 11 | 90 days after sight | Feb. 15 | Feb. 18 |
| 8. | June 14 | 3 months after date | June 18 | June 20 |
| 9. | July 29 | 3 " " sight | Aug. 1 | Aug. 5 |
| 10. | May 10 | 45 days after date | May 12 | May 14 |

## EXERCISE 157

Solve the following problems, and be careful in each case to note whether the draft is a *sight* draft or a *date* draft.

1. A draft for $3600 maturing 30 days after sight is dated Nov. 10, accepted Nov. 17, and discounted Nov. 21 at 6%. The bank charges $\frac{1}{10}$% for collection. What are the proceeds?

2. A draft maturing 60 days after date is dated September 19, accepted September 25, and discounted September 29 at 5%. The bank charges $\frac{1}{8}$% for collection, and the proceeds are $4284.60. What is the face amount of the draft?

3. A draft for $1800 maturing 90 days after date is dated August 18, accepted August 23, and discounted August 27. The bank charges $\frac{1}{8}$% for collection, and the proceeds are $1780.20. What is the bank's rate of discount?

4. A draft for $1600 maturing 60 days after sight is dated September 9, accepted September 12, and discounted September 15 at $4\frac{1}{2}$%. The bank charges $\frac{1}{8}$% for collection. What are the proceeds?

5. A draft maturing 90 days after sight is dated August 5, accepted August 8, and discounted August 12 at 4%. The bank charges $\frac{1}{10}$% for collection, and the proceeds are $2671.50. What is the face amount of the draft?

6. A draft for $3200 maturing 120 days after date is dated March 19, accepted March 30, and discounted April 8. The bank charges

$\frac{1}{8}\%$ for collection and the proceeds are $3156. What is the bank's rate of discount?

7. A draft for $5040 maturing 60 days after date is dated May 18, accepted May 21, and discounted May 25 at 5%. The bank charges $\frac{1}{5}\%$ for collection. What are the proceeds?

8. A draft for $1200 maturing 30 days after sight is dated June 11, accepted June 13, and discounted June 15 at 6%. The bank charges $\frac{1}{10}\%$ for collection. What are the proceeds?

9. A draft for $4200 maturing 45 days after date is dated March 10, accepted March 16, and discounted March 22. The bank charges $\frac{1}{10}\%$ for collection, and the proceeds are $4172.70. What is the bank's rate of discount?

10. A draft for $5400 maturing 90 days after sight is dated July 10, accepted July 15, and discounted July 20. The bank charges $\frac{1}{8}\%$ for collection, and the proceeds are $5312.50. What is the bank's rate of discount?

11. A draft for $6480 maturing 120 days after sight is dated July 7, accepted July 11, and discounted July 21 at 5%. The bank charges $\frac{1}{8}\%$ for collection. What are the proceeds?

12. A draft maturing 60 days after sight is dated July 7, accepted July 10, and discounted July 15 at 5%. The bank charges $\frac{1}{8}\%$ for collection, and the proceeds are $7849.60. What is the face amount of the note?

13. A draft for $4500 is dated October 16, accepted October 20, and discounted October 24 at 4%. The bank charges $\frac{1}{5}\%$ for collection, and the proceeds are $4480. How long did the draft have to run?

14. A draft for $6300 maturing 45 days after sight is dated January 16, accepted January 20, and discounted January 26. The bank charges $\frac{1}{10}\%$ for collection, and the proceeds are $6266.40. What is the bank's rate of discount?

15. A draft for $5600 maturing 120 days after sight is dated April 15, and discounted April 20 at $4\frac{1}{2}\%$. The bank charges $\frac{1}{8}\%$ for collection, and the proceeds are $5511.80. When was the draft accepted?

16. A draft for $1040 maturing 90 days after date is accepted June 20 and discounted June 25 at $4\frac{1}{2}\%$. The bank charges $\frac{1}{10}\%$ for collection, and the proceeds are $1028.56. What was the date of the draft?

17. A draft for $6000 maturing 60 days after date is dated July 18, accepted July 20, and discounted July 22 at 6%. The bank charges $\frac{1}{10}\%$ for collection. What are the proceeds?

18. A draft maturing 60 days after sight is dated April 12, accepted

# BANKING AND LOANS

April 16, and discounted April 20 at 4%. The bank charges $\frac{1}{10}$% for collection, and the proceeds are $8041.50. What is the face amount of the draft?

19. A draft for $9360 maturing 30 days after sight is dated February 20, accepted February 24, and discounted February 28. The bank charges $\frac{1}{8}$% for collection, and its total charges come to $45.50. What are the proceeds, and what is the bank's rate of discount?

20. A draft maturing 30 days after date is dated May 17, accepted May 21, and discounted May 23. The bank charges $\frac{1}{8}$% for collection; and, after deducting $5.78 for collection and discount, yields $1364.22 to the payee. What is the face amount of the draft and what is the bank's rate of discount?

## ANSWERS

### EXERCISE 147

1. $865.00; $680; $915; $1391; $1154; $1133.25; $1028.75; $1042.35 (interest of $13.60); $923.90; $973.40; $879.65; $897.23 (interest of $17.58).
2. $195.40; $592.90; $425.41; $467.64; $30.14; $217.63; $218.23 (interest of $.60); $314.73; $226.85; $659.95; $30.95; $361.14; $36.14; $36.86 (interest of $.72).

### EXERCISE 148

1. $275.02     2. $315.16     3. $267.28     4. $297.87

### EXERCISE 149

1. $2.50; $497.50.     2. $5.25; $519.75.     3. $20.25; $1329.75.
4. $18.75; $1856.25.     5. $27.63; $1814.37.     6. $9.81; $1952.19.
7. $5.80; $594.20.     8. $43.00; $5957.00.     9. $17.00; $1483.00.
10. $.95; $299.05.

### EXERCISE 150

1. July 26, 42 days.     2. February 10, 71 days.     3. May 10, 50 days.
4. February 28, 105 days.     5. August 22, 48 days.

### EXERCISE 151

1. $796.50     2. $296.60     3. $963.16     4. $890.70
5. $287.16     6. $3894     7. $268.89     8. $417.34
9. $215.46     10. $6532.90     11. $1200     12. two months; 42 days
13. July 14; 53 days     14. January 23     15. September 18; August 19
16. 111 days; February 16     17. 6%     18. 90 days; May 7
19. October 29; August 29     20. $1800

### EXERCISE 152

1. $1860.32     2. $650.70     3. $1668.66     4. $9719.23     5. $642.40

### EXERCISE 153

1. 90 days     2. 60 days     3. 120 days     4. 30 days     5. 60 days

### EXERCISE 154

1. 6%     2. 5%     3. $4\frac{1}{2}$%     4. 4%     5. 3%

### EXERCISE 155
1. $304   2. $1230   3. $1152   4. $336   5. $7434

### EXERCISE 156

| No. | Date | Term | No. | Date | Term |
|---|---|---|---|---|---|
| 1. | Apr. 2 | 51 days | 6. | Feb. 9 | 52 days |
| 2. | June 21 | 83 " | 7. | May 16 | 87 " |
| 3. | Sept. 10 | 121 " | 8. | Sept. 14 | 86 " |
| 4. | Aug. 28 | 53 " | 9. | Nov. 1 | 88 " |
| 5. | Oct. 19 | 24 " | 10. | June 24 | 41 " |

### EXERCISE 157
1. $3580.80   2. $4320   3. 4%   4. $1586.60
5. $2700   6. $4\frac{1}{2}$%   7. $4992.82   8. $1193.20
9. 6%   10. 6%   11. $6376.50   12. $7920
13. 30 days after date   14. 4%   15. April 16   16. June 15
17. $5938   18. $8100   19. $9314.50; 5%   20. $1360; $4\frac{1}{2}$%

## CHAPTER XXII
## Investments
### STOCKS

THERE are two principal kinds of stocks—*common stock* and *preferred stock*.

Common stock entitles the owner to a *proportionate share* of the profits of a corporation.

Preferred stock entitles the owner to a *fixed dividend*, provided the profits of the corporation are sufficient to meet this dividend. The dividend on the preferred stock is paid before any dividend is declared on the common stock.

The face value of a share of stock as stated on the certificate when issued is called the *par value* of the stock. The par value of a stock is generally $100 a share.

The amount for which a share of stock can be sold in the market is called the *market value* of the stock. If it sells for more than the par value, it is said to be *above par*. If it sells for less than the par value, it is said to be *below par*.

Corporations as a rule do not pay out in dividends the full amount of their profits. They lay aside a part of their earnings, called *surplus*, for future emergencies.

On stocks which have a par value, dividends are reckoned as a percent of the par value, and not as a percent of the market value. This is an important fact for the investor to bear in mind.

### EXAMPLES

1. The A B C Shoe Company's capital stock of $250,000 is divided into 2500 shares of common stock with a par value of $100 each. Mr. Smith bought 30 shares at $125 per share ($25 above par). The net profit of the company for 1938 was $12,985.59. A dividend of 5% was paid to the stockholders, and the remainder was placed in the surplus account against emergencies. Find:

(a) The dividend per share.
(b) The total amount paid out in dividends.

(c) The amount laid aside as surplus.
(d) The amount of the dividend received by Mr. Smith.

(a) Dividend per share = 5% of $100 (par value)    = $5.00
(b) Total amount paid out in dividends
        = 2500 shares × $5                      = $12,500.00
(c) Amount laid aside as surplus = $12,985.59 − $12,500 = $485.59
(d) Amount of dividend received by Mr. Smith
        = 30 shares × $5                         = $150.00
        Answer: (a) $5.00; (b) $12,500.00; (c) $485.59; (d) $150.00

2. A certain company's capital stock of $450,000 is issued in two lots: 1500 shares at 6% preferred stock, and 3000 shares of common stock, all stock having a par value of $100. The company makes a net profit of $46,453.28, lays aside $1453.28 as surplus, and pays out the remainder in dividends. If Mr. Brown owns 50 shares of common stock, how much does he receive in dividends?

| | |
|---|---|
| Net profit for year | = $46,453.28 |
| Surplus | = 1,453.28 |
| Total dividend paid to stockholders | = $45,000.00 |
| Dividend paid on preferred stock | |
|   = $100 × 6% × 1500 shares | = 9,000.00 |
| Dividend paid to common stockholders | = $36,000.00 |
| Since there are 3000 shares of common stock, | |
|   the dividend on each share = $36,000 ÷ 3000 | = $12.00 |
| Amount of dividend received by Mr. Brown | |
|   = 50 shares × $12 | = $600.00 |

Answer, $600.00

## EXERCISE 158

A. Find the amount of the annual dividend per share in each of the following examples:

| | Par Value per Share | Market Value per Share | Annual Dividend Rate | Amount of Annual Dividend |
|---|---|---|---|---|
| 1. | $100 | $123 | 5% | ? |
| 2. | $ 50 | $ 27 | 6% | ? |
| 3. | $75 | $ 75 | 8% | ? |
| 4. | $100 | $249 | 7% | ? |
| 5. | $ 75 | $ 64 | 5% | ? |

# INVESTMENTS 261

B. The capital stock of the Independent Knitting Mills, Incorporated, was $1,250,000, divided as follows: 2500 shares of 7% preferred stock, and 10,000 shares of common stock at a par value of $100 a share. In 1938 the company paid out $37,000 in dividends to its stockholders. How much did each of the following stockholders receive?

| Stockholder | 7% Preferred Shares | Common Shares |
|---|---|---|
| 1. Mr. Brown | 20 | |
| 2. Mr. Black | | 250 |
| 3. Mr. Green | 12 | 100 |
| 4. Mr. White | 24 | 25 |
| 5. Mr. Gray | | 150 |
| 6. Mr. Jones | 15 | 70 |

## STOCK REPORTS

The following is a list of quotations selected from a typical stock report as printed in the daily newspapers:

| Stocks and Dividends in Dollars | Sales | High | Low | Last Sale |
|---|---|---|---|---|
| Am Can (4) | 2000 | $111\frac{1}{4}$ | 110 | $110\frac{1}{8}$ |
| Am Ice | 200 | 2 | 2 | 2 |
| Col Carbon (4) | 700 | $44\frac{3}{8}$ | $43\frac{1}{2}$ | $44\frac{3}{8}$ |
| Consol Oil (.80) | 5300 | 9 | $8\frac{3}{4}$ | $8\frac{3}{4}$ |
| First Nat Stores ($2\frac{1}{2}$) | 2000 | $42\frac{3}{8}$ | $41\frac{3}{8}$ | $41\frac{1}{2}$ |
| Gen Foods (2) | 2900 | $40\frac{3}{4}$ | $40\frac{1}{4}$ | $40\frac{5}{8}$ |
| Gillette (.60) | 1000 | $6\frac{5}{8}$ | $6\frac{1}{2}$ | $6\frac{1}{2}$ |
| Ill Central | 4500 | $15\frac{3}{8}$ | $14\frac{1}{2}$ | $14\frac{3}{4}$ |
| Kresge S S (1.20) | 1900 | $23\frac{3}{4}$ | $23\frac{1}{4}$ | $23\frac{1}{4}$ |
| Texas Corp (2) | 6700 | 49 | 47 | $47\frac{1}{8}$ |
| Union Pacific (6) | 700 | 101 | 100 | $100\frac{1}{4}$ |
| U S Steel | 62100 | $80\frac{5}{8}$ | $77\frac{1}{8}$ | $77\frac{3}{8}$ |
| U S Steel pr. (7) | 800 | $118\frac{5}{8}$ | $117\frac{7}{8}$ | $118\frac{3}{8}$ |
| Vanadium | 7300 | 39 | $36\frac{5}{8}$ | $36\frac{7}{8}$ |

Explanation: The first line of the above report means that American Can pays a dividend of $4 a share, that 2000 shares of this stock were sold during the day's transactions on the Stock Exchange, that the prices of these shares ranged from a high of $111.25 to a low of $110 per share, and that the last sale was made at $110.12½ per share.

## COMMISSION RATES

Stock brokers charge their clients a commission on each purchase or sale. This commission is called *brokerage*. Following is a table of commission rates commonly charged by brokers on the Stock Exchange:

| On Stock Selling At | Rate Charged |
| --- | --- |
| $.50 to $.99 | $.03 per share |
| $1.00 to $9⅞ | $.07½ per share |
| $10.00 to $24⅞ | $.12½ per share |
| $25.00 to $49⅞ | $.15 per share |
| $50.00 to $74⅞ | $.17½ per share |
| $75.00 to $99⅞ | $.20 per share |
| $100.00 to $199⅞ | $.25 per share |
| $200.00 to $249⅞ | $.30 per share |

For stock selling at $250 or more, 5 cents per share is added for each $50 or fraction thereof.

## TAXES ON STOCK TRANSFERS

When a person *sells* stocks through the New York Stock Exchange, he must pay both a Federal tax and a State tax in addition to the brokerage fee. When a person *buys* stocks, he must pay a tax only on *odd* lots. No tax is required on purchases of *full* lots. (An *odd* lot means any number of shares from 1 to 99. A *full* lot, sometimes called a *round* lot, means 100 shares or any multiple of 100 shares. Thus, 547 shares equals 5 *full* lots of 100 shares each, plus 1 *odd* lot of 47 shares.)

# INVESTMENTS

## TABLES OF FEDERAL AND STATE TAXES

### 1. New York State Tax

| Market Price per Share | Tax |
|---|---|
| Selling under $20 | 3 cents |
| Selling at $20 or over | 4 cents |

### 2. Federal Tax

| Stock | Market Price per Share | Tax |
|---|---|---|
| When there is no par value | Selling under $20 | 4 cents |
| | Selling at $20 or over | 5 cents |
| When there is a par value | Selling under $20 | 4 cents on each $100 of par value or fraction thereof |
| | Selling at $20 or over | 5 cents on each $100 of par value or fraction thereof |

## EXAMPLES

1. Mr. Jackson bought 200 shares of Montgomery Ward (no par value) at $51\frac{1}{2}$. How much did he pay for the stock?

Buying price = $51.50 × 200      = $10,300.00
Brokerage = 200 shares at $.17$\frac{1}{2}$      = 35.00
Total paid for stock      = $10,335.00

Answer, $10,335.00

2. Mr. Stevens bought 125 shares (no par) American Locomotive at $26\frac{1}{2}$. How much did he pay for the stock?

Buying price = $26.50 × 125      = $3312.50
Brokerage = 125 shares × $.15      = 18.75
State tax on odd lot of 25 shares
     = 25 shares × $.04      = 1.00
Federal tax on odd lot of 25 shares
     = 25 shares × $.05      = 1.25
Total paid for stock      = $3333.50

Answer, $3333.50

3. Mr. Winters instructed his broker to sell for him 70 shares of Standard Oil of New Jersey (par value $25) at 48. How much did he receive from his broker?

| | | |
|---|---|---|
| Gross proceeds = $48 × 70 | | = $3360.00 |
| Less: | | |
|    Brokerage = 70 × $.15 | = $10.50 | |
|    State tax = 70 × $.04 | = 2.80 | |
|    Federal tax on par value of $1750 | | |
|      ($25 × 70) 5% on each $100 of | | |
|      par value or fraction thereof | | |
|      = 18 × $.05 | = .90 | 14.20 |
| Amount received by Mr. Winters | | $3345.80 |

Answer, $3345.80

4. Mrs. Grover bought some stock at a total cost of $65\frac{3}{4}$ a share. She received an annual dividend of $5 a share. What was the approximate percentage of her yield?

Percentage of yield = dividend ÷ cost
" " " $5 ÷ $65.75 = .076+
Answer, 7.6% approximately.

## EXERCISE 159

A. Find the total cost of buying each group of the following stocks:

| | No. of Shares | Stock | Par Value | Price per Share |
|---|---|---|---|---|
| 1. | 400 | Am Locomotive | None | 18 |
| 2. | 125 | Anaconda | None | 25 |
| 3. | 300 | Beth Steel | None | $56\frac{1}{2}$ |
| 4. | 900 | Ches & Ohio | 25 | 33 |
| 5. | 500 | Int Tel & Tel | None | $6\frac{1}{2}$ |

B. Find the net proceeds of each of the following sales of stock:

| | No. of Shares | Stock | Par Value | Price per Share |
|---|---|---|---|---|
| 1. | 600 | Am Locomotive | None | 18 |
| 2. | 800 | Miami Copper | 5 | $7\frac{1}{4}$ |
| 3. | 200 | Mont Ward | None | 50 |
| 4. | 60 | Union Pacific | 100 | 95 |
| 5. | 400 | U S Rubber | 100 | 45 |

C. Find the percentage of the yield in the following cases:

| | Stock Cost per Share | Annual Dividend |
|---|---|---|
| 1. | 75 | $6.00 |
| 2. | $87\frac{7}{8}$ | $3.60 |
| 3. | $24\frac{1}{2}$ | $ .24\frac{1}{2}$ |
| 4. | $124\frac{3}{4}$ | $5.00 |
| 5. | $47\frac{1}{2}$ | $3.75 |

## BONDS

When a man borrows money, he generally gives a promissory note as a proof of his debt. In like manner, when a corporation or a government borrows money, it issues promissory notes known as *bonds*.

Bonds are usually issued with a *face value*, or *par value*, of $1000, although occasionally they are issued in smaller denominations of $500, $100, or even $50.

The purchase of a bond entitles the holder not only to receive the interest regularly, but to get back the par value of the bond when it matures.

The *maturity* of a bond is the date on which the corporation or the government promises to pay back to the owner the par value of the bond.

Interest on bonds is generally paid twice a year. To facilitate the collection of interest by the owner, bonds are generally provided with coupons. These coupons are attached to the bond, and each one bears the date on which the interest is due. The owner merely detaches the right coupon at the right date and presents it to a bank for collection.

A bond may be bought at par, above par, or below par, depending upon the market conditions under which it is bought. At maturity, however, the owner will receive the par value of the bond.

Bonds are usually sold through investment houses that buy the complete issue from the corporation at a little below par and try to sell them to the public at higher prices. When bonds are bought and sold on the Stock Exchange, a commission

266  MATHEMATICS MADE EASY

is charged for buying and selling. The general commission is from $1.50 to $3 for each $1000 of par value, but a minimum of $5 is frequently charged on any one transaction.

A person who *buys* a bond is not required to pay any transfer tax. But a person who *sells* a bond is required to pay a Federal tax of $.40 per $1000 face value, regardless of the market price.

When bonds are quoted at 100, it means that they sell at 100% of the par value. When they are quoted at $98\frac{1}{2}$, it means that they sell at $98\frac{1}{2}\%$ of the par value. For example, a bond at a $1000 par value quoted at 100 sells for $1000. If it is quoted at $98\frac{1}{2}$, it sells for $985. And so on.

### EXAMPLES

1. A man buys 7 bonds par value $1000 each on June 13. The coupon rate is 5%, and the interest is payable April 1 and October 1. The market price per bond is $98\frac{1}{2}$. The brokerage commission is $2.50 per $1000 of par value. What is the total cost of the bonds?

*Note:* In computing the interest, use the 30-day-a-month and 360-day-a-year method.

*Solution:* Since the preceding interest date is April 1, the interest accrued on the note from April 1 to June 13, or 72 days, must be paid by the purchaser.

Interest for 72 days at 5% per bond
   of $1000 par value $=\frac{5}{100}\times\frac{72}{360}\times 1000$    = $10.00
Brokerage per bond of $1000 par value    =   2.50
Price per bond    =  985.00
Total cost per bond    = $997.50
Total cost of 7 bonds $997.50×7    =$6982.50

                  Answer, $6982.50

2. A man sells 5 bonds, par value $1000, on April 1. The coupon rate is 6%, and the interest is payable January 1 and July 1. The market price per bond is $105\frac{1}{2}$. The brokerage commission is $3 per $1000 of par value. What are his net proceeds?

Since the interest accrued from January 1 to April 1 must be paid by the purchaser, it is received by the seller.

# INVESTMENTS

| | | |
|---|---|---|
| Interest for 90 days at 5% per bond of $1000 par value | = | $15.00 |
| Price per bond | = | $1055.00 |
| Gross proceeds per bond | = | $1070.00 |
| Less: | | |
|     Brokerage per bond | = $3.00 | |
|     Tax per bond of $1000 par value | = .40 | 3.40 |
| Net proceeds per bond | | = $1066.60 |
| Net proceeds from 5 bonds = $1066.60 × 5 | | = $5333.00 |

Answer, $5333.00

## EXERCISE 160

A. Find the total cost of buying each group of the following bonds:

| | Number of Bonds | Par Value | Coupon Rate | Date Bought | Last Date of Interest | Market Price | Brokerage Commission |
|---|---|---|---|---|---|---|---|
| 1. | 5 | $1000 | 6% | Aug. 1 | June 1 | 99 | $2.50 |
| 2. | 3 | $1000 | 3% | Feb. 7 | Jan. 1 | 96 | $3.00 |
| 3. | 4 | $1000 | 4% | Mar. 13 | Jan. 1 | $98\frac{1}{2}$ | $2.50 |
| 4. | 6 | $1000 | 5% | June 21 | Apr. 1 | $95\frac{3}{4}$ | $2.50 |
| 5. | 7 | $1000 | 2% | Nov. 11 | Oct. 1 | $93\frac{1}{4}$ | $2.50 |

B. Find the total proceeds from the sales of the following groups of bonds:

| | Number of Bonds | Par Value | Coupon Rate | Date Sold | Last Date of Interest | Market Price | Brokerage Commission |
|---|---|---|---|---|---|---|---|
| 1. | 4 | $1000 | 3% | Mar. 1 | Jan. 1 | $98\frac{1}{2}$ | $2.50 |
| 2. | 5 | $1000 | 2% | Jul. 11 | Apr. 11 | $99\frac{1}{4}$ | $2.50 |
| 3. | 5 | $1000 | 5% | Dec. 13 | Oct. 1 | 100 | $3.00 |
| 4. | 6 | $1000 | $2\frac{1}{2}$% | Apr. 1 | Jan. 1 | 103 | $3.00 |
| 5. | 3 | $1000 | $2\frac{1}{4}$% | Nov. 1 | July 1 | $100\frac{7}{8}$ | $2.50 |

## ANSWERS
### EXERCISE 158 A

1. $5.—     2. $3.—     3. $6.—     4. $7.—     5. $3.75

### EXERCISE 158 B

1. $140     4. $218
2. $500     5. $300
3. $284     6. $245

## EXERCISE 159
A. 1, $7250;  2, $3146;  3, $17,002.50;  4, $29,835;  5, $3287.50.
B. 1, $10,683;  2, $5714.40;  3, $9947;  4, $5684.10  5, $17,904.
C. 1, 8%;  2, about 4%;  3, 1%;  4, about 4%;  5, about 7.8%.

## EXERCISE 160
A. 1, $5012.50;  2, $2898;  3, $3982;  4, $5826.66;  5, $6578.04.
B. 1, $3948.40;  2, $4975.80;  3, $5033;  4, $6197.10;  5, $3040.05.

## CHAPTER XXIII
## Property Taxes

PROPERTY TAXES are computed as follows:

Suppose a tax of $70,400 is to be raised by a town which has taxable property assessed at $6,400,000.

a. Find the rate of taxation per $100.

b. Find the tax paid by Mr. Jones, if his property is assessed at $11,920.

a. The tax on $1 = $70,400 ÷ 6,400,000 = $.011

That is, the tax on $1 is 11 mills (1 cent and 1 mill).

Therefore the tax on $100 is $.011 × 100 = $1.10

b. To get the tax paid (T) by Mr. Jones, divide the assessed value of his property (A) by 100 and multiply the quotient by the rate per $100, or $1.10 (R).

That is, $T = \dfrac{AR}{100}$

T = $11,920 ÷ 100 × 1.10 = $131.12

Answer: (a) $1.10; (b) $131.12

### EXERCISE 161

A. In the following problems, find the tax rate per hundred dollars from the assessed value of the community and the tax to be raised:

| No. | Assessed Value of Community | Tax to Be Raised | Tax Rate per $100 |
|---|---|---|---|
| 1. | $ 16,872,000 | $ 126,540 | .......... |
| 2. | 124,432,000 | 2,190,003.20 | .......... |
| 3. | 12,765,000 | 217,005 | .......... |
| 4. | 69,264,000 | 432,900 | .......... |
| 5. | 10,744,800 | 188,034 | .......... |
| 6. | 108,878,000 | 2,221,111.20 | .......... |
| 7. | 26,640,000 | 692,640 | .......... |
| 8. | 93,324,000 | 1,414,080.80 | .......... |
| 9. | 89,991,000 | 1,421,857.80 | .......... |

270  MATHEMATICS MADE EASY

| No. | Assessed Value of Community | Tax to Be Raised | Tax Rate per $100 |
|---|---|---|---|
| 10. | 32,432,000 | 405,400 | .......... |
| 11. | 35,409,000 | 994,992.90 | .......... |
| 12. | 53,835,000 | 277,250.25 | .......... |
| 13. | 92,685,000 | 1,418,080.50 | .......... |
| 14. | 23,421,000 | 142,656.90 | .......... |
| 15. | 77,145,000 | 1,087,744.50 | .......... |
| 16. | 19,092,000 | 282,561.60 | .......... |
| 17. | 3,599,964,000 | 99,359,006.40 | .......... |
| 18. | 101,565,000 | 1,797,700.50 | .......... |
| 19. | 31,524,000 | 807,014.40 | .......... |
| 20. | 363,297,000 | 9,918,008.10 | .......... |

B. For a recent year the tax rates on real property in New York City were:

| Bronx | $2.74 per $100 |
| Brooklyn | 2.78 " " |
| Manhattan | 2.76 " " |
| Queens | 2.84 " " |
| Richmond | 2.74 " " |

Using these rates, find the tax to be paid on the property whose value is given in the following problems:

| No. | Assessed Value | Borough | Tax |
|---|---|---|---|
| 1. | $ 5,000 | Bronx | .......... |
| 2. | 8,000 | Manhattan | .......... |
| 3. | 6,500 | Richmond | .......... |
| 4. | 9,000 | Queens | .......... |
| 5. | 7,500 | Brooklyn | .......... |
| 6. | 8,750 | Queens | .......... |
| 7. | 6,250 | Richmond | .......... |
| 8. | 3,750 | Brooklyn | .......... |
| 9. | 1,400 | Manhattan | .......... |
| 10. | 7,900 | Bronx | .......... |
| 11. | 8,960 | Brooklyn | .......... |
| 12. | 9,420 | Queens | .......... |
| 13. | 18,310 | Richmond | .......... |
| 14. | 25,840 | Manhattan | .......... |
| 15. | 196,740 | Bronx | .......... |
| 16. | 237,510 | Manhattan | .......... |

# PROPERTY TAXES

| 17. | 894,120 | Richmond | .......... |
| 18. | 873,460 | Brooklyn | .......... |
| 19. | 933,800 | Bronx | .......... |
| 20. | 424,860 | Queens | .......... |

## FINDING THE ASSESSED VALUE

Suppose the tax rate for a certain town is $2.75 per $100. What is the assessed value on Mr. A's property if he pays $165 in taxes?

$$T = \frac{AR}{100}$$
$$100T = AR$$
$$\$165 \times 100 = \$2.75 \times A$$
$$A = \$16,500 \div 2.75 = \$6,000$$

Answer, $6,000

## EXERCISE 162

Using the same tax rates as in Exercise 161B, find the assessed value from the tax given in the following problems:

| No. | Tax Paid | Borough | Assessed Value |
|---|---|---|---|
| 1. | $ 142.00 | Queens | .............. |
| 2. | 1,918.00 | Bronx | .............. |
| 3. | 1,668.00 | Brooklyn | .............. |
| 4. | 10,960.00 | Richmond | .............. |
| 5. | 16,560.00 | Manhattan | .............. |
| 6. | 1,163.68 | Bronx | .............. |
| 7. | 3,717.17 | Manhattan | .............. |
| 8. | 20,740.16 | Richmond | .............. |
| 9. | 11,524.44 | Queens | .............. |
| 10. | 1,260.73 | Brooklyn | .............. |
| 11. | 2,739.97 | Brooklyn | .............. |
| 12. | 59,296.44 | Bronx | .............. |
| 13. | 12,141.09 | Brooklyn | .............. |
| 14. | 2,942.81 | Queens | .............. |
| 15. | 12,199.44 | Richmond | .............. |
| 16. | 12,793.06 | Bronx | .............. |
| 17. | 72,108.04 | Manhattan | .............. |
| 18. | 5,517.63 | Richmond | .............. |
| 19. | 24,130.05 | Queens | .............. |
| 20. | 7,845.02 | Manhattan | .............. |

## FINDING THE TAX RATE

The assessed value on a piece of property is $68,000, and the tax paid is $850. What is the tax rate per $100?

$$T = \frac{AR}{100}$$

$$\$850 = \frac{68000R}{100}$$

$$\$85000 = 68000R$$

$$R = \$1.25$$

Answer, $1.25

## EXERCISE 163

In the following problems find the tax rate per $100 from the assessed value and the tax paid:

| No. | Assessed Value | Tax Paid | Rate per $100 |
|---|---|---|---|
| 1. | $152,000 | $ 570.00 | ............ |
| 2. | 115,000 | 977.50 | ............ |
| 3. | 96,800 | 847.00 | ............ |
| 4. | 240,000 | 1,560.00 | ............ |
| 5. | 81,000 | 639.90 | ............ |
| 6. | 112,000 | 985.60 | ............ |
| 7. | 104,000 | 650.00 | ............ |
| 8. | 98,000 | 999.60 | ............ |
| 9. | 84,000 | 636.40 | ............ |
| 10. | 136,000 | 1,700.00 | ............ |
| 11. | 211,000 | 3,987.90 | ............ |
| 12. | 172,000 | 2,545.60 | ............ |
| 13. | 284,000 | 7,270.40 | ............ |
| 14. | 319,000 | 8,963.90 | ............ |
| 15. | 485,000 | 2,497.75 | ............ |
| 16. | 695,000 | 4,899.75 | ............ |
| 17. | 835,000 | 6,387.75 | ............ |
| 18. | 915,000 | 8,097.75 | ............ |
| 19. | 327,000 | 8,927.10 | ............ |
| 20. | 324,000 | 8,942.40 | ............ |

## DELINQUENT TAXES AND DISCOUNTED TAXES

When the tax is paid some time *after* it is due, a penalty is generally imposed upon the payer. When it is paid some time *before* it is due, a discount is generally allowed to the payer.

## PROPERTY TAXES

In order that we may see how the penalty and the discount are computed, let us consider a few examples:

1. In a certain community, the tax rate is $2.50, and the taxes are due in two installments—on April 1 and October 1. They become delinquent if they are not paid by May 1 and November 1, and a penalty is imposed at the rate of 6% for the exact time of the delinquency. On the other hand, if the first installment has been paid, the second installment may be discounted at the rate of 4% for the exact period of the discount.

With the above information, find the tax imposed, the penalty, and the total paid in the following case:

|  | 1st Installment | 2nd Installment |
|---|---|---|
| Assessed Value | Date Paid | Date Paid |
| $90,000 | May 24 | October 31 |

$T = \dfrac{AR}{100} = \dfrac{\$90{,}000 \times 2.50}{100}$ = $2250.00

1st installment = $1125

Penalty on 1st installment for 24 days
(May 1–May 24) $1125 \times \frac{6}{100} \times \frac{1}{15}$ (of a yr.) = 4.50

Total paid = $2254.50

### Answer

| Tax Imposed | Penalty | Total Paid |
|---|---|---|
| $2250 | $4.50 | $2254.50 |

2. With the same rates as above, find the tax imposed, the penalty, the discount, and the total paid, in the following case:

|  | 1st Installment | 2nd Installment |
|---|---|---|
| Assessed Value | Date Paid | Date Paid |
| $60,000 | May 20 | September 1 |

$T = \dfrac{\$60{,}000 \times 2.50}{100}$ = $1500

Add penalty on 1st installment
$750 \times \frac{6}{100} \times \frac{20}{360}$ = 2.50

= $1502.50

Deduct discount on 2nd installment
$750 \times \frac{4}{100} \times \frac{80}{360}$ = 2.50

Balance paid $1500.00

### Answer

| Tax Imposed | Penalty | Discount | Total Paid |
|---|---|---|---|
| $1500 | $2.50 | $2.50 | $1500 |

## EXERCISE 164

In New York City, taxes may be paid in two installments—on April 1 and October 1. Taxes become delinquent on May 1 and November 1, respectively, and interest is charged at the rate of 7% for exact time of the delinquency (including the first day of May or November). If the first half of the tax is paid, the second half may be discounted at the rate of 4%. With this information, and using the tax rate of $2.76 per $100, find the tax imposed, penalty, discount, and total paid in each of the following problems of Manhattan taxes:

| No. | Assessed Value | 1st Installment Date Paid | 2nd Installment Date Paid |
|---|---|---|---|
| 1. | $ 81,260 | Apr. 18 | Oct. 31 |
| 2. | 45,360 | May 18 | Oct. 26 |
| 3. | 11,200 | May 24 | June 2 |
| 4. | 16,200 | Apr. 19 | Oct. 28 |
| 5. | 8,400 | Apr. 15 | Sept. 15 |
| 6. | 119,450 | May 1 | Oct. 31 |
| 7. | 962,000 | Apr. 30 | July 17 |
| 8. | 875,000 | June 29 | Oct. 31 |
| 9. | 125,000 | June 14 | Dec. 6 |
| 10. | 963,000 | July 14 | Nov. 8 |
| 11. | 375,000 | July 2 | Oct. 24 |
| 12. | 427,500 | May 9 | Dec. 15 |
| 13. | 750,000 | Apr. 30 | Aug. 1 |
| 14. | 43,200 | June 14 | Oct. 31 |
| 15. | 73,800 | May 18 | Nov. 27 |
| 16. | 69,300 | July 29 | Oct. 15 |
| 17. | 24,300 | June 27 | Dec. 24 |
| 18. | 21,600 | Apr. 28 | Dec. 10 |
| 19. | 894,600 | May 27 | Oct. 31 |
| 20. | 915,400 | Apr. 20 | Nov. 9 |

### GENERAL PROBLEMS IN TAXATION

1. The total tax to be collected in a certain town is $70,850. The assessed value of the real and personal property is $6,400,000. There is a poll tax of $1 per poll on each of the 450 male voters. Find (a) the rate of taxation per $100, and (b) the amount of tax paid by a man whose property is assessed at $6500.

# PROPERTY TAXES

a. Total tax to be collected.................................$70,850
   Deduct poll taxes.................................... 450
   Net property tax to be collected....................$70,400
   Tax on $1 = \$70,400 \div 6,400,000 = \$.011$
   Tax on $100 = 100 \times \$.011 = \$1.10$

b. Property tax $= \dfrac{\$6500 \times 1.10}{100} = \$71.50$

   Poll tax                    =    1.00
   Total tax paid              = $72.50

   Answer: (a) $1.10; (b) $72.50

2. A man's property is assessed at $45,000. How much tax will he have to pay if the rate is $1.75 per $100 and the collector's fee is 1% of the tax?

$\dfrac{\$45,000 \times 1.75}{100} = \$787.50$

Collector's fee = 1% of $787.50 =   7.88
Total tax                        = $795.38

Answer, $795.38

3. A man's property is assessed at $27,000. The combined village and state tax rate is $1.25 per $100. The school tax rate is $.75 per $100. He must pay for two polls at $1 per poll. The collector's fee is 1%. What is the total tax that he has to pay?

Village and state tax rate.....................$1.25 per $100
School tax rate.................................. .75 " "
Total property tax rate........................$2.00 " "

Property tax $= \dfrac{\$27,000 \times 2.00}{100}$ = $540

Poll tax                                       =    2
                                                  $542
Collector's fee, @ 1%                          =    5.42
Total tax                                      = $547.42

Answer, $547.42

## EXERCISE 165

Solve the following problems:

1. The total tax to be collected in a certain town is $40,400. The assessed value of the real and personal property is $1,960,000. There

276   MATHEMATICS MADE EASY

is a poll tax of $1 per poll on each of the 560 male voters. Find the rate of taxation, and the amount of tax paid by a man whose property is assessed at $5600, and who pays for 1 poll.

2. A man's property is assessed at $36,000. How much tax will he have to pay if the rate is $1.375 per $100 and the collector's fee is 1% (of the tax).

3. A man's property is assessed at $54,000. How much tax will he have to pay if the combined village, county, and state rate is $1.023 per $100; the school tax rate is $.852 per $100; he must pay for two polls at $1 per poll; and the collector's fee is 2%?

4. A certain state assesses property at 75% of its actual value. If the tax rate is $2.56 per $100, and the actual value of a man's property is $25,000, how much tax does he pay?

5. In a certain town the school tax is $.40 per $100 of assessed valuation. The town budget is $17,500, and the assessed valuation of property in the town is $5,000,000. The county budget is $187,500 and the assessed valuation of property in the county is $30,000,000. The state budget is $7,500,000, and the assessed valuation of property in the state is $2,000,000,000. What is the tax rate per $100 of assessed valuation payed by property owners in the town?

6. In New York City for a recent year, the basic tax rate per $100 of assessed valuation was $2.64. The gross tax rate in Manhattan was $2.76, the addition being for citywide and borough assessments. If the total assessed valuation of property in Manhattan for that year was $8,252,020,105, and if all taxes were collected, how much was collected in Manhattan for citywide and borough assessments?

7. Under the same circumstances, how much was raised by the Bronx with a gross tax rate of $2.74 and an assessed valuation of $1,923,709,614?

8. How much by Brooklyn, with a gross tax rate of $2.78 and an assessed valuation of $3,939,292,859?

9. How much by Queens, with a gross tax rate of $2.84 and an assessed valuation of $2,186,323,584?

10. How much by Richmond, with a gross tax rate of $2.74 and an assessed valuation of $298,349,032?

ANSWERS
EXERCISE 161A

| 1. $.75 | 2. $1.76 | 3. $1.70 | 4. $.625 |
| 5. $1.75 | 6. $2.04 | 7. $2.60 | 8. $1.52 |
| 9. $1.58 | 10. $1.25 | 11. $2.81 | 12. $.515 |
| 13. $1.53 | 14. $1.89 | 15. $1.41 | 16. $1.48 |
| 17. $2.76 | 18. $1.77 | 19. $2.56 | 20. $2.73 |

## PROPERTY TAXES

### EXERCISE 161B

| | | | |
|---|---|---|---|
| 1. $137 | 2. $220.80 | 3. $178.10 | 4. $255.60 |
| 5. $208.50 | 6. $248.50 | 7. $191.25 | 8. $104.25 |
| 9. $38.64 | 10. $216.46 | 11. $249.09 | 12. $267.53 |
| 13. $501.69 | 14. $713.18 | 15. $5390.68 | 16. $6555.28 |
| 17. $24,398.89 | 18. $24,282.19 | 19. $25,568.12 | 20. $12,065.02 |

### EXERCISE 162

| | | | |
|---|---|---|---|
| 1. $5000 | 2. $70,000 | 3. $60,000 | 4. $400,000 |
| 5. $600,000 | 6. $42,470 | 7. $134,680 | 8. $756,940 |
| 9. $405,290 | 10. $45,350 | 11. $98,560 | 12. $2,164,140 |
| 13. $436,730 | 14. $103,620 | 15. $447,060 | 16. $466,900 |
| 17. $2,612,610 | 18. $201,410 | 19. $849,720 | 20. $284,240 |

### EXERCISE 163

| | | | |
|---|---|---|---|
| 1. $.375 | 2. $.85 | 3. $.875 | 4. $.65 |
| 5. $.79 | 6. $.88 | 7. $.625 | 8. $1.02 |
| 9. $.76 | 10. $1.25 | 11. $1.89 | 12. $1.48 |
| 13. $2.56 | 14. $2.81 | 15. $.515 | 16. $.705 |
| 17. $.765 | 18. $.885 | 19. $2.73 | 20. $2.76 |

### EXERCISE 164

| No. | Tax Imposed | Penalty | Discount | Total Paid |
|---|---|---|---|---|
| 1. | $ 2,242.78 | $ — | $ — | $ 2,242.78 |
| 2. | 1,251.94 | 2.19 | | 1,254.13 |
| 3. | 309.12 | .72 | 2.06 | 307.78 |
| 4. | 447.12 | | | 447.12 |
| 5. | 231.84 | | .19 | 231.65 |
| 6. | 3,296.82 | .32 | | 3,297.14 |
| 7. | 26,551.20 | | 110.63 | 26,440.57 |
| 8. | 24,150 | 140.88 | | 24,290.88 |
| 9. | 3,450 | 27.17 | | 3,477.17 |
| 10. | 26,578.80 | 240.31 | | 26,819.11 |
| 11. | 10,350 | 33.21 | | 10,383.21 |
| 12. | 11,809 | 61.99 | | 11,870.99 |
| 13. | 20,700 | | 69.00 | 20,631.00 |
| 14. | 1,192.32 | 5.22 | | 1,197.54 |
| 15. | 2,036.88 | 8.91 | | 2,045.79 |
| 16. | 1,912.68 | 16.74 | | 1,929.42 |
| 17. | 670.68 | 7.04 | | 677.72 |
| 18. | 596.16 | 1.87 | | 598.03 |
| 19. | 24,690.96 | 64.81 | | 24,755.77 |
| 20. | 25,265.04 | 22.11 | | 25,287.15 |

### EXERCISE 165

1. $2.04 per $100; $115.24   2. $499.95   3. $1034.79   4. $480
5. $1.75 per $100   6. $9,902,424.13   7. $1,923,709.61   8. $4,515,910
9. $4,372,647.17   10. $298,349.03

## CHAPTER XXIV
## Insurance

INSURANCE is a coöperative arrangement whereby a large group of persons, by contributing comparatively small sums of money called premiums, enable the company to reimburse the losses of those members who belong to the group.

Insurance protection covers a very great number of different kinds of risks, including dangers from fire, factory labor, land and sea and air travel, accidents, storms, lightning, boiler explosions, sickness, death, etc. In this chapter we shall consider the two kinds of insurance that concern practically all of us—*fire insurance* and *life insurance*.

### I
### FIRE INSURANCE

The company which sells insurance, or protection against loss, is known as the *insurer*, or the *underwriter*. The property-owner who buys the protection is known as the *insured*.

The regular payment which the owner makes to the company for his protection is called the *premium*.

The contract made between the insurer and the insured is known as the *policy*.

The amount of the protection as given in the policy is called the *face of the policy*.

#### PREMIUM RATES

The premium rates for fire insurance depend upon what is known as the *fire hazard*. These rates vary in accordance with the nature of the building that is to be insured, its location, the use to which it is being put, and the protection which it possesses against destruction by fire. The rates are generally computed in terms of cents per $100 for 1 year.

# INSURANCE

Let us, for example, look at the following policies:

1.  | Amount of Policy | Rate per $100 | Years in Force | Total Premium Paid |
    |---|---|---|---|
    | $80,000 | $1.20 | 1 | ? |

    80,000 ÷ 100 = 800
    800 × $1.20 = $960 = total premium paid.
    Answer, $960.00

2.  | Amount of Policy | Rate per $100 | Years in Force | Total Premium Paid |
    |---|---|---|---|
    | $125,000 | $.90 | 3 | ? |

    125,000 ÷ 100 = 1250
    1250 × $.90 = $1125
    $1125 × 3 = $3375 = total premium paid.
    Answer, $3375.00

3.  | Value of Property | Face of Policy | Rate per $100 | Years in Force | Total Premium Paid |
    |---|---|---|---|---|
    | $70,000 | 80% of value | $1.10 | 5 | ? |

    80% of $70,000 = $56,000
    56,000 ÷ 100 = 560
    560 × $1.10 = $616
    $616 × 5 = $3080 = total premium paid.
    Answer, $3080.00

## EXERCISE 166

Find the total amount paid in premiums in each of the following problems:

| | Amount of Policy | Rate per $100 | Years in Force |
|---|---|---|---|
| 1. | $40,000 | $1.10 | 1 |
| 2. | 65,000 | 1.25 | 2 |
| 3. | 50,000 | .80 | 5 |
| 4. | 43,000 | .65 | 3 |
| 5. | 75,000 | .75 | 6 |
| 6. | 60,000 | 1.14 | 4 |
| 7. | 35,000 | 1.23 | 3 |
| 8. | 70,000 | .89 | 6 |
| 9. | 26,000 | 1.11 | 4 |
| 10. | 30,000 | .94 | 7 |

## EXERCISE 167

Find the total premiums in the following problems if the property is insured at only 80% of its full value:

| | Value of Property | Rate per $100 | Years in Force |
|---|---|---|---|
| 1. | $35,000 | $1.10 | 1 |
| 2. | 30,000 | 1.25 | 2 |
| 3. | 75,000 | .95 | 7 |
| 4. | 40,000 | 1.12 | 4 |
| 5. | 65,000 | .90 | 6 |
| 6. | 80,000 | 1.24 | 3 |
| 7. | 48,000 | 1.15 | 4 |
| 8. | 53,000 | .75 | 6 |
| 9. | 68,000 | .65 | 3 |
| 10. | 42,000 | .80 | 5 |

## CO-INSURANCE

In a large city a property-owner may sometimes feel that the municipal fire department is sufficiently effective to save him from heavy losses in the event of a fire. Supported by this feeling, he may decide to insure his property for only a small part of its value. This means a smaller premium investment on his own part, and consequently a larger risk for the insurance company. In order to protect themselves against this risk, most insurance companies insert a co-insurance clause in their policies. In accordance with this clause, the property-owner must either insure his property at a certain percentage of the value of the property, or else he must agree to share with the company in whatever losses may be caused to his property by fire.

For example:

1. A man has a piece of property valued at $100,000. He insures it for $50,000, or 50% of its value. The policy bears a co-insurance clause of 80%—that is, a clause to the effect that if the owner wants to be indemnified for the total loss caused by fire, he must insure his property for no less than 80% of its value. Suppose, now, there is a fire causing a loss of $40,000 to his property. How much of the loss will the company pay?

## INSURANCE

### Solution

Value of property....................................= $100,000
Insurance expected, 80% of $100,000..................= 80,000
Amount of insurance taken out, 50% of $100,000.......= 50,000
Loss caused by fire..................................= 40,000
The company will pay $\frac{50000}{80000}$ of $40,000, or         $25,000

The formula for co-insurance, therefore, is as follows:

$$\frac{\text{Insurance taken out}}{\text{Insurance expected}} \times \text{loss caused by fire} = \text{amount of insurance paid by company.}$$

2. The owner of a building valued at $120,000 insures it for $70,000. The policy contains an 80% co-insurance clause, and the premium is $.70 per $100. Fire causes a damage of $36,000. (a) What was the loss to the insurance company? (b) What was the loss to the policy-holder?

Value of property....................................= $120,000
Insurance expected, 80% of $120,000..................= 96,000
Amount of insurance taken out........................= 70,000
Damage caused by fire................................= 36,000
$\frac{70000}{96000} \times 36,000$ ................................= 26,250
Premium = $70,000 at $.70 per $100...................= 490
Company loses $26,250 − $490.........................= $ 25,760
Policy-owner loses $36,000 − $25,760.................= $10,240

Answer: (a) $25,760; (b) $10,240

When the percentage in the co-insurance clause is not specified, it is understood to equal 100%, or the total, of the assessed value. Let us, for example, consider the folllowing case:

3. The owner of a building valued at $150,000 insures it for $120,000. The policy contains a co-insurance clause, and the premium is $.85 per $100. Fire causes a damage of $78,000. (a) What was the loss to the insurance company? (b) What was the loss to the policy-holder?

Value of property....................................= $150,000
Insurance expected...................................= 150,000
Amount of insurance taken out........................= 120,000
Damage caused by fire................................= 78,000
$\frac{120000}{150000} \times 78,000$ ................................= 62,400
Premium = $120,000 at $.85 per $100..................= 1,020

Company loses $62,400 − $1,020 ............ = $61,380
Policy-owner loses $78,000 − $61,380 ............ = $16,620
Answer: (a) $61,380; (b) $16,620

## EXERCISE 168

Solve the following problems:

1. The owner of a building valued at $100,000 insures it for $60,000. The policy contains an 80% co-insurance clause, and the premium is $.90 per $100. Fire causes a damage of $40,000. (a) What was the loss to the insurance company? (b) What was the loss to the policy-holder.

2. The owner of a building valued at $80,000 insures it for $50,000. The policy contains an 80% co-insurance clause, and the premium is $.85 per $100. Fire causes a damage of $32,000. (a) What was the loss to the insurance company? (b) What was the loss to the policy-holder?

3. The owner of a building valued at $60,000 insures it for $35,000. The policy contains an 80% co-insurance clause, and the premium is $.70 per $100. Fire causes a damage of $18,000. (a) What was the loss to the insurance company? (b) What was the loss to the policy-holder?

4. The owner of a building valued at $40,000 insures it for $25,000. The policy contains an 80% co-insurance clause, and the premium is $.80 per $100. Fire causes a damage of $20,000. (a) What was the loss to the insurance company? (b) What was the loss to the policy-holder?

5. The owner of a building valued at $30,000 insures it for $20,000. The policy contains an 80% co-insurance clause, and the premium is $1.20 per $100. Fire causes a damage of $10,000. (a) What was the loss to the insurance company? (b) What was the loss to the policy-holder?

6. The owner of a building valued at $50,000 insures it for $30,000. The policy contains an 80% co-insurance clause, and the premium is $1.15 per $100. Fire causes a damage of $18,000. (a) What was the loss to the insurance company? (b) What was the loss to the policy-holder?

7. The owner of a building valued at $70,000 insures it for $50,000. The policy contains an 80% co-insurance clause, and the premium is $.95 per $100. Fire causes a damage of $24,000. (a) What was the loss to the insurance company? (b) What was the loss to the policy-holder?

8. The owner of a building valued at $90,000 insures it for $65,000.

# INSURANCE

The policy contains an 80% co-insurance clause, and the premium is $1.12 per $100. Fire causes a damage of $36,000. (a) What was the loss to the insurance company? (b) What was the loss to the policy-holder?

9. The owner of a building valued at $120,000 insures it for $85,000. The policy contains an 80% co-insurance clause, and the premium is $.93 per $100. Fire causes a damage of $48,000. (a) What was the loss to the insurance company? (b) What was the loss to the policy-holder?

10. The owner of a building valued at $140,000 insures it for $100,000. The policy contains an 80% co-insurance clause, and the premium is $1.14 per $100. Fire causes a damage of $84,000. (a) What was the loss to the insurance company? (b) What was the loss to the policy-holder?

## EXERCISE 169

Solve the following problems:

1. The owner of a building valued at $100,000 insures it for $70,000. The policy contains a co-insurance clause, and the premium is $.80 per $100. Fire causes a damage of $40,000. (a) What was the loss to the insurance company? (b) What was the loss to the policy-holder?

2. The owner of a building valued at $135,000 insures it for $90,000. The policy contains a co-insurance clause, and the premium is $1.04 per $100. Fire causes a damage of $72,000. (a) What was the loss to the insurance company? (b) What was the loss to the policy-holder?

3. The owner of a building valued at $125,000 insures it for $85,000. The policy contains a co-insurance clause, and the premium is $.83 per $100. Fire causes a damage of $40,000. (a) What was the loss to the insurance company? (b) What was the loss to the policy-holder?

4. The owner of a building valued at $95,000 insures it for $70,000. The policy contains a co-insurance clause, and the premium is $1.02 per $100. Fire causes a damage of $57,000. (a) What was the loss to the insurance company? (b) What was the loss to the policy-holder?

5. The owner of a building valued at $75,000 insures it for $60,000. The policy contains a co-insurance clause, and the premium is $.85 per $100. Fire causes a damage of $39,000. (a) What was the loss to the insurance company? (b) What was the loss to the policy-holder?

6. The owner of a building valued at $65,000 insures it for $50,000. The policy contains a co-insurance clause and the premium is $1.05 per $100. Fire causes a damage of $20,800. (a) What was the loss to the insurance company? (b) What was the loss to the policy-holder?

7. The owner of a building valued at $43,000 insures it for $35,000. The policy contains a co-insurance clause and the premium is $1.10 per $100. Fire causes a damage of $25,800. (a) What was the loss to the insurance company? (b) What was the loss to the policy-holder?

8. The owner of a building valued at $98,000 insures it for $80,000. The policy contains a co-insurance clause and the premium is $.70 per $100. Fire causes a damage of $34,300. (a) What was the loss to the insurance company? (b) What was the loss to the policy-holder?

9. The owner of a building valued at $67,000 insures it for $50,000. The policy contains a co-insurance clause and the premium is $.83 per $100. Fire causes a damage of $46,900. (a) What was the loss to the insurance company? (b) What was the loss to the policy-holder?

10. The owner of a building valued at $89,000 insures it for $60,000. The policy contains a co-insurance clause and the premium is $.64 per $100. Fire causes a damage of $53,400. (a) What was the loss to the insurance company? (b) What was the loss to the policy-holder?

## DIVISION OF LOSSES

The fire insurance on a building is often divided between two or more companies. In the event of a loss by fire, each company pays to the insured its proportional share of the loss.

For example:

The owner of a building valued at $60,000 insures it for $44,000 as follows: With Company A—for $8,000; with Company B—for $10,000; with Company C—for $12,000; with Company D—for $14,000. Fire causes a damage of $36,000. (a) How much does the owner get from each company if each policy contains an 80% co-insurance clause? (b) How much does he lose?

Value of property.................................... = $60,000
Insurance expected, 80% of $60,000.................. =  48,000
Total amount of insurance taken out................. =  44,000
Damage caused by fire............................... =  36,000
Total indemnity due owner, $\frac{44000}{48000} \times 36,000$ ............. =  33,000
Since owner insured his property with Company A
 for $8,000, Company A owes him $\frac{8000}{44000}$ of $33,000, or      $6,000

## INSURANCE

In like manner, Company B owes him $\frac{10000}{44000}$ of $33,000, or $7,500
" " " Company C owes him $\frac{12000}{44000}$ of $33,000, or $9,000
" " " Company D owes him $\frac{14000}{44000}$ of $33,000, or $10,500
Owner's loss = $36,000 − $33,000........................ = $3,000
    Answer: (a) $6,000; $7,500; $9,000; $10,500. (b) $3,000.

### EXERCISE 170

Solve the following problems:

1. The owner of a building valued at $30,000 insures it for $4000 with Company A; $5000 with Company B; $6000 with Company C; and $7000 with Company D. Fire causes a damage of $18,000. (a) How much is recoverable from each company if each policy contains an 80% co-insurance clause? (b) How much is lost by the owner?

2. The owner of a building valued at $80,000 containing merchandise valued at $24,000 insures both for $65,000 as follows: With Company A—$15,000; with Company B—$20,000; with Company C—$30,000. Fire causes a damage of $28,000 to the building and a total loss of the merchandise. (a) Find the amount recoverable from each insurance company if each policy had a co-insurance clause. (b) How much was lost by the owner?

3. How much could have been recovered from each company in Problem 2 if each policy contained an 80% co-insurance clause? (b) How much would have been lost by the owner?

4. The owner of a building valued at $40,000 containing merchandise valued at $12,000 insures both for 60% of their value. Fire causes a damage of $12,000 to the building and a loss of 70% of the contents. How much is recoverable from the insurance company if the policy contained an 80% co-insurance clause—(a) for the loss to the building? (b) for the loss to the contents? (c) What was the loss to the owner?

5. The owner of a building valued at $45,000 insured it for $35,000. The policy contained an 80% co-insurance clause and ran for 10 years at an annual premium of $1\frac{1}{4}$%. Just before the end of the tenth year, fire and water caused a 60% damage to the building. (a) Find the loss to the insurance company (disregard interest on the premiums). (b) Find the loss to the owner of the building.

### SHORT-TERM INSURANCE

When a policy is taken out for less than 1 year, the protection is called *short-term insurance*. The premium for a short-term policy is computed by means of a short-rate table such as the following:

SHORT-TERM RATES

| Policy Term | Per Cent of Annual Premium | Policy Term | Per Cent of Annual Premium |
|---|---|---|---|
| 1 day | 2 | 70 days | 36 |
| 2 days | 4 | 75 days | 37 |
| 3 days | 5 | 80 days | 38 |
| 4 days | 6 | 85 days | 39 |
| 5 days | 7 | 90 days | 40 |
| 6 days | 8 | 105 days | 46 |
| 8 days | 9 | 120 days | 50 |
| 10 days | 10 | 135 days | 56 |
| 12 days | 11 | 150 days | 60 |
| 13 days | 12 | 165 days | 65 |
| 15 days | 13 | 180 days | 70 |
| 16 days | 14 | 195 days | 73 |
| 17 days | 15 | 210 days | 75 |
| 19 days | 16 | 225 days | 78 |
| 20 days | 17 | 240 days | 80 |
| 25 days | 19 | 255 days | 83 |
| 30 days | 20 | 270 days | 85 |
| 35 days | 23 | 285 days | 88 |
| 40 days | 25 | 300 days | 90 |
| 45 days | 27 | 315 days | 93 |
| 50 days | 28 | 330 days | 95 |
| 55 days | 29 | 345 days | 98 |
| 60 days | 30 | 360 days | 100 |
| 65 days | 33 | | |

In using the above table, consider a month as 30 days. For any term not given in the table, such as 108 days, or 140 days, use the next longer term (120 days, or 150 days).

Find the cost of the premium in the following short-term policy:

| Amount of Policy | Rate | Time | Cost |
|---|---|---|---|
| $13,000 | $1\frac{1}{2}\%$ | 25 da. | ? |

Cost for 1 year = $\$13,000 \times 1\frac{1}{2}\% = \$13,000 \times \frac{3}{2} \times \frac{1}{100} = \$195$.
Cost for 25 days = 19% of cost for 1 year = $\frac{19}{100} \times \$195 = \$37.05$

Answer, $37.05

# INSURANCE

## EXERCISE 171

Find the cost of the premium in each of the following cases of short-term insurance.

| | Amount of Policy | Rate | Time | Cost |
|---|---|---|---|---|
| 1. | $16,000 | $\frac{5}{8}$% | 10 days | .......... |
| 2. | 36,000 | $\frac{3}{4}$% | 1 month | .......... |
| 3. | 24,000 | $\frac{7}{8}$% | 15 days | .......... |
| 4. | 48,000 | $1\frac{5}{8}$% | 4 months | .......... |
| 5. | 24,800 | $1\frac{1}{8}$% | 20 days | .......... |
| 6. | 46,400 | $1\frac{3}{8}$% | 2 months | .......... |
| 7. | 26,000 | $1\frac{1}{2}$% | 25 days | .......... |
| 8. | 56,000 | $\frac{7}{8}$% | 5 months | .......... |
| 9. | 32,000 | $\frac{5}{8}$% | 3 months | .......... |
| 10. | 73,100 | $1\frac{1}{4}$% | 8 months | .......... |

## CANCELLATION OF INSURANCE

Sometimes an insurance company cancels a policy before the term expires. In that case, the company retains only that portion of the premium which corresponds to the length of the time during which the policy has been in force. It returns the balance of the premium to the policy-holder.

For example:

Find the amount of the premium which must be returned to the policy-holder in the following case:

| Amount of Policy | Rate | Time | Amount Returned |
|---|---|---|---|
| $48,000 | $1.25 per $100 (or $1\frac{1}{4}$%) | 1 month | ? |

$48,000 \times \frac{5}{4} \times \frac{1}{100} = \$600 =$ premium for 1 year

The policy is in force 1 month, or $\frac{1}{12}$ of 1 year

The policy is *not* in force 11 months, or $\frac{11}{12}$ of 1 year

Hence the company returns $\frac{11}{12}$ of $600, or $550.

## EXERCISE 172

In each of the following cases the insurance company cancels the policy at the end of the indicated time. Find the amount of the premium which must be returned by the insurance company to the policy-holder.

| | Amount of Policy | Rate | Time |
|---|---|---|---|
| 1. | $96,000 | $1\frac{1}{4}\%$ | 1 month |
| 2. | 19,200 | $\frac{7}{8}\%$ | 5 months |
| 3. | 57,600 | $1\frac{3}{8}\%$ | 2 months |
| 4. | 15,600 | $1\frac{5}{8}\%$ | 8 months |
| 5. | 16,800 | $\frac{5}{8}\%$ | 3 months |

## II
## LIFE INSURANCE

Generally speaking, there are three kinds of life insurance policies—the *ordinary life policy*, the *limited-payment life policy*, and the *endowment policy*.

The *ordinary life policy*, sometimes called the *whole-life policy*, is one in which the policy-holder agrees to pay to the insurance company a specified premium each year until his death, and the insurance company agrees to pay the face of the policy to the beneficiary at the death of the policy-holder.

The *limited-payment life policy*, generally known as the *ten-payment life*, the *twenty-payment life*, the *thirty-payment life*, etc., is a policy in which the policy-holder agrees to pay a specified premium each year for a specified number of years (10, 20, or 30), and the company agrees to pay the face of the policy at the death of the policy-holder. The premiums on the *limited-payment life policy* are naturally higher than those on the ordinary life policy.

The *endowment policy* is one in which the policy-holder agrees to pay premiums for a fixed number of years, and the company agrees to pay the face of the policy to the beneficiary if the policy-holder dies before the completion of the specified period, or to the policy-holder himself if he is still alive at the completion of the specified period. The premiums on the endowment policy are higher than on either of the other two policies described above.

## PREMIUM RATES

The premium rates on all kinds of insurance may be computed from tables issued by the various companies. The following tables, for example, will show you at a glance just how much per $1000 you will have to pay annually if you take out any kind of insurance at any age between 20 and 40:

### TABLE I

*Ordinary Life Policies and Limited-Payment Life Policies*

Schedule of Annual Premium Rates per $1000.

| Age | Annual Premium (Ordinary Life) | 10 Annual Premiums (Limited Payment) | 20 Annual Premiums (Limited Payment) |
|---|---|---|---|
| 20 | $17.80 | $46.70 | $27.66 |
| 21 | 18.20 | 47.38 | 28.07 |
| 22 | 18.60 | 48.08 | 28.50 |
| 23 | 19.03 | 48.81 | 28.94 |
| 24 | 19.47 | 49.55 | 29.40 |
| 25 | 19.94 | 50.33 | 29.88 |
| 26 | 20.42 | 51.13 | 30.37 |
| 27 | 20.95 | 51.95 | 30.88 |
| 28 | 21.49 | 52.81 | 31.41 |
| 29 | 22.06 | 53.69 | 31.96 |
| 30 | 22.64 | 54.60 | 32.52 |
| 31 | 23.27 | 55.54 | 33.11 |
| 32 | 23.94 | 56.51 | 33.73 |
| 33 | 24.64 | 57.51 | 34.37 |
| 34 | 25.38 | 58.55 | 35.03 |
| 35 | 26.15 | 59.62 | 35.72 |
| 36 | 26.96 | 60.73 | 36.44 |
| 37 | 27.83 | 61.87 | 37.20 |
| 38 | 28.75 | 63.06 | 37.98 |
| 39 | 29.72 | 64.28 | 38.81 |
| 40 | 30.70 | 65.52 | 39.66 |

## Table II
### Endowment Policies

| Age | 10 Year Endowment | 15 Year Endowment | 20 Year Endowment | 25 Year Endowment |
|---|---|---|---|---|
| 20 | $104.30 | $66.78 | $48.43 | $37.72 |
| 21 | 104.34 | 66.82 | 48.48 | 37.78 |
| 22 | 104.37 | 66.87 | 48.53 | 37.85 |
| 23 | 104.41 | 66.91 | 48.58 | 37.92 |
| 24 | 104.45 | 66.96 | 48.64 | 38.00 |
| 25 | 104.49 | 67.01 | 48.71 | 38.08 |
| 26 | 104.53 | 67.07 | 48.78 | 38.17 |
| 27 | 104.58 | 67.13 | 48.86 | 38.27 |
| 28 | 104.63 | 67.20 | 48.95 | 38.38 |
| 29 | 104.68 | 67.27 | 49.04 | 38.50 |
| 30 | 104.74 | 67.35 | 49.14 | 38.64 |
| 31 | 104.81 | 67.44 | 49.26 | 38.79 |
| 32 | 104.89 | 67.54 | 49.39 | 38.97 |
| 33 | 104.98 | 67.64 | 49.53 | 39.16 |
| 34 | 105.06 | 67.76 | 49.68 | 39.37 |
| 35 | 105.16 | 67.88 | 49.86 | 39.61 |
| 36 | 105.26 | 68.02 | 50.06 | 39.88 |
| 37 | 105.38 | 68.18 | 50.28 | 40.18 |
| 38 | 105.51 | 68.37 | 50.53 | 40.51 |
| 39 | 105.65 | 68.56 | 50.80 | 40.89 |
| 40 | 105.80 | 68.76 | 51.08 | 41.29 |

With the help of the above tables, let us look at the following examples:

1. A young man of 25 takes out an ordinary life policy for $3000. What annual premium does he pay?

The annual premium rate for $1000 on an ordinary life policy at the age of 25 (table I) is $19.94.

The annual premium for $3000 is $\frac{3000}{1000} \times \$19.94 = 3 \times \$19.94 = \$59.82$.

2. A young woman of 21 takes out a ten-year endowment policy for $7500. What annual premium does she pay?

The annual premium rate for $1000 on a ten-year endowment policy at the age of 21 (table II) is $104.34.

The annual premium for $7500 = \$104.34 \times \frac{7500}{1000} = \$104.34 \times 7.5 = \$782.55$.

# INSURANCE

3. A man aged 30 takes out a twenty-payment life insurance policy for $6000. What annual premium does he pay?

The annual premium rate for $1000 on a twenty-payment life policy at the age of 30 (table I) is $32.52.

The annual premium for $6000 = \$32.52 \times \frac{6000}{1000} = \$32.52 \times 6 = \$195.12$.

From the foregoing examples, we get this formula:

$$\text{Annual Premium} = \text{Rate per } \$1000 \times \frac{\text{Face Amount of Policy}}{\$1000}$$

That is, $P = R \times \frac{F}{1000}$, or $P = \frac{RF}{1000}$

Using this formula, let us now try to solve the following examples:

4. A man of 33 takes out a twenty-five-year endowment policy and pays an annual premium of $166.43. What is the face amount of the policy?

Annual rate for $1000 on a 25-year endowment policy at 33 = $39.16

$P = \frac{RF}{1000}$

$\$166.43 = \frac{39.16 \times F}{1000}$

$\$166,430 = 39.16F$

$F = \$166,430 \div 39.16 = \$4250.$

Answer, $4250.

5. A woman takes out a twenty-year endowment policy for $18000 and pays an annual premium of $882.72. What is her age when she takes out the policy?

$P = \frac{RF}{1000}$

$\$882.72 = \frac{18000R}{1000}$

$\$882.72 = 18R$

$R = \$49.04$

Referring to table II, we find that $49.04 is the 20-year endowment rate at the age of 29.

6. A man of 24 takes out an $8000 policy and pays an annual premium of $535.68. What type of policy does he take out?

$$P = \frac{RF}{1000}$$
$$\$535.68 = \frac{8000R}{1000}$$
$$\$535.68 = 8R$$
$$R = \$66.96$$

Referring to our tables, we find that the annual rate of $66.96 at the age of 24 represents a 15-year endowment policy.

## EXERCISE 173

Solve the following problems:

1. A young man of 20 takes out an ordinary life insurance policy for $2000. What annual premium does he pay?

2. A teacher aged 27 takes out a 10-payment life insurance policy for $5500. What annual premium does he pay?

3. A business man aged 31 takes out a twenty-payment life insurance policy for $8000. What annual premium does he pay?

4. A young woman aged 21 takes out a ten-year endowment policy for $2500. What annual premium does she pay?

5. A doctor aged 32 takes out a fifteen-year endowment policy for $6,000. What annual premium does he pay?

6. A lawyer aged 28 takes out an ordinary life insurance policy for $12,000. What annual premium does he pay?

7. A young man aged 22 takes out a 20-year endowment policy for $3000. What annual premium does he pay?

8. A business man aged 33 takes out a 25-year endowment policy and pays an annual premium of $332.86. What is the face amount of the policy?

9. A dentist aged 36 takes out a ten-year endowment policy and pays an annual premium of $1578.90. What is the face amount of the policy?

10. A young man aged 23 takes out a ten-payment life insurance policy and pays an annual premium of $170.84. What is the face amount of the policy?

11. A business man takes out a 25-year endowment policy for $6500 and pays an annual premium of $261.17. What is his age when he takes out the policy?

12. A teacher takes out a 20-year endowment policy for $9000 and

# INSURANCE

pays an annual premium of $441.36. What is his age when he takes out the policy?

13. A young business executive aged 24 takes out a $16000 life insurance policy and pays an annual premium of $1071.36. What type of policy does he take out?

14. A business man aged 34 takes out an ordinary life insurance policy and pays an annual premium of $101.52. What is the face amount of his policy?

15. A doctor takes out a 20-payment life insurance policy for $7000 and pays an annual premium of $265.86. What is his age at the time he takes out the policy?

16. A teacher aged 25 takes out a life insurance policy for $10,000 and pays an annual premium of $1044.90. What type of policy does he take out?

17. A lawyer aged 39 takes out a life insurance policy for $4500 and pays an annual premium of $228.60. What type of policy does he take out?

18. A business man aged 35 takes out a 10-payment life insurance policy and pays an annual premium of $447.15. What is the face amount of his policy?

19. A lawyer aged 26 takes out a 15-year endowment policy and pays an annual premium of $737.77. What is the face amount of his policy?

20. A business man aged 30 takes out a 20-payment life insurance policy and pays an annual premium of $162.60. What is the face amount of his policy?

## ANSWERS
### EXERCISE 166

1. $440.00  2. $1625.00  3. $2000.00  4. $838.50
5. $3375.00  6. $2736.00  7. $1291.50  8. $3738.00
9. $1154.40  10. $1974.00

### EXERCISE 167

1. $308.00  2. $600.00  3. $3990.00  4. $1433.60
5. $2340.00  6. $2380.80  7. $1766.40  8. $1908.00
9. $1060.80  10. $1344.00

### EXERCISE 168

1. (a) $29,460.00  (b) $10,540      2. (a) $24,575.00  (b) $7,425.00
3. (a) $12,880.00  (b) $5,120.00    4. (a) $15,425.00  (b) $4,575.00
5. (a) $8,093.33   (b) $1,906.67    6. (a) $13,155.00  (b) $4,845.00
7. (a) $20,953.57  (b) $3,046.43    8. (a) $31,772.00  (b) $4,228.00
9. (a) $41,709.50  (b) $6,290.50    10. (a) $73,860.00 (b) $10,140.00

## EXERCISE 169

1. (a) $27,440.00  (b) $12,560.00
2. (a) $47,064.00  (b) $24,936.00
3. (a) $26,494.50  (b) $13,505.50
4. (a) $41,286.00  (b) $15,714.00
5. (a) $30,690.00  (b) $8,310.00
6. (a) $15,475.00  (b) $5,325.00
7. (a) $20,615.00  (b) $5,185.00
8. (a) $27,440.00  (b) $6,860.00
9. (a) $34,585.00  (b) $12,315.00
10. (a) $35,616.00  (b) $17,784.00

## EXERCISE 170

1. (a) Company A, $3,000.00  Company B, $3,750.00.  Company C, $4,500.00. Company D, $5,250.00.  (b) $1500.00.
2. (a) Company A, $7,500.00.  Company B, $10,000.000  Company C, $15,000.00. (b) $19,500.00.
3. (a) Company A, $9,375.00.  Company B, $12,500.00.  Company C, $18,750.00. (b) $11,375.00.
4. (a) $9,000.00.  (b) $6,300.00.  (c) $5,100.00.
5. (a) $21,875.00.  (b) $5,125.00.

## EXERCISE 171

1. $10.00
2. $54.00
3. $27.30
4. $390.00
5. $47.43
6. $191.40
7. $74.10
8. $294.00
9. $80.00
10. $731.00

## EXERCISE 172

1. $1100
2. $98.00
3. $660.00
4. $84.50
5. $78.75

## EXERCISE 173

1. $35.60
2. $285.73
3. $264.88
4. $260.85
5. $405.24
6. $257.88
7. $145.59
8. $8500
9. $15,000
10. $3500
11. 37 years
12. 29 years
13. 15-year endowment
14. $4000
15. 38 years
16. 10-year endowment
17. 20-year endowment
18. $7500
19. $11,000
20. $5000

## CHAPTER XXV
## Advertising

BUSINESS MEN are frequently called upon to figure out the cost of a certain advertisement, to determine how much space they can get for a specified sum, and to calculate the possible profit or loss that may result from a proposed advertisement in a newspaper or magazine.

Newspaper advertising is generally computed in agate lines. *Agate* is a term used in printing. It represents a type so small that 14 printed lines can go into a space of one inch. Hence an advertising space 1 inch long and 1 column wide is said to consist of 14 agate lines. Advertising rates are as a rule based upon that unit. An advertisement is said to cost such-and-such a sum *per agate line*, or 14 times that sum *per inch*.

For example:

A business man places an advertisement 3 columns wide and 5 inches deep in a newspaper which charges $.65 per agate line. As a result of this advertisement, he sells 200 units of merchandise at $2.73 per unit. Find:

(a) The cost of the advertisement.
(b) The advertising cost per unit sold.
(c) The advertising cost as a percentage of the selling price.

(a) Space taken for advertisement = 3×5 inches = 15 inches
    Number of agate lines = 15×14 = 210 lines
    Cost of the advertisement = 210×$.65 = $136.50
(b) Advertising cost per unit = $136.50 ÷ 200 = $.68¼
(c) Selling price = 200×$2.73 = $546.00
    Advertising cost = $\frac{\$136.50}{\$546.00}$ = $.25 = 25%

Answer: (a) $136.50; (b) $.68¼; (c) 25%.

### EXERCISE 174

Solve the following problems:

1. A man places an advertisement two columns wide and four inches deep in a metropolitan newspaper which charges $.95 per agate

line. As a result of the advertisement, he sells 118 units of merchandise at $4.00 per unit. Find (a) the cost of the advertisement, (b) the advertising cost per unit sold and (c) the advertising cost as a percentage of the selling price.

2. A man places an advertisement four columns wide and nine inches deep in a country newspaper which charges $.12 per agate line. As a result of the advertisement, he sells 84 units of merchandise at $3.50 per unit. Find (a) the cost of the advertisement, (b) the advertising cost per unit sold and (c) the advertising cost as a percentage of the selling price.

3. A man places an advertisement three columns wide and eight inches deep in a Sunday issue of a metropolitan newspaper at a rate of $1.05 per agate line. As a result of the advertisement, he sells 25 units of merchandise at $75.00 each. Find (a) the cost of the advertisement, (b) the advertising cost per unit sold and (c) the advertising cost as a percentage of the selling price.

4. A man places an advertisement two columns wide and six inches deep in a country newspaper at the rate of $.12 per agate line. As a result of the advertisement, he sells 80 units of merchandise at $1.50 each. Find (a) the cost of the advertisement, (b) the advertising cost per unit sold and (c) the advertising cost as a percentage of the selling price.

5. A man places an advertisement one column wide and five inches deep in the Sunday issue of a metropolitan newspaper at a rate of $1.05 per agate line. As a result of the advertisement he sells 500 units of merchandise at $.50 each. Find (a) the cost of the advertisement, (b) the advertising cost per unit sold and (c) the advertising cost as a percentage of the selling price.

6. A man places an advertisement three columns wide and seven inches deep in a metropolitan newspaper at the rate of $.95 per agate line. As a result of the advertisement he sells 72 units of merchandise at $10.00 each. Find (a) the cost of the advertisement, (b) the advertising cost per unit sold and (c) the advertising cost as a percentage of the selling price.

7. A man places an advertisement one column wide and three inches deep in a metropolitan newspaper at the rate of $.95 per agate line. As a result of the advertisement he sells 19 units of merchandise at $5.00 each. Find (a) the cost of the advertisement, (b) the advertising cost per unit sold and (c) the advertising cost as a percentage of the selling price.

8. A man places an advertisement two columns wide and five inches deep in the Sunday edition of a metropolitan newspaper at the rate of

# ADVERTISING

$1.05 per agate line. As a result of the advertisement he sells 46 units of merchandise at $8.00 each. Find (a) the cost of the advertisement, (b) the advertising cost per unit sold and (c) the advertising cost as a percentage of the selling price.

9. A man places an advertisement two columns wide and seven inches deep in a country newspaper at the rate of $.12 per agate line. As a result of the advertisement he sells 160 units of merchandise at $.75 each. Find (a) the cost of the advertisement, (b) the advertising cost per unit sold and (c) the advertising cost as a percentage of the selling price.

10. A man places an advertisement two columns wide and five inches deep in a country newspaper at the rate of $.12 per agate line. As a result of the advertisement he sells 216 units of merchandise at $.50 each. Find (a) the cost of the advertisement, (b) the advertising cost per unit sold and (c) the advertising cost as a percentage of the selling price.

If you want to keep the cost of an advertisement down to a definite percentage of the expected sales resulting from that advertisement, how do you figure out the cost?

Let us take a specific case:

A man places an advertisement 4 columns wide and 4 inches deep in a newspaper at a cost of $.85 per agate line. The merchandise advertised is sold at $5.00 per unit and 15% of the selling price is allowable for advertising. Find:

(a) The cost of the advertisement.
(b) The advertising cost (in dollars and cents) per unit of merchandise.
(c) The number of units which must be sold if the advertising cost is not to exceed the allowed 15%. (Count any fraction as a complete unit.)

(a) Cost of advertisement = 4×4×14×$.85     = $190.40
(b) Advertising cost per unit = 15% of $5.00     = $.75
(c) Total cost of advertisement, or $190.40,
    = 15% of total sales necessary
  Hence total sales necessary = $190.40 ÷ 15%     = $1269.33
  Number of units to be sold = $1269.33 ÷ $5.00     = 254
        Answer: (a) $190.40; (b) $.75; (c) 254.

## EXERCISE 175

Solve the following problems:

1. A man places an advertisement three columns wide and five inches deep in a metropolitan newspaper at a cost of $.95 per agate line. The merchandise advertised is sold at $4.00 per unit and 19% of the selling price is allowable for advertising. Find (a) the cost of the advertisement, (b) the advertising cost (in dollars and cents) per unit of merchandise, and (c) the number of units which must be sold if the advertising cost is not to exceed the allowed 19%. (Count any fraction as a complete unit.)

2. A man places an advertisement four columns wide and three inches deep in a metropolitan newspaper at a cost of $.95 per agate line. The merchandise advertised is sold at $5.00 per unit and 11% of the selling price is allowable for the advertising. Find (a) the cost of the advertisement, (b) the advertising cost (in dollars and cents) per unit of merchandise, and (c) the number of units of merchandise which must be sold if the advertising cost is not to exceed the allowed 11%.

3. A man places an advertisement five columns wide and eight inches deep in a country newspaper at a cost of $.12 per agate line. The merchandise advertised is sold at $2.50 per unit and 12% of the selling price is allowable for the advertising. Find (a) the cost of the advertisement, (b) the advertising cost per unit of merchandise, and (c) the number of units of merchandise which must be sold if the advertising cost is not to exceed the allowed 12%.

4. A man places an advertisement one column wide and four inches deep in a metropolitan newspaper at a cost of $.95 per agate line. The merchandise advertised is sold at $1.75 per unit and 16% of the selling price is allowable for the advertising. Find (a) the cost of the advertisement, (b) the advertising cost per unit of merchandise, and (c) the number of units of merchandise which must be sold if the advertising cost is not to exceed the allowed 16%.

5. A man places an advertisement two columns wide and three inches deep in the Sunday edition of a metropolitan newspaper at a cost of $1.05 per agate line. The merchandise advertised is sold at $6.00 per unit and 13% of the selling price is allowable for the advertising. Find (a) the cost of the advertisement, (b) the advertising cost per unit of merchandise and (c) the number of units of merchandise which must be sold if the advertising cost is not to exceed the allowed 13%.

6. A man places an advertisement four columns wide and six inches

deep in a metropolitan newspaper at a cost of $.95 per agate line. The merchandise advertised is sold at $15.00 per unit and 18% of the selling price is allowable for the advertising. Find (a) the cost of the advertisement, (b) the advertising cost per unit of merchandise and (c) the number of units of merchandise which must be sold if the advertising cost is not to exceed the allowed 18%.

7. A man places an advertisement five columns wide and six inches deep in a country newspaper at a cost of $.12 per agate line. The merchandise advertised is sold at $.75 per unit and 12% of the selling price is allowable for the advertising. Find (a) the cost of the advertisement, (b) the advertising cost per unit of merchandise and (c) the number of units of merchandise which must be sold if the advertising cost is not to exceed the allowed 12%.

8. A man places an advertisement four columns wide and five inches deep in the Sunday edition of a metropolitan newspaper at a cost of $1.05 per agate line. The merchandise advertised is sold at $45.00 per unit and 17% of the selling price is allowable for the advertising. Find (a) the cost of the advertisement, (b) the advertising cost per unit of merchandise and (c) the number of units of merchandise which must be sold if the advertising cost is not to exceed the allowed 17%.

9. A man places an advertisement three columns wide and six inches deep in a metropolitan newspaper at a cost of $.95 per agate line. The merchandise advertised is sold at $50.00 per unit and 15% of the selling price is allowable for the advertising. Find (a) the cost of the advertisement, (b) the advertising cost per unit of merchandise and (c) the number of units of merchandise which must be sold if the advertising cost is not to exceed the allowed 15%.

10. A man places an advertisement six columns wide and eight inches deep in a country newspaper at a cost of $.12 per agate line. The merchandise advertised is sold at $.50 per unit and 10% of the selling price is allowable for the advertising. Find (a) the cost of the advertisement, (b) the advertising cost per unit of merchandise and (c) the number of units of merchandise which must be sold if the advertising cost is not to exceed the allowed 10%.

## ANSWERS
### EXERCISE 174

|    | (a)      | (b)    | (c)   |
|----|----------|--------|-------|
| 1. | $106.40  | $ .90  | 22.5% |
| 2. | 60.48    | .72    | 20.6% |
| 3. | 352.80   | 14.11  | 18.8% |
| 4. | 20.16    | .25    | 16.7% |
| 5. | 73.50    | .15    | 29.4% |
| 6. | 279.30   | 3.89   | 38.9% |
| 7. | 39.90    | 2.10   | 42%   |
| 8. | 147.00   | 3.20   | 40%   |
| 9. | 23.52    | .15    | 19.6% |
| 10.| 16.80    | .08    | 15.6% |

### EXERCISE 175

|    | (a)      | (b)    | (c)  |
|----|----------|--------|------|
| 1. | $199.50  | $ .76  | 263  |
| 2. | 159.60   | .55    | 291  |
| 3. | 67.20    | .30    | 224  |
| 4. | 53.20    | .28    | 190  |
| 5. | 88.20    | .78    | 114  |
| 6. | 319.20   | 2.70   | 119  |
| 7. | 50.40    | .09    | 560  |
| 8. | 294.00   | 7.65   | 39   |
| 9. | 239.40   | 7.50   | 36   |
| 10.| 80.64    | .05    | 1613 |

## CHAPTER XXVI
# Problems of Manufacturers

### DEPRECIATION

EVERY MANUFACTURER owns various things—such as machinery, or equipment, or buildings, or fixtures—which constantly depreciate in value. For example, a shoe manufacturer buys machinery for $50,000. He may use this machinery for about 12 years, and then he may be obliged to scrap it as useless or to sell it at a very small fraction of its original cost. When he buys the machinery, he has in his factory something which is worth $50,000. At the end of the first year, it is worth less than $50,000; at the end of the second year, less than at the end of the first year; at the end of the third year, less than at the end of the second year; and so on.

In order to allow for this depreciation, the wise manufacturer lays aside each year a certain sum of money to cover the depreciation. The simplest way to determine this annual depreciation, is to use the *constant-value method*. By this method the amount of depreciation is regarded as constant, or equal, during each year of the depreciation. The difference between the original cost and the value at the end is distributed equally over the estimated number of years.

For example:

A manufacturer buys an office building for $63,000. The building has a life of 25 years and a salvage value of $7875. (a) How much does its value depreciate each year? (b) What is the percent of annual depreciation? (c) What is the book value of the building after 10 years?

(a) The total depreciation of the building is the original cost less the salvage value at the end.

That is, total depreciation = $63,000 − $7875 = 55,125

$$\text{Annual depreciation} = \frac{\$55,125}{25} = \$2205.$$

(b) The percent of annual depreciation is the annual depreciation divided by the original cost.

That is, percent of annual depreciation $=\dfrac{2205}{63{,}000}=3.5\%$

(c) The book value of the building after 10 years is the original cost of the building less the depreciation for 10 years.

That is, value after 10 years $=\$63{,}000-(\$2205\times 10)=\$40{,}950$.

Answer: (a) $2205; (b) 3.5%; (c) $40,950.

## EXERCISE 176

Solve the following problems:

1. A manufacturer buys machinery for $36,000.00. If the machinery has a life of 12 years and a scrap value of $4500.00, (a) how much does its value depreciate each year, (b) what is the percent of annual depreciation and (c) what is the book value of the machinery after 5 years?

2. A manufacturer buys a truck for $1,500.00. If the truck has a life of 6 years and a trade-in value of $150.00, (a) how much does its value depreciate each year, (b) what is the percent of annual depreciation and (c) what is the book value of the truck after 5 years?

3. A manufacturer buys an office building for $84,000.00. If the building has a life of 25 years and a salvage value of $10,500.00, (a) how much does its value depreciate each year, (b) what is the percent of annual depreciation and (c) what is the book value of the building after 5 years?

4. A manufacturer buys a factory building for $19,600.00. If the building has a life of 20 years and a salvage value of $3,920.00, (a) how much does its value depreciate each year, (b) what is the percent of annual depreciation and (c) what is the book value of the building after 5 years?

5. A manufacturer buys machinery for $14,080.00. If the machinery has a life of 16 years and a scrap value of $5,280.00, (a) how much does its value depreciate each year, (b) what is the percent of annual depreciation and (c) what is the book value of the machinery after 5 years?

6. A manufacturer buys machinery for $23,250.00. If the machinery has a life of 10 years and a scrap value of $3,875.00, (a) how much does its value depreciate each year, (b) what is the percent of annual depreciation and (c) what is the book value of the machinery after 5 years?

7. A manufacturer buys machinery for $15,000.00. If the machin-

## PROBLEMS OF MANUFACTURERS

ery has a life of 18 years and a scrap value of $2,850.00, (a) how much does its value depreciate each year, (b) what is the percent of annual depreciation and (c) what is the book value of the machinery after 5 years?

8. A manufacturer buys a factory building for $72,525. If the building has a life of 15 years and a salvage value of $14,505, (a) how much does its value depreciate each year, (b) what is the percent of annual depreciation and (c) what is the book value of the building after 5 years?

9. A manufacturer buys furniture for $2,850.00. If the furniture has a life of 14 years and junk value of $456.00, (a) how much does its value depreciate each year, (b) what is the percent of annual depreciation and (c) what is the book value of the furniture after 5 years?

10. A manufacturer buys machinery for $12,000.00. If the machinery has a life of 19 years and a scrap value of $1740.00, (a) how much does its value depreciate each year, (b) what is the percent of annual depreciation and (c) what is the book value of the machinery after 5 years?

### FACTORY COSTS

When a manufacturer who produces neckties wants to compute the factory-cost of each necktie, he must include in this factory-cost such items as the cost of the raw material, the cost of labor, the overhead, etc. Then he must divide the total of these costs by the number of neckties he produces.

Let us, for example, look at the following case:

| Cost of Raw Material | Cost of Labor | Overhead (Based on Cost of Material Plus Cost of Labor) | Number of Ties Manufactured | Cost of Each Tie |
|---|---|---|---|---|
| $29,136 | $42,864 | $11\frac{1}{9}\%$ | 320,000 | ? |

Overhead = $11\frac{1}{9}\%$ of $29,136 + $42,864 = $8000
Total Cost = $29,136 + $42,864 + $8000 = $80,000
Cost per Tie = $80,000 ÷ 320,000 = $.25

Answer, $.25

## EXERCISE 177

In each of the following problems the overhead is expressed as a percent of the prime cost (cost of raw materials plus the cost of direct labor). Find the factory cost of each article manufactured.

|  | Cost of Raw Material | Cost of Direct Labor | Overhead | Number Manufactured |
|---|---|---|---|---|
| 1. | $ 7,634.40 | $2,365.60 | 10% | 1100 |
| 2. | 3,567.00 | 4,433.00 | $12\frac{1}{2}$% | 720 |
| 3. | 1,943.00 | 4,057.00 | $8\frac{1}{3}$% | 1300 |
| 4. | 2,856.00 | 5,144.00 | $6\frac{1}{4}$% | 3400 |
| 5. | 8,674.00 | 11,326.00 | 15% | 4000 |
| 6. | 3,896.00 | 8,104.00 | $16\frac{2}{3}$% | 35,000 |
| 7. | 7,284.00 | 10,716.00 | $11\frac{1}{9}$% | 80,000 |
| 8. | 11,867.00 | 23,133.00 | $14\frac{2}{7}$% | 16,000 |
| 9. | 8,395.00 | 13,605.00 | $9\frac{1}{11}$% | 1200 |
| 10. | 14,472.00 | 17,528.00 | $18\frac{3}{4}$% | 4000 |

### ANSWERS
#### EXERCISE 176

1. (a) $2,625.00     (b) 7.29%         (c) $22,875.00
2. (a) $225.00       (b) 15%           (c) $375.00
3. (a) $2,940.00     (b) $3\frac{1}{2}$%    (c) $69,300.00
4. (a) $784.00       (b) 4%            (c) $15,680.00
5. (a) $550.00       (b) $3\frac{28}{32}$%  (c) $11,330.00
6. (a) $1,937.50     (b) $8\frac{1}{3}$%    (c) $13,562.50
7. (a) $675.00       (b) $4\frac{1}{2}$%    (c) $11,625.00
8. (a) $3,868.00     (b) $5\frac{1}{3}$%    (c) $53,185.00
9. (a) $171.00       (b) 6%            (c) $1,995.00
10. (a) $540.00      (b) $4\frac{1}{2}$%    (c) $9,300.00

#### EXERCISE 177

1. $10.00   2. $12.50   3. $5.00   4. $2.50
5. $5.75    6. $.40     7. $.25    8. $2.50
9. $20.00   10. $9.50

## CHAPTER XXVII
# Problems of Wholesalers and Retailers
## A
### PROBLEMS OF WHOLESALERS

A JOBBER BUYS AN AUTOMOBILE listed at $1408 with trade discounts of 20%, $16\frac{2}{3}$%, $16\frac{2}{3}$%, and 10%. He wants to sell it to the retailer at a profit of $33\frac{1}{3}$% based on the cost to the retailer and must mark it so as to realize that profit and still allow a trade discount of 20% to his customer. Find: (a) His real selling price—that is, the cost to the retailer. (b) The price at which he actually marks it.

(a) He buys the automobile for $1408 less 20%, less $16\frac{2}{3}$%, less $16\frac{2}{3}$%, less 10%.

That is, he buys the automobile for $1408 × (100% − 20% − $16\frac{2}{3}$% − $16\frac{2}{3}$% − 10%)  = $1408 × 50% = $704

He wants to sell the automobile at a profit of $33\frac{1}{3}$% based on the cost to the retailer.

Cost to the retailer = 100% of itself.
Price jobber paid for it = 100% − $33\frac{1}{3}$% of the cost to the retailer.
Price jobber paid for it = $66\frac{2}{3}$% of the cost to the retailer.
$704 = $66\frac{2}{3}$%, or $\frac{2}{3}$ of the cost to the retailer.
Cost to the retailer = $704 ÷ $\frac{2}{3}$ = $1056.

(b) Jobber marks the automobile at 20% higher than the price to the retailer.

Price marked = 100% of itself.
Price to retailer = 100% − 20% of marked price.
$1056 = 80%, or $\frac{4}{5}$ of marked price.
Marked price = $1056 ÷ $\frac{4}{5}$ = $1320
Answer: (a) $1056; (b) $1320.

### EXERCISE 178

Solve the following problems:

Note: In each of these ten problems, "the cost" or "the net cost" means the *cost to the retailer*.

1. A jobber buys a typewriter listed at $128.00 with trade discounts of 20%, $16\frac{2}{3}$%, $16\frac{2}{3}$% and 10%. He wishes to sell it at a profit

of $33\frac{1}{3}\%$ based on the cost and must mark it so as to realize that profit and still allow a trade discount of 20% to his customer. Find: (a) His real selling price. (b) The price at which he actually marks it.

2. A jobber buys a radio listed at $45.00 with trade discounts of 20%, $16\frac{2}{3}\%$ and $16\frac{2}{3}\%$. He wishes to sell it at a profit of $37\frac{1}{2}\%$ of the net cost and must mark it so as to allow a discount of $16\frac{2}{3}\%$. Find: (a) His intended selling price. (b) The price at which he actually marks it.

3. A jobber buys a set of dishes listed at $24.00 with trade discounts of 25% and $16\frac{2}{3}\%$. He wishes to sell it at a profit of 25% of the net cost and must mark it so as to allow a discount of 20% and $16\frac{2}{3}\%$. Find: (a) His intended selling price. (b) The price at which he actually marks it.

4. A jobber buys a lamp listed at $20.00 with trade discounts of 20%, $16\frac{2}{3}\%$ and 10%. He wishes to sell it at a profit of $33\frac{1}{3}\%$ of the net cost and must mark it so as to allow a discount of $16\frac{2}{3}\%$ and 10%. Find: (a) His intended selling price. (b) The price at which he actually marks it.

5. A jobber buys neckties listed at $100.00 per gross with trade discounts of 25% and 20%. He wishes to sell them at a profit of $37\frac{1}{2}\%$ of the net cost and must mark them so as to allow a discount of 20% and $16\frac{2}{3}\%$. Find: (a) His intended selling price per dozen. (b) The price at which he actually marks them.

6. A jobber buys toys listed at $96.00 per gross with trade discounts of 20%, $16\frac{2}{3}\%$ and 10%. He wishes to sell them at a profit of $33\frac{1}{3}\%$ of the net cost and must mark them so as to allow a discount of $33\frac{1}{3}\%$ and 10%. Find: (a) His intended selling price per dozen. (b) The price at which he actually marks them.

7. A jobber buys gloves listed at $450.00 per gross with trade discounts of $33\frac{1}{3}\%$ and 10%. He wishes to sell them at a profit of 25% of the net cost and must mark them so as to allow a discount of 25% and $16\frac{2}{3}\%$. Find: (a) His intended selling price per dozen. (b) The price at which he actually marks them.

8. A jobber buys Ladies' compacts listed at $216.00 per gross with trade discounts of 20%, $16\frac{2}{3}\%$ and 10%. He wishes to sell them at a profit of $30\frac{10}{13}\%$ of the net cost and must mark them so as to allow a discount of 35%. Find: (a) His intended selling price per dozen. (b) The price at which he actually marks them.

9. A jobber buys handkerchiefs listed at $180.00 per gross with trade discounts of $33\frac{1}{3}\%$ and 10%. He wishes to sell them at a profit of $33\frac{1}{3}\%$ of the net cost and must mark them so as to allow a

discount of 20% and 16⅔%. Find: (a) His intended selling price per dozen. (b) The price at which he actually marks them.

10. A jobber buys wallets listed at $135.00 per gross with trade discounts of 33⅓%, 16⅔% and 10%. He wishes to sell them at a profit of 33⅓% of the net cost and must mark them so as to allow a discount of 33⅓% and 10%. Find: (a) His intended selling price per dozen. (b) The price at which he actually marks them.

## B
## PROBLEMS OF RETAILERS

A grocer buys 14 cartons of canned soup (24 cans to a carton) at $1.40 a carton.

(a) What is the total amount of the purchase?
(b) If there is a 2% cash discount, what is the cost of the purchase?
(c) If he sells each can at a profit of 40% based on the selling price, at what price does he sell each can? (Find the price to the nearest cent.)
(d) What total percent profit will he make on all the cans if he sells them all at the price computed in question c? (1) Profit based on the net cost to the grocer (assuming he pays cash for the order)? (2) Profit based on the selling price?

(a) Total amount of purchase = 15 cartons at $1.40 a carton = $19.60
(b) Cash cost of purchase     = $19.60 − 2% of $19.60    = $19.21
(c) Sales price of all the cans = 100% of itself.
    Cost of all the cans    = 100% − 40% = 60% of the sales price.
    $19.60    = 60%, or ⅗ of the sales price.
    Hence sales price    = $19.60 ÷ ⅗    = $32.67
    Sales price on each can = $32.67 ÷ 336 cans = $.097   = $.10
(d) Net cost to grocer
    (on cash basis)    = $19.21
    Total amount of sales = 336 cans × 10 cents per can = $33.60
    Profit    = $33.60 − $19.21    = $14.39
    Percent profit based on
      cost    = $14.39 ÷ $19.21    = 74.9%
    Percent profit based on
      selling price    = $14.39 ÷ $33.60    = 42.8%

Note: You will observe that the percent profit on the sales, as computed here, is a little higher than the 40% as given in question c. This is because he sells each can at $.10 instead of $.097, which is the actual price at a 40% profit.

## EXERCISE 179

A grocer orders the following merchandise:

1. 3 Cartons Soap (48 Bars to the Carton) at $1.50
2. 2 Cartons Baked Beans (24 to a Carton) at $1.40
3. 5 Cartons Sardines (12 Tins to a Carton) at $.75
4. 2 Cartons Ketchup (24 Bottles to a Carton) at $2.10
5. 3 Cartons Tomato Juice (24 12-ounce Cans each) at $.80
6. 2 Cartons Tomato Juice (18 14-ounce Cans each) at $.90
7. 6 Cartons Soup Brand "A" (24 Cans each) at $1.50
8. 2 Cartons Soup Brand "B" (24 Cans each) at $1.80
9. 3 Cartons Evaporated Milk (24 Cans each) at $.70
10. 2 Cartons Salt (24 Boxes each) at $1.45

Answer the following questions based on the above:

1. What is the amount of each purchase?
2. If there is a 2% cash discount what does each item cost?
3. What is the total amount of the bill without a cash discount?
4. What is the total amount of the bill with a 2% cash discount?
   (a) If the 10 items are considered as a single order?
   (b) If each item is paid for separately?
5. If the grocer sells each item at a profit of 40% based on the selling price, at what price does he sell each item? (Find the price to the nearest cent.)
6. If all the merchandise is sold at the prices just computed, what will the gross sales amount to?
7. What percent profit will the grocer make if he sells all the merchandise at the prices computed in question 5? (a) Profit based on the net cost to him (assuming he pays cash for the entire order)?
   (b) Profit based on the selling price?
8. On which item does the grocer make a bigger profit—the 14-ounce or the 12-ounce can of tomato juice?
9. Does the grocer make a bigger profit on Brand "A" or Brand "B" of soup?
10. On which items is the grocer's profit larger than 40% of the selling price?

## COMPUTING OVERHEAD AND PROFIT

A clothier pays an annual rent of $7500, insurance premiums of $1000, taxes amounting to $2250, and salaries of $9000. Depreciation and miscellaneous expenses amount to $1250.

## PROBLEMS OF WHOLESALERS AND RETAILERS

(a) What is his total overhead?

(b) What is the amount of gross sales he must make in a year to meet his overhead if his profit is 35% of the selling price?

(c) What is the amount of the gross sales he must make in one month to meet expenses?

(d) What is the amount of gross sales he must make in one month to make a net profit of 10% (of the gross sales)?

(a) Total overhead = sum of his expenses = $21,000
(b) His profit = 35% of the gross sales
But his profit must just meet his overhead.
Hence his overhead = 35% of his gross sales
$21,000 = 35% of his gross sales
His gross sales = $21,000 ÷ 35% = $60,000
(c) His gross sales, just enough to cover his overhead each month = $60,000 ÷ 12 = $5,000
(d) His gross profit (See b) = 35% of the gross sales.
But his gross profit = his net profit plus his overhead.
Computing this per month,
35% of S (gross sales) = 10% of S + $1750 (overhead per month)

35% of S − 10% of S = $1750
25%, or ¼ of S = $1750
S = $7000 per month

Answer: (a) $21,000; (b) $60,000; (c) $5,000; (d) $7,000.

## EXERCISE 180

Solve the following problems:

1. A grocer pays an annual rent of $2400.00, insurance premiums of $200, taxes amounting to $800 and salaries of $1500. Depreciation and miscellaneous expenses amount to $500.00 per year. Find (a) the total of these annual expenses, (b) the gross sales he must make in a year to meet expenses if his profit is 20% of the selling price, (c) the gross sales he must make in one month to meet expenses (d) the gross sales he must make in one month to make a net profit of 10% (of the gross sales).

2. The owner of a hardware store pays an annual rent of $2160.00, insurance premiums of $150.00, taxes amounting to $520.00 and salaries of $2000.00. Depreciation and miscellaneous expenses amount to $770.00 per year. Find (a) the total of these annual expenses, (b) the gross sales he must make in a year to meet expenses if his profit is 35% of the selling price, (c) the gross sales he must

make in one month to meet expenses, (d) the gross sales he must make in one month to make a net profit of 10% (of the gross sales).

3. A baker pays an annual rent of $1800.00, insurance premiums of $240.00, taxes amounting to $500.00 and salaries of $2400.00. Depreciation and miscellaneous expenses amount to $220.00 per year. Find (a) the total of these annual expenses, (b) the gross sales he must make in a year to meet expenses if his profit is 25% of the selling price, (c) the gross sales he must make in one month to meet expenses, (d) the gross sales he must make in one month to make a net profit of 10% (of the gross sales).

4. A butcher pays an annual rent of $1800.00, insurance premiums of $180.00, taxes amounting to $420.00 and salaries of $2000.00. Depreciation and miscellaneous expenses amount to $400.00 per year. Find (a) the total of these annual expenses, (b) the gross sales he must make in a year to meet expenses if his profit is $33\frac{1}{3}$% of the selling price, (c) the gross sales he must make in one month to meet expenses, (d) the gross sales he must make in one month to make a net profit of 10% (of the gross sales).

5. A haberdasher pays an annual rent of $2100.00, insurance premiums of $180.00, taxes amounting to $400.00 and salaries of $1800.00. Depreciation and miscellaneous expenses amount to $200.00 per year. Find (a) the total of these annual expenses, (b) the gross sales he must make in a year to meet expenses if his profit is 40% of the selling price, (c) the gross sales he must make in one month to meet expenses, (d) the gross sales he must make in one month to make a net profit of 10% (of the gross sales).

6. A stationer pays an annual rent of $1800.00, insurance premiums of $240.00, taxes amounting to $400.00 and salaries of $1560.00. Depreciation and miscellaneous expenses amount to $260.00 per year. Find (a) the total of these annual expenses, (b) the gross sales he must make in a year to meet expenses if his profit is 40% of the selling price, (c) the gross sales he must make in one month to meet expenses (d) the gross sales he must make in one month to make a net profit of 10% (of the gross sales).

7. A clothier pays an annual rent of $2100.00, insurance premiums of $240.00, taxes amounting to $560.00 and salaries of $2000.00. Depreciation and miscellaneous expenses amount to $740.00 per year. Find (a) the total of these annual expenses, (b) the gross sales he must make in a year to meet expenses if his profit is 40% of the selling price, (c) the gross sales he must make in one month to meet expenses, (d) the gross sales he must make in one month to make a net profit of 10% (of the gross sales).

# PROBLEMS OF WHOLESALERS AND RETAILERS

8. The owner of a shoe store pays an annual rent of $1800.00, insurance premiums of $290.00, taxes amounting to $700.00 per year and salaries of $3000.00. Depreciation and miscellaneous expenses amount to $210.00 per year. Find (a) the total of these annual expenses, (b) the gross sales he must make in a year to meet expenses if his profit is 40% of the selling price, (c) the gross sales he must make in one month to meet expenses (d) the gross sales he must make in one month to make a net profit of 10% (of the gross sales).

9. A pharmacist pays an annual rent of $3000.00, insurance premiums of $400.00, taxes amounting to $900.00 and salaries of $3600.00. Depreciation and miscellaneous expenses amount to $500.00 per year. Find (a) the total of these annual expenses, (b) the gross sales he must make in a year to meet expenses if his profit is 35% of the selling price, (c) the gross sales he must make in one month to meet expenses (d) the gross sales he must make in one month to make a net profit of 10% (of the gross sales).

10. The owner of a gift and book shop pays an annual rent of $1200.00, insurance premiums of $150.00, taxes amounting to $200.00 and salaries of $1300.00. Depreciation and miscellaneous expenses amount to $150.00 per year. Find (a) the total of these annual expenses, (b) the gross sales he must make in a year to meet expenses if his profit is 40% of the selling price (c) the gross sales he must make in one month to meet expenses (d) the gross sales he must make in one month to make a net profit of 10% (of the gross sales).

## ANSWERS
### EXERCISE 178

|    | (a)     | (b)      |     | (a)     | (b)     |
|----|---------|----------|-----|---------|---------|
| 1. | $96.00  | $120.00  | 6.  | $7.20   | $12.00  |
| 2. | $40.00  | $48.00   | 7.  | $30.00  | $48.00  |
| 3. | $20.00  | $30.00   | 8.  | $15.60  | $24.00  |
| 4. | $18.00  | $24.00   | 9.  | $12.00  | $18.00  |
| 5. | $8.00   | $12.00   | 10. | $7.50   | $12.50  |

### EXERCISE 179

1. (1) $4.50  (2) $2.80  (3) $3.75  (4) $4.20  (5) $2.40
   (6) $1.80  (7) $9.00  (8) $3.60  (9) $2.10  (10) $2.90
2. (1) $4.41  (2) $2.74  (3) $3.67  (4) $4.12  (5) $2.35
   (6) $1.76  (7) $8.82  (8) $3.53  (9) $2.06  (10) $2.84
3. $37.05
4. (a) $36.31  (b) $36.30
5. (1) $.05  (2) $.10  (3) $.10  (4) $.15  (5) $.05
   (6) $.08  (7) $.10  (8) $.12  (9) $.05  (10) $.10
6. $60.24
7. (a) 65.9%  (b) 39.7%

8. The 14-ounce Can
9. Brand "A"
10. The Baked Beans, Ketchup, Evaporated Milk, and Salt.

## EXERCISE 180

|    | (a)      | (b)        | (c)       | (d)       |
|----|----------|------------|-----------|-----------|
| 1. | $5400.00 | $27,000.00 | $2,250.00 | $4,500.00 |
| 2. | $5600.00 | $16,000.00 | $1,333.33 | $1,866.67 |
| 3. | $5160.00 | $20,640.00 | $1,720.00 | $2,866.67 |
| 4. | $4800.00 | $14,400.00 | $1,200.00 | $1,714.29 |
| 5. | $4680.00 | $11,700.00 | $ 975.00  | $1,300.00 |
| 6. | $4260.00 | $10,650.00 | $ 887.50  | $1,183.33 |
| 7. | $5640.00 | $14,100.00 | $1,175.00 | $1,566.67 |
| 8. | $6000.00 | $15,000.00 | $1,250.00 | $1,666.67 |
| 9. | $8400.00 | $24,000.00 | $2,000.00 | $2,800.00 |
| 10.| $3000.00 | $77,500.00 | $ 625.00  | $ 833.33  |

# MATHEMATICS FOR THE HOME

## CHAPTER XXVIII
## Invoices and Payments

THIS SECTION deals with some of the more common household expenses—telephone, gas and electric bills, purchases of family commodities, garage rentals, and so forth.

### A. TELEPHONE BILLS

The cost of Mr. A's telephone service is $4.50 a month for 100 calls. Additional calls are charged at the rate of 5 cents a call and a 2% tax for unemployment relief.

Find (a) the amount due for additional calls, and (b) the total amount due, under the following circumstances:

| Balance from Previous Month | Total Calls for Month | Long Distance Calls and Telegrams |
|---|---|---|
| $5.87 | 119 | $1.34 |

| | |
|---|---|
| Cost of additional calls................19×$.05 | $.95 |
| 2% of $.95................................ | .02 |
| | $.97 |
| Long distance calls and telegrams................ | $1.34 |
| | $2.31 |
| Monthly charge for 100 calls................ | 4.50 |
| Balance from previous month................ | 5.87 |
| Total................................ | $12.68 |

Answer: (a) $2.31; (b) $12.68

### EXERCISE 181

In the following problems based on telephone bills the cost for monthly service is uniformly $4.38; additional local calls are charged at the rate of $.05 per call and a 3% for tax for unemployment relief. In each case the balance due from the previous month is given together with the additional local calls and charges for out-of-town calls and telegrams. Find (a) the amount due for additional local calls and (b) the total amount due.

|  | Balance from Previous Month | Additional Local Calls | Long Distance and Telegrams |
|---|---|---|---|
| 1. | $6.43 | 22 | $.95 |
| 2. | $5.36 | 38 | $.35 |
| 3. | $5.45 | 19 | none |
| 4. | $5.79 | 15 | $.30 |
| 5. | $5.49 | 19 | $.30 |
| 6. | $4.85 | 5 | $1.35 |
| 7. | $6.59 | 8 | $.70 |
| 8. | $4.54 | 33 | none |
| 9. | $6.69 | 34 | $.30 |
| 10. | $4.53 | 3 | none |

## B. GAS BILLS

In order to compute your gas bill, read your meter at the beginning and at the end of each month, and then multiply the difference in cubic feet—that is, the number of cubic feet used up during the month—by the rate per cubic foot. If there is an unemployment tax in your vicinity, add it to your bill.

For example: Suppose on March 1 your gas meter reads 24,000 cubic feet and on April 1 it reads 25,400 cubic feet. The rate is $11\frac{3}{7}$¢ per 100 cubic feet, plus a 2% tax for unemployment relief. What is your bill for the month of March?

25,400 cu. ft. − 24,000 cu. ft. = 1400 cu. ft. = 14 units of 100 cu. ft each.

$14 \times \$.11\frac{3}{7} = \$1.60$
Tax = .03
Total $1.63

Answer, $1.63

## EXERCISE 182

In the following problems based on bills for gas service, the rate is $11\frac{1}{2}$ cents per hundred cubic feet, plus a 3% tax for unemployment relief. In each problem you are given the meter reading at the beginning and end of the month. Find the amount of the bill.

*Note*: These readings are given in terms of hundreds of cubic feet.

## INVOICES AND PAYMENTS

|    | Previous Reading |   | Present Reading |     | Previous Reading |   | Present Reading |
|----|------------------|---|-----------------|-----|------------------|---|-----------------|
| 1. | 282              |   | 290             | 6.  | 432              |   | 450             |
| 2. | 240              |   | 246             | 7.  | 450              |   | 471             |
| 3. | 336              |   | 341             | 8.  | 471              |   | 483             |
| 4. | 390              |   | 412             | 9.  | 483              |   | 506             |
| 5. | 412              |   | 432             | 10. | 506              |   | 531             |

### C. ELECTRICITY BILLS

Suppose the electricity service rates in your community are as follows:

For the first 10 kilowatt hours—$.09 per kilowatt hour (KWH)
For the next 35 kilowatt hours—$.06 per KWH
For the next 35 kilowatt hours—$.05 per KWH
For the next 50 kilowatt hours—$.03 per KWH
For all additional service         —$.02 per KWH

In addition to the regular rates, suppose there is a charge of $.0002 per KWH for "fuel cost adjustment," and a 3% tax for unemployment relief. What is your electric bill for May if on May 1 the reading is 5362 and on June 1, 5507?

$$5507 - 5362 = 145 \text{ KWH}$$

$$10 \times \$.09 = \$ \ .90$$
$$35 \times \$.06 = \$2.10$$
$$35 \times \$.05 = \$1.75$$
$$50 \times \$.03 = \$1.50$$
$$15 \times \$.02 = \ \ .30$$
$$\overline{\$6.55}$$
$$145 \times \$.0002 = \ \ .03$$
$$\overline{\$6.58}$$
$$\$6.58 \times .03 = \ \ .20$$
$$\text{Total bill} = \overline{\$6.78}$$

Answer, $6.78

### EXERCISE 183

In the following problems based on bills for electricity service the rates are the following:

For the first 10 kilowatt hours    —$.90
For the next 35 kilowatt hours   —$.05 per KWH
"    "    "   40    "         "        —$.04   "      "
"    "    "   40    "         "        —$.03   "      "
All additional                          —$.02   "      "

In each case you are given the previous and present readings (the reading at the beginning and at the end of the month). In addition to the regular rates there is a charge of $.0002 per kilowatt hour for "fuel cost adjustment"; and a 3% tax for unemployment relief. Find the total amount of each bill.

|    | Previous Reading | Present Reading |     | Previous Reading | Present Reading |
|----|------------------|-----------------|-----|------------------|-----------------|
| 1. | 5531             | 5622            | 6.  | 5988             | 6099            |
| 2. | 5622             | 5719            | 7.  | 6099             | 6223            |
| 3. | 5719             | 5802            | 8.  | 6223             | 6378            |
| 4. | 5802             | 5888            | 9.  | 6378             | 6525            |
| 5. | 5888             | 5988            | 10. | 6525             | 6701            |

## EXERCISE 184
### Miscellaneous Examples

Solve the following problems:

1. A housewife bought a vacuum cleaner for $77.50 plus a sales tax of 2%. She was allowed $7.50 as the trade-in value of her old vacuum cleaner; and paid $28.65 on delivery of the new machine. Find the balance due.

2. A housewife sent a rug 9'×12' to be cleaned. The cleaners charged $.07 per square foot. What was the amount of the bill?

3. A garage charges a man $10.00 per month for garaging his car. During the course of the month the man buys 9 gallons of gasoline at 15½ cents and 29 gallons at $.164. There is a 2% sales tax on the gasoline. Find the amount of the bill, for the month.

4. Find the amount of the garage bill if the customer bought 19 gallons of gasoline at $.175 and 1 gallon of anti-freeze fluid at $2.95.

Note: In this, and in the following examples, don't forget the sales tax.

5. Find the amount of the garage bill if the customer buys 26 gallons of gasoline at $.175, 10 gallons of special gasoline at $.195 and one quart of oil at $.30.

6. Find the amount of the garage bill if the customer buys 8 gallons of gasoline at $.175, 33 gallons of gasoline at $.164; is charged $.50 for fixing a "flat" and $.15 for a "patch" on the inner tube. (No sales tax is charged on the amount for fixing the "flat.")

7. Find the amount of the garage bill if the customer buys 38 gallons of gasoline at $.155, 9 gallons of gasoline at $.163 and two quarts of oil at $.25.

# INVOICES AND PAYMENTS

**ANSWERS**

**EXERCISE 181**

| | | | | |
|---|---|---|---|---|
| (a) 1. $1.13 | 2. $1.96 | 3. $.98 | 4. $.77 | 5. $.98 |
| (6) $.26 | 7. $.41 | 8. $1.70 | 9. $1.75 | 10. $.16 |
| (b) 1. $12.89 | 2. $12.05 | 3. $10.81 | 4. $11.24 | 5. $11.15 |
| 6. $10.84 | 7. $12.08 | 8. $10.62 | 9. $13.12 | 10. $9.07 |

**EXERCISE 182**

| | | | | |
|---|---|---|---|---|
| 1. $.95 | 2. $.71 | 3. $.60 | 4. $2.61 | 5. $2.37 |
| 6. $2.13 | 7. $2.49 | 8. $1.55 | 9. $2.73 | 10. $2.97 |

**EXERCISE 183**

| | | | | |
|---|---|---|---|---|
| 1. $4.58 | 2. $4.77 | 3. $4.32 | 4. $4.43 | 5. $4.86 |
| 6. $5.20 | 7. $5.60 | 8. $6.26 | 9. $6.10 | 10. $6.71 |

**EXERCISE 184**

| | | | |
|---|---|---|---|
| 1. $42.90 | 2. $7.56 | 3. $16.28 | 4. $16.41 |
| 5. $16.94 | 6. $17.60 | 7. $18.02 | |

## CHAPTER XXIX
# Budgets

IT IS WELL for every family with a moderate income to budget its annual expenditures somewhat as follows:

| | |
|---|---|
| Rent | 20% |
| Food | 25% |
| Clothing | 15% |
| Household Expenses | 5% |
| Miscellaneous Expenses | 10% |
| Entertainment | 10% |
| Insurance and Medical Care | 7% |
| Savings | 8% |

Suppose the rent is $416 per year.
(a) What is the weekly income?
(b) What is the annual amount saved?
(c) What is the monthly outlay for clothing?

(a) $416 = 20\%$, or $\frac{1}{5}$ of annual income
Annual income $= \$416 \div \frac{1}{5} = \$2080$
Weekly income $= \$2080 \div 52 = \$40$
(b) Annual amount saved $= 8\%$ of $\$2080 = \$166.40$
(c) Annual outlay for clothing $= 15\%$ of $\$2080 = \$312$
   Monthly outlay for clothing $= \$312 \div 12 = \$26$

Answer: (a) $40; (b) $166.40; (c) $26

## EXERCISE 185

Using the above budget, you are given one of the items and you are to find the amount spent on the other items:

1. Annual Income, $2000.00
2. Rent, $460.00
3. Food, $525.00
4. Clothing, $360.00
5. Miscellaneous Household Expenses, $110.00
6. Miscellaneous Work Expenses, $252.00
7. Entertainment, $288.00

# BUDGETS

8. Insurance and Medical Care, $184.80
9. Savings, $249.60
10. Insurance and Medical Care, $193.20

## MONTHLY AND WEEKLY SALARIES

52 weeks = 12 months
1 week = $\frac{12}{52}$ of a month = .23 of a month (approximately).
From this we get the following formula:
A monthly salary can be translated into a weekly amount by *multiplying* by .23. A weekly wage can be translated into a monthly salary by *dividing* by .23.

### EXERCISE 186

Using the above formula, change the weekly wages of the first 10 problems into monthly salaries; and the monthly salaries of the last 10 problems into weekly wages:

| | Weekly Wage | Monthly Salary | | Monthly Salary | Weekly Wage |
|---|---|---|---|---|---|
| 1. | $30.00 | .......... | 11. | $100.00 | .......... |
| 2. | $50.00 | .......... | 12. | $200.00 | .......... |
| 3. | $35.00 | .......... | 13. | $125.00 | .......... |
| 4. | $55.00 | .......... | 14. | $225.00 | .......... |
| 5. | $40.00 | .......... | 15. | $150.00 | .......... |
| 6. | $60.00 | .......... | 16. | $250.00 | .......... |
| 7. | $45.00 | .......... | 17. | $175.00 | .......... |
| 8. | $53.00 | .......... | 18. | $ 40.00 | .......... |
| 9. | $4.60 | .......... | 19. | $ 65.00 | .......... |
| 10. | $5.78 | .......... | 20. | $ 55.00 | .......... |

### EXERCISE 187

Mr. Smith has an annual income of $2400.00. His expenditures for a certain year were as follows:

January: Rent, $40.00; Food, $51.36; Clothing, $60.00; Misc. Household Exp., $11.24; Misc. Work Exp. (such as carfares, etc.), $20.00; Entertainment, $14.16; Insurance and Med. Care, $17.00.

February: Rent, $40.00; Food, $52.04; Clothing, $5.00; Misc. Household Exp., $11.53; Misc. Work Exp., $20.00; Entertainment, $13.85; Insurance and Med. Care, $7.00.

March: Rent, $40.00; Food, $51.48; Clothing, $4.80; Misc. Household Exp., $11.07; Misc. Work Exp., $20.00; Entertainment, $15.40; Insurance and Med. Care, $13.00.

April: Rent, $40.00; Food, $50.36; Clothing, $33.00; Misc. Household Exp., $9.84; Misc. Work Exp., $20.00; Entertainment, $17.95; Insurance and Med. Care, $7.00.

May: Rent, $40.00; Food, $49.84; Clothing, $41.28; Misc. Household Exp., $9.21; Misc. Work Exp., $20.00; Entertainment, $22.14; Insurance and Med. Care, $7.00.

June: Rent, $40.00; Food, $49.60; Clothing, $42.48; Misc. Household Exp., $8.79; Misc. Work Exp., $20.00; Entertainment, $24.18; Insurance and Med. Care, $7.00.

July: Rent, $40.00; Food, $48.20; Clothing, $7.23; Misc. Household Exp., $8.81; Misc. Work Exp., $20.00; Entertainment, $30.14; Insurance and Med. Care, $35.00.

August: Rent, $40.00; Food, $45.48; Clothing, $9.68; Misc. Household Exp., $8.93; Misc. Work Exp., $20.00; Entertainment, $31.18; Insurance and Med. Care, $24.00.

September: Rent, $40.00; Food, $47.49; Clothing, $53.14; Misc. Household Exp., $8.98; Misc. Work Exp., $20.00; Entertainment, $22.64; Insurance and Med. Care, $7.00.

October: Rent, $40.00; Food, $49.73; Clothing, $18.41; Misc. Household Exp., $9.24; Misc. Work Exp., $20.00; Entertainment, $19.47; Insurance and Med. Care, $7.00.

November: Rent, $40.00; Food, $41.24; Clothing, $35.84; Misc. Household Exp., $11.86; Misc. Work Exp., $20.00; Entertainment, $16.59; Insurance and Med. Care, $7.00.

December: Rent, $40.00; Food, $52.83; Clothing, $29.76; Misc. Household Exp., $11.51; Misc. Work Exp., $20.00; Entertainment, $44.84; Insurance and Med. Care, $18.00.

Prepare a budget showing these expenditures for the various months together with the totals for the year for each item and the total spent during each month. Show also the amount saved each month and the annual amount budgeted for each item of expense according to the schedule given earlier.

## ANSWERS
### EXERCISE 185

1. Rent, $400.00; Food, $500.00; Clothing, $300.00; Misc. Household Exp., $100.00; Misc. Work Exp., $200.00; Entertainment, $200.00; Insurance and Med. Care, $140.00; Savings, $160.00.
2. Income, $2300.00; Rent, $460.00; Food, $575.00; Clothing, $345.00; Misc. Household Exp., $115.00; Misc. Work Exp., $230.00; Entertainment, $230.00; Insurance and Med. Care, $161.00; Savings, $184.00.
3. Income, $2100.00; Rent, $420.00; Clothing, $315.00; Misc. Household Exp., $105.00; Misc. Work Exp., $210.00; Entertainment, $210.00; Insurance and Med. Care, $147.00; Savings, $168.00.

# BUDGETS

4. Income, $2400.00; Rent, $480.00; Food, $600.00; Misc. Household Exp., $120.00; Misc. Work Exp., $240.00; Entertainment, $240.00; Insurance and Med. Care, $168.00; Savings, $192.00.
5. Income, $2200.00; Rent, $440.00; Food, $550.00; Clothing, $330.00; Misc. Work Exp., $220.00; Entertainment, $220.00; Insurance and Med. Care, $154.00; Savings, $176.00.
6. Income, $2520.00; Rent, $504.00; Food, $630.00; Clothing, $378.00; Misc. Household Exp., $126.00; Entertainment, $252.00; Insurance and Med. Care, $176.40; Savings, $201.60.
7. Income $2880.00; Rent, $576.00; Food, $720.00; Clothing, $432.00; Misc. Household Exp., $144.00; Misc. Work Exp., $288.00; Insurance and Med. Care, $201.60; Savings, $230.40.
8. Income, $2640.00; Rent, $528.00; Food, $660.00; Clothing, $396.00; Misc. Household Exp., $132.00; Misc. Work Exp., $264.00; Entertainment, $264.00; Insurance and Med. Care, $184.80; Savings, $211.20.
9. Income, $3120.00; Rent, $624.00; Food, $780.00; Clothing, $468.00; Misc. Household Exp., $156.00; Misc. Work Expenses, $312.00; Entertainment, $312.00; Insurance and Med. Care, $218.40.
10. Income, $2760.00; Rent, $552.00; Food, $690.00; Clothing, $414.00; Misc. Household Exp., $138.00; Misc. Work Expenses, $276.00; Entertainment, $276.00; Savings, $220.80; Insurance and Medical Care, $193.20.

## EXERCISE 186

1. $130.43
2. $217.39
3. $152.17
4. $239.13
5. $173.91
6. $260.87
7. $195.65
8. $230.43
9. $20.00
10. $25.13
11. $23.00
12. $46.00
13. $28.75
14. $51.75
15. $34.50
16. $57.50
17. $40.25
18. $9.20
19. $14.95
20. $12.65

## EXERCISE 187

| INCOME | | 200 | 200 | 200 | 200 | 200 | 200 | 200 | 200 | 200 | 200 | 200 | 200 | 2400 |
|---|---|---|---|---|---|---|---|---|---|---|---|---|---|
| | | | | | | | Monthly Expenditures | | | | | | | |
| | Budget per Year | Jan. | Feb. | Mar. | Apr. | May | June | July | Aug. | Sept. | Oct. | Nov. | Dec. | Totals |
| Rent | $480 | $40.00 | $40.00 | $40.00 | $40.00 | $40.00 | $40.00 | $40.00 | $40.00 | $40.00 | $40.00 | $40.00 | $40.00 | $480.00 |
| Food | 600 | 51.36 | 52.04 | 51.48 | 50.36 | 49.84 | 49.60 | 48.20 | 45.48 | 47.49 | 49.73 | 51.24 | 52.83 | 599.65 |
| Clothing | 360 | 60.00 | 5.00 | 4.80 | 33.00 | 41.28 | 42.48 | 7.23 | 9.68 | 53.14 | 18.41 | 35.84 | 29.76 | 340.62 |
| Misc. House | 120 | 11.24 | 11.53 | 11.07 | 9.84 | 9.21 | 8.79 | 8.81 | 8.93 | 8.98 | 9.24 | 11.06 | 11.51 | 120.21 |
| Carfare etc. | 240 | 20.00 | 20.00 | 20.00 | 20.00 | 20.00 | 20.00 | 20.00 | 20.00 | 20.00 | 20.00 | 20.00 | 20.00 | 240.00 |
| Entertain | 240 | 14.16 | 13.85 | 15.40 | 17.95 | 22.14 | 24.18 | 30.14 | 31.18 | 22.64 | 19.47 | 16.59 | 44.84 | 272.54 |
| Ins. & Medicine | 168 | 17.00 | 7.00 | 13.00 | 7.00 | 7.00 | 7.00 | 35.00 | 24.00 | 7.00 | 7.00 | 7.00 | 18.00 | 156.00 |
| Savings | 192 | −13.76 | 50.58 | 44.25 | 21.85 | 10.53 | 7.95 | 10.62 | 20.73 | .75 | 36.15 | 18.27 | −16.94 | 190.98 |
| Totals Spent | 2208 | 213.76 | 149.42 | 155.75 | 178.15 | 189.47 | 192.05 | 189.38 | 179.27 | 199.25 | 163.85 | 181.73 | 216.94 | 2209.02 |

Note: You will observe that Mr. Smith's expenditures for the year amounted to $1.02 *more* than his budget; and that his savings, therefore, amounted to $1.02 *less* than his budget.

CHAPTER XXX
# Income Taxes
## I. THE FEDERAL INCOME TAX

THE FEDERAL INCOME TAX is levied on the incomes of those who are citizens or residents of the United States. This tax is graduated, or proportioned, in accordance with the financial ability of each person to contribute his share to the national expenses. Nobody is required to pay a tax on his entire income. As a matter of fairness to all, especially to those whose incomes are in the lower brackets, certain exemptions are allowed. A single person who is not the head of a household is allowed $1000; and a married person or the head of a family is allowed $2500. Other exemptions include: $400 for each dependent; expenses in conducting a man's business or profession; money paid out in taxes (other than income taxes); losses from fire or from bad debts; gifts made to religious or to charitable organizations; an earned-income credit amounting to $\frac{1}{10}$ of the earned income; etc.

### NORMAL TAX AND SURTAX

There are two kinds of Federal taxes: *normal taxes* and *surtaxes*.

1. A *normal tax* of 4% is levied on all incomes up to and including $4000 (subject to the exemptions as specified above).

2. A *surtax* is levied on all incomes over $4000. The only exemptions allowed on the surtax are the personal exemptions of $1000 for a single person, $2500 for the head of a family, and $400 for each dependent. This surtax is distinct from, and added to, the normal tax. The amount of the surtax is computed in accordance with the following schedule:

| Amount Taxable | Surtax |
|---|---|
| Up to $4,000 | None |
| Over $4,000, and up to $6,000 | 4% of the amount over $4,000 |
| Over $6,000, and up to $8,000 | $80+5% of amount over $6,000 |
| Over $8,000, and up to $10,000 | $180+6% of amount over $8,000 |
| Over $10,000, and up to $12,000 | $300+7% of amount over $10,000 |
| Over $12,000, and up to $14,000 | $440+8% of amount over $12,000 |

## MATHEMATICS MADE EASY

| Amount Taxable | Surtax |
|---|---|
| Over $14,000, and up to $16,000 | $600+9% of amount over $14,000 |
| Over $16,000, and up to $18,000 | $780+11% of amount over $16,000 |
| Over $18,000, and up to $20,000 | $1000+13% of amount over $18,000 |

And so on.

And now let us see how the Federal income tax computations work out in actual practice:

1. A married man with 1 child earns $75 a week. He gives $125 to charity and writes off $100 in bad debts. Find:
   (a) His net income
   (b) His earned-income credit
   (c) His personal exemption
   (d) Exemption for dependent
   (e) The balance taxable
   (f) The amount of the tax.

(a) His earned income = $75×52                          = $3900
    His net income     = $3900 − ($125+$100)       = $3675
(b) His earned-income credit = $\frac{1}{10}$ of his earned income     = $390
(c) His personal exemption                              = $2500
(d) Exemption for dependent                            = $400
(e) Balance taxable = $3675 − ($390+$2500+$400)    = $385
(f) Amount of tax = 4% of $385                       = $15.40

2. A single man earns $100 a week and draws interest at 3% on $6000 in bonds. He supports his mother and donates $350 in charity, and he pays other taxes amounting to $25. What is the amount of his Federal tax?

| | |
|---|---|
| Earned income = $100×52 | = $5200 |
| Income from bonds = 3% of $6000 | = 180 |
| Gross income | = $5380 |
| Less amount given in charity | 350 |
| Balance | = $5030 |
| Less other taxes | 25 |
| Balance = net income | = $5005 |
| Exemptions: | |
|   Personal                 $1000 | |
|   1 dependent            400 | |
|   Earned-income credit   520 | $1920 |
| Balance taxable | = $3085 |
| Amount of Federal tax = 4% of $3085    = $123.40 | |

Answer, $123.40.

# INCOME TAXES

3. Frederick Brown receives a salary of $14,000 together with $2500 from bonds. He is married and has 4 dependent children. What is the amount of his Federal income tax?

(a) Normal Tax:

| | | |
|---|---|---|
| Total net income = $14,000+$2500 | | =$16,500 |
| Exemptions: | | |
|   Personal | =$2500 | |
|   4 dependents at $400 | = 1600 | |
|   Earned-income credit | = 1400 | 5,500 |
| Balance subject to normal tax | | =$11,000 |

Amount of normal tax = 4% of $11,000 = $440

(b) Surtax:

| | | |
|---|---|---|
| Total net income | | =$16,500 |
| Exemptions: | | |
|   Personal | $2500 | |
|   4 dependents | 1600 | 4,100 |
| Balance subject to surtax | | $12,400 |

Surtax on $12,400 (see table on page 323):
  $440+8% of $400          =$472
Total Federal income tax = $440+$472      = $912

                Answer, $912.00

## EXERCISE 188

In each of the following Federal income tax problems, find the net income, the earned income credit, personal exemption, exemption for dependents, the balance taxable, and the amount of the tax.

1. A single man earns $26.00 per week.
2. A single man earns $33.25 per week and supports his mother.
3. A married man with two children earns $90.00 per week, gives $100.00 to charity during the year and writes off $90.00 in bad debts.
4. A married man with three children earns $84.00 per week and draws annual interest on bonds of $250.00. During the course of the year, he gives $150.00 to charity and pays other taxes of $18.00.
5. A married man earns $35.50 per week, donates $15.00 to charity, and writes off $10.00 in bad debts.
6. A single man who supports his mother earns $39.75 per week, draws annual interest at 3% on a $1000.00 bond, and donates $25.00 to charity.
7. A married man earns $72.00 per week and donates $50.00 to charity.
8. A single man earns $88.00 per week and draws interest at 4% on $5000.00 in bonds; he donates $300.00 to charity.

9. A married man with one child earns $65.00 per week.
10. A single man earns $31.50 per week.

## II. THE STATE INCOME TAX

The rate of the income tax for the various states may differ somewhat from the Federal tax rates. The general principles that govern the taxes for the various states, however, are similar to those that govern the Federal taxes.

For example:

Suppose in a certain state there is an emergency tax rate of 2% based upon the taxable balance of each of its residents; and also a normal tax rate of 1% on the first thousand of the taxable balance, 2% on the second and third thousands, 3% on the fourth thousand, and so on. A single man in that state earns $80 a week. He draws a 4% interest on a bank balance of $2000, and a 5% interest on a $1000 bond. He supports his mother, gives $200 to charity, and pays $25 in other taxes. (a) What is his emergency state tax? (b) What is his normal state tax?

| | | |
|---|---|---|
| Earned income = $80×52 | | = $4160 |
| Income from bank balance = 4% of $2000 | | = 80 |
| Income from bond = 5% of $1000 | | = 50 |
| Gross income | | = $4290 |
| Less: | | |
| Amount he pays to charity | $200 | |
| Amount he pays in other taxes | 25 | $225 |
| Net income | | = $4065 |
| Exemptions: | | |
| Personal | = $1000 | |
| 1 dependent | = 400 | $1400 |
| Balance taxable | | $2665 |

(a) Emergency tax = 2% of $2665     = $53.30
(b) Normal tax = 1% of $1000 + 2% of $1665
          = $10 + $33.30      = $43.30

Answer: (a) $53.30; (b) $43.30

## EXERCISE 189

In the following State income tax problems find the net income, personal exemption, deduction for dependents, balance taxable, normal tax and emergency tax. Compute the emergency tax by taking

# INCOME TAXES

1% of the balance taxable; compute the normal tax by taking 2% of the first thousand (of the balance taxable), 3% of the second and third thousands, and four percent of the fourth thousand.

1. A single man who supports his mother earns $42.00 per week.

2. A married man earns $74.00 per week, draws interest at 4% on $2000.00 in a savings bank, donates $25.00 to charity and pays state taxes amounting to $36.24.

3. A single man earns $95.00 per week, draws interest at 5% on a $1000.00 bond and interest at 4% on a balance of $3000.00 in his savings bank; he donates $125.00 to charity and pays state taxes amounting to $50.52.

4. A married man earns $85.00 per week, draws interest at 4% on a bank balance of $1500.00; he donates $35.00 to charity and pays state taxes amounting to $56.17.

5. A married man with one child earns a monthly salary of $450.00, draws interest at 5% on a $1000.00 bond and at 4% on a bank balance of $840.00; he donates $50.00 to charity, writes off bad debts of $217.00 and pays off interest at 6% on a $5000.00 mortgage; his state taxes amount to $69.54.

## ANSWERS
### EXERCISE 188

| | Net Income | Earned Income Credit | Personal Exemption | Deduction for Dependents | Balance Taxable | Tax |
|---|---|---|---|---|---|---|
| 1. | $1352.00 | $135.20 | $1000.00 | | $216.80 | $ 8.67 |
| 2. | 1729.00 | 172.90 | 1000.00 | $400.00 | 156.10 | 6.24 |
| 3. | 4490.00 | 468.00 | 2500.00 | 800.00 | 722.00 | 28.88 |
| 4. | 4450.00 | 436.80 | 2500.00 | 1200.00 | 314.20 | 12 57 |
| 5. | 1821.00 | 184.60 | 2500.00 | | | |
| 6. | 2072.00 | 206.70 | 1000.00 | 400.00 | 465.30 | 18.61 |
| 7. | 3694.00 | 374.40 | 2500.00 | | 819.60 | 32.78 |
| 8. | 4476.00 | 457.60 | 1000.00 | | 3018.40 | 120.74 |
| 9. | 3380.00 | 338.00 | 2500.00 | 400.00 | 142.00 | 5.68 |
| 10. | 1638.00 | 163.80 | 1000.00 | | 474.20 | 18.97 |

### EXERCISE 189

| | Net Income | Personal Exemption | Deduction for Dependents | Balance Taxable | Normal Tax | Emergency Tax |
|---|---|---|---|---|---|---|
| 1. | $2184.00 | $1000 | $400.00 | $ 784.00 | $ 15.68 | $ 7.84 |
| 2. | 3867.76 | 2500 | | 1367.76 | 31.03 | 13.68 |
| 3. | 4934.48 | 1000 | | 3934.48 | 117.38 | 39.34 |
| 4. | 4285.83 | 2500 | | 1785.83 | 43.57 | 17.86 |
| 5. | 4847.06 | 2500 | 400.00 | 1947.06 | 48.41 | 19.47 |

## CHAPTER XXXI
# Interior and Exterior Decorating

IT IS BECOMING more and more customary for home owners to paint and to decorate their homes, inside and out, and to keep them generally in tip-top shape, without resorting to hired help. If you are planning to do this sort of thing in your own home, here is how you can figure the cost:

Suppose you wish to paint the walls and ceiling of your living room which measures 22'×14'×9'. There are two windows 6'×3'3" and one door 6'6"×3'. The paint is to be of oil base with a flat finish to be applied on plaster and there are to be two coats. You wish to apply three coats of varnish to the hardwood floor of the living room and to lay a broadloom rug costing $4.00 per square yard to cover all of the floor except a one-foot margin on each side. Find: (a) The net surface in square feet to be painted. (b) The number of gallons of paint required (see the table which follows this problem). (c) The number of gallons of varnish required. (d) The cost of the rug.

### SPREAD OF PAINT, ETC., PER GALLON

|   | 1 Coat | 2 Coats | 3 Coats |
|---|---|---|---|
| 1. Oil paint, gloss finish, on plaster | 450 sq. ft. | 250 | 175 |
| 2. Oil paint, gloss finish, on hard brick | 400 | 225 | 160 |
| 3. Oil paint, gloss finish, on rough wood | 350 | 200 | 135 |
| 4. Oil paint, flat finish, on plaster | 400 | 225 | 160 |
| 5. Oil paint, flat finish, on hard brick | 350 | 200 | 150 |
| 6. Interior finishing varnish on smooth wood | 500 | 275 | 200 |
| 7. Asphalt roof paint on smooth surface | 250 | | |
| 8. Asphalt roof paint on rough surface | 150 | | |
| 9. Calcimine (5-pound powder) on plaster | 400 | | |
| 10. Whitewash (1-pound hydrated lime) on wood | 45 | | |

# INTERIOR AND EXTERIOR DECORATING 329

(a) Area of 2 walls = 22 ft. × 9 ft. each = 2 × 22 × 9     = 396 sq. ft.
   "    "   "   "    = 14 ft. × 9 ft. each = 2 × 14 × 9     = 252 sq. ft.
   "    "   ceiling = 22 ft. × 14 ft.     = 308 sq. ft.
Total area of 4 walls and ceiling     = 956 sq. ft.
Less:
   Area of 2 windows = 2 × 6 ft. × 3$\frac{1}{4}$ ft. = 39 sq. ft.
   Area of door     = 6$\frac{1}{2}$ ft. × 3 ft.    = 19$\frac{1}{2}$ sq. ft.   = 58$\frac{1}{2}$ sq. ft.
Net surface to be painted     = 897$\frac{1}{2}$ sq. ft.
(b) Number of gallons of paint required (see table)
   = 897$\frac{1}{2}$ ÷ 225 = 3.988 gallons +,     = 4 gallons
(c) Area of floor = 22 ft. × 14 ft.     = 308 sq. ft.
Number of gallons of varnish required (see table)
   = 308 ÷ 200 = 1$\frac{1}{2}$ gallons +,     = 2 gallons

(d)

Area of rug = 20 ft. × 12 ft. = 240 sq. ft. ÷ 9 sq. ft.    = 26$\frac{2}{3}$ sq. yd.
Cost of rug = 26$\frac{2}{3}$ × $4     = $106.67
Answer: (a) 897$\frac{1}{2}$ sq. ft.; (b) 4 gallons; (c) 2 gallons; (d) $106.67

## EXERCISE 190

1. A man wishes to paint the walls and ceiling of his kitchen and dinette (one large room) which measures 16′ × 10′ × 9′. There is one window 4′ × 6′ and a door 6′6″ by 3′. The paint is to be of oil base gloss finish to be applied on plaster and there are to be two coats. He also wishes to varnish the floor and lay a linoleum over the entire floor at a cost of $2.00 per square yard. Find: (a) The net surface in square feet to be painted. (b) The number of gallons of paint needed. (c) The number of gallons of varnish needed. (d) The cost of the linoleum.

2. A man wishes to paint the walls and ceiling of his bedroom measuring 14′ × 12′ × 9′. There are two windows 6′ × 3′3″ and one door 6′6″ × 3′. There are to be two coats of oil paint flat finish to be applied on plaster. He also wishes to put two coats of varnish on the

floor and then cover the entire floor surface with a light rug which costs $2.25 per square yard. Find (a) The net surface in square feet to be painted. (b) The number of gallons of paint needed. (c) The number of gallons of varnish needed. (d) The cost of the rug.

3. A man wishes to calcimine the walls and ceiling of his basement measuring 29'×22'×8'. There are four windows 2'×3' and a door 6'6"×3'. Find (a) the net surface in square feet to be painted and (b) the number of 5-pound bags of powder he will need.

4. A man wishes to paint the walls of his house measuring 6'×40' by 20'. There are 20 windows 6'×3' and two doors 6'6"×3'. There are to be two coats of paint flat finish on hard brick. Find (a) the net surface in square feet to be painted and (b) the number of gallons of paint required.

5. A man wishes to paint a gable roof each half of which measures 60'×26', with asphalt roof paint. The surface of the roof is rough. Find (a) the net surface in square feet to be painted and (b) the number of gallons of paint required.

6.

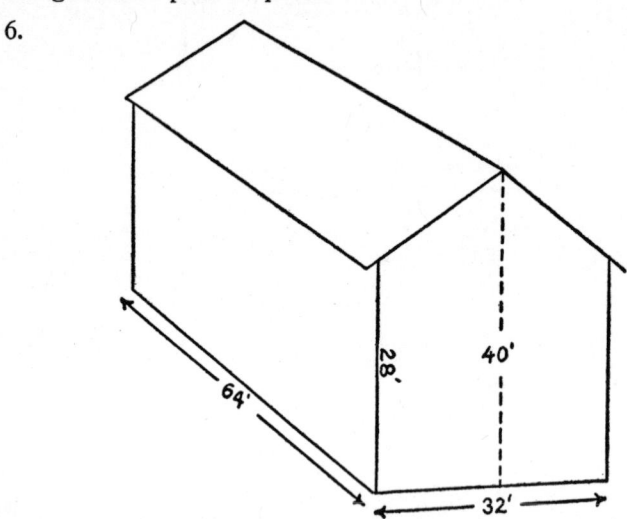

A man wishes to paint the roof of his barn (see diagram) with asphalt roof paint. The surface is smooth. Find (a) The measurements of the roof if there is a one-foot overhang in each direction, (b) the net surface in square feet to be painted, and (c) the number of gallons of paint needed. (The paint can be bought in quantities of one-gallon or one-half-gallon.)

7. If the walls of the barn are to be painted with oil paint gloss

# INTERIOR AND EXTERIOR DECORATING 331

finish on rough wood, (a) how many gallons of paint will be required, (b) what is the net surface in square feet to be painted?

8. If the inside walls and ceiling (made of wood) are to be whitewashed, how many pounds of hydrated lime will be needed for the job, (b) what is the net surface in square feet to be painted?

9. A silo is 32' high and 14' in diameter. A farmer wishes to paint it with oil paint flat finish on wood. (The spread on such a surface is 275 square feet to the gallon.) Find (a) the net surface in square feet to be painted and (b) the number of gallons of paint required.

### ANSWERS
### EXERCISE 190

1. (a) 584½ Sq. Ft.   (b) 2½ Gallons   (c) ½ Gallon   (d) $35.56
2. (a) 577½ Sq. Ft.   (b) 3 Gallons   (c) 1 Gallon   (d) $42.00
3. (a) 1410½ Sq. Ft.   (b) 3 Bags
4. (a) 3601 Sq. Ft.   (b) 18 Gallons
5. (a) 3120 Sq. Ft.   (b) 21 Gallons
6. (a) 66' × 21'   (b) 2772 Sq. Ft.   (c) 11¼ Gallons
7. (a) 30½ Gallons   (b) 6096 Sq. Ft.
8. (a) 207 Lbs.   (b) 9296 Sq. Ft.
9. (a) 1408 Sq. Ft.   (b) 5½ Gallons

## CHAPTER XXXII
# Ingredients for Cooking

CONSCIOUSLY or unconsciously, every good cook is a good mathematician. If you want your recipe to taste right, you must make certain that the proportions of the ingredients are mathematically correct. You must be able to add, subtract, multiply and divide fractions, to reduce cups of water to pints, tablespoons of flour to ounces, and teaspoons of syrup to drops. You must estimate the time it takes several pounds of meat to boil or to roast or to stew. And you must be able to reduce a recipe for five or for six portions to an equivalent recipe for two or for three portions, and vice versa.

For example:

1. One pound of powdered sugar equals $2\frac{2}{3}$ cups. How many cups does $\frac{1}{3}$ of a pound equal?

$\frac{1}{3}$ of $2\frac{2}{3}$ cups = $\frac{8}{9}$, or a little less than 1 cup.

2. If it takes 25 minutes to roast 1 pound of veal, how long will it take to roast $4\frac{3}{5}$ pounds? Allow 10 minutes extra to let the meat warm through.

25 minutes $\times 4\frac{3}{5}$ = 115 minutes

115 minutes + 10 minutes = 125 minutes = 2 hours, 5 minutes.

3. A recipe for two portions of tomato bouillon soup calls for the following ingredients:

    2 cups of boiling water.
    6 teaspoons tomato ketchup.
    $\frac{1}{4}$ teaspoon beef extract.
    $1\frac{1}{2}$ tablespoons whipped cream.

Find the quantities of the same ingredients for 5 portions of tomato bouillon.

First find the quantities necessary for 1 portion, by dividing each ingredient by 2:

    2 cups of boiling water ÷ 2         = 1 cup
    6 teaspoons tomato ketchup ÷ 2    = 3 teaspoons

# INGREDIENTS FOR COOKING

$\frac{1}{4}$ teaspoon beef extract ÷ 2      = $\frac{1}{8}$ teaspoon
$1\frac{1}{2}$ tablespoons whipped cream ÷ 2      = $\frac{3}{4}$ tablespoons
Now multiply these quantities by 5:
1 cup of boiling water × 5      = 5 cups
3 teaspoons tomato ketchup × 5      = 15 teaspoons
$\frac{1}{8}$ teaspoon beef extract × 5 = $\frac{5}{8}$ = a little over $\frac{1}{2}$ teaspoon
$\frac{3}{4}$ tablespoon whipped cream × 5 = $1\frac{5}{4}$      = 4 tablespoons

## EXERCISE 191

Use this table to solve the 20 problems which follow.

| | | |
|---|---|---|
| 60 drops | equals | 1 teaspoon |
| 3 teaspoons | " | 1 tablespoon |
| 2 tablespoons | " | 1 liquid ounce |
| 4 tablespoons | " | $\frac{1}{4}$ cup |
| 16 tablespoons | " | 1 cup |
| 2 cups | " | 1 pint |
| 2 pints | " | 1 quart |
| 4 quarts | " | 1 gallon |
| 4 cups of flour | " | 1 pound |
| 2 cups of granulated sugar | " | 1 pound |
| $2\frac{2}{3}$ cups of powdered sugar | " | 1 pound |
| $2\frac{2}{3}$ cups of brown sugar | " | 1 pound |
| 2 cups of solid butter | " | 1 pound |
| 4 tablespoons of flour | " | 1 ounce |
| 2 tablespoons of butter, sugar or salt | " | 1 ounce |

1. Express 2 gallons as quarts.
2.   "    3 gallons as pints.
3.   "    2 liquid ounces as drops.
4.   "    3 cups as tablespoons.
5.   "    32 pints as gallons.
6.   "    $\frac{1}{4}$ cup as tablespoons.
7.   "    $\frac{1}{3}$ cup as teaspoons.
8.   "    9 teaspoons as tablespoons.
9.   "    9 pints as quarts.
10.   "    3 pounds of butter as cups.
11.   "    $\frac{1}{3}$ cup powdered sugar as ounces.
12.   "    1 pint as tablespoons.
13.   "    $\frac{1}{4}$ pound flour as tablespoons.
14.   "    4 tablespoons as cups.
15.   "    $\frac{2}{3}$ cup brown sugar as pounds.
16.   "    1 cup of flour as pounds.

17. Express 1 pint as teaspoons.
18. " $\frac{1}{2}$ cup of flour as ounces.
19. " $\frac{1}{4}$ pound granulated sugar as cups.
20. " 2 liquid ounces as teaspoons.

## EXERCISE 192

Use this table for the problems which follow:

### Cooking Meat
#### Amount of Time for Roasting

Beef.................rare, 15 minutes per pound.
                     medium, 20 minutes per pound.
                     well done, 30 minutes per pound.
Lamb...............30 to 35 minutes per pound.
Veal................25 minutes per pound.
Pork...............30 minutes per pound.
Ham................25 to 30 minutes per pound.

#### Amount of time for boiling or stewing

Beef................40 to 60 minutes per pound.
Lamb...............15 to 20 minutes per pound.
Ham................25 minutes per pound.

Allow 10 minutes in addition to the above in order to let the meat warm through.

Find the time required for each of the following:

1. 5 pounds of rare roast beef.
2. 3 pounds of roast lamb.
3. 2 pounds of roast veal.
4. 3 pounds of beef stew.
5. $3\frac{1}{2}$ pounds of well-done roast beef.
6. 4 pounds of lamb stew.
7. $2\frac{1}{2}$ pounds of roast pork.
8. 3 pounds of medium done roast beef.
9. 3 pounds of boiled ham.
10. $4\frac{1}{2}$ pounds of roast ham.

## EXERCISE 193

Solve the following problems:

1. A recipe for oatmeal calls for 1 cup of oats to 2 cups of water for three large portions. Find the amount of oats and water necessary for (a) 2 small portions, (b) 2 large portions, (c) 5 small portions. (Note: 1 small portion $=\frac{3}{4}$ of 1 large portion.)

# INGREDIENTS FOR COOKING 335

2. A cereal recipe calls for 6 cups of boiling water one teaspoon full of salt and 1 cup of cereal for six portions. Find the amount of water, salt and cereal necessary for (a) 2 portions, (b) 3 portions, (c) 5 portions, (d) 8 portions.

3. A recipe for beef stew calls for the following ingredients for five portions:

$3\frac{1}{2}$ lb. beef      2 potatoes
$\frac{1}{2}$ onion         $\frac{1}{4}$ cup flour
$\frac{1}{4}$ cup carrots    2 tablespoons fat.
$\frac{1}{4}$ cup turnips

Find the quantities of the same ingredients if only three portions are desired.

## ANSWERS
### EXERCISE 191

1. 8 qts.
2. 24 pints
3. 360 drops
4. 48 tablespoons
5. 4 gallons
6. 4 tablespoons
7. 16 teaspoons
8. 3 tablespoons
9. $4\frac{1}{2}$ qts.
10. 6 cups
11. 2 ounces
12. 32 tablespoons
13. 16 tablespoons
14. $\frac{1}{4}$ cup
15. $\frac{1}{4}$ pound
16. $\frac{1}{2}$ pound
17. 96 teaspoons
18. 2 ounces
19. $\frac{1}{2}$ cup
20. 12 teaspoons

### EXERCISE 192

1. 1 hour, 25 minutes
2. 1 hour, 55 minutes
3. 1 hour
4. 2 to 3 hours
5. 1 hour, 55 minutes
6. 1 hour, 10 minutes to $1\frac{1}{2}$ hours
7. 1 hour, 25 minutes.
8. 1 hour, 10 minutes.
9. 1 hour, 25 minutes.
10. 2 hours to 2 hours, 25 minutes

### EXERCISE 193

1. (a) $\frac{1}{2}$ cup oats and 1 cup water.
   (b) $\frac{2}{3}$ cup oats and $1\frac{1}{3}$ cups water.
   (c) $1\frac{1}{4}$ cups oats and $2\frac{1}{2}$ cups water.
2. (a) 2 cups of water, $\frac{1}{3}$ teaspoon salt (a good sized pinch) $\frac{1}{3}$ cup cereal.
   (b) 3 cups of water, $\frac{1}{2}$ teaspoon salt, $\frac{1}{2}$ cup cereal.
   (c) 5 cups water, $\frac{5}{8}$ teaspoon salt, $\frac{5}{8}$ cup cereal.
   (d) 8 cups water, $1\frac{1}{3}$ teaspoons salt, $1\frac{1}{3}$ cups cereal.
3. A little over 2 pounds of beef, about $\frac{1}{3}$ of an onion, $\frac{1}{8}$ cup each of carrots and turnips, 1 large potato, $2\frac{1}{2}$ tablespoons flour and a little over one tablespoon of fat.

PART III

Mathematics for Entertainment

## CHAPTER XXXIII
# Oddities and Curiosities

FIGURES, like words, tell many a strange and interesting story. Certain of the numbers seem to possess almost magical peculiarities, as we shall see from the following examples:

### NUMBER 1

It hardly seems possible, but it is true that—

$$1 \times 9 + 2 = 11$$
$$12 \times 9 + 3 = 111$$
$$123 \times 9 + 4 = 1111$$
$$1234 \times 9 + 5 = 11111$$
$$12345 \times 9 + 6 = 111111$$
$$123456 \times 9 + 7 = 1111111$$
$$1234567 \times 9 + 8 = 11111111$$
$$12345678 \times 9 + 9 = 111111111$$
$$123456789 \times 9 + 10 = 1111111111$$

And now notice the magical symmetry in the manipulations of the following groupings of the figure 1:

$$11 \times 11 = 121$$
$$111 \times 111 = 12321$$
$$1111 \times 1111 = 1234321$$
$$11111 \times 11111 = 123454321$$
$$111111 \times 111111 = 12345654321$$
$$1111111 \times 1111111 = 1234567654321$$
$$11111111 \times 11111111 = 123456787654321$$
$$111111111 \times 111111111 = 12345678987654321$$

### NUMBERS 3 AND 7

The numbers 3 and 7 have always had a mystical connotation in the human mind. Thus, there are the *Three* Wise Men, the Holy *Trinity*, the *trefoil* on the mariner's compass, the *three* dimensions of space, the *Three* Sisters, the *Seven* Wonders of the World, the *seven* intervals in the musical scale, the *seven* days in the week, the *seven* great branches of learning, the *seventh* heaven, and the *seventh* son of a *seventh* son. Throughout the history of the world, these two numbers have been closely associated with the extraordinary and the miraculous in human affairs.

And, strangely enough, the numbers formed by the digits 3 and 7—that is, 37 and 73—have several peculiar properties. Here are some of them:

$$37 \times 3 = 111$$
$$37 \times 6 = 222$$
$$37 \times 9 = 333$$
$$37 \times 12 = 444$$
$$37 \times 15 = 555$$
$$37 \times 18 = 666$$
$$37 \times 21 = 777$$
$$37 \times 24 = 888$$
$$37 \times 27 = 999$$

And now, when you multiply 73 by the same numbers, you will notice that the last digits of the products form the descending order—9, 8, 7, 6, 5, 4, 3, 2, 1:

$$73 \times 3 = 219$$
$$73 \times 6 = 438$$
$$73 \times 9 = 657$$
$$73 \times 12 = 876$$
$$73 \times 15 = 1095$$
$$73 \times 18 = 1314$$
$$73 \times 21 = 1533$$
$$73 \times 24 = 1752$$
$$73 \times 27 = 1971$$

### NUMBER 8

If you like the number 8, try the following calculations:

$$9 \times 9 + 7 = 88$$
$$9 \times 98 + 6 = 888$$
$$9 \times 987 + 5 = 8888$$
$$9 \times 9876 + 4 = 88888$$
$$9 \times 98765 + 3 = 888888$$
$$9 \times 987654 + 2 = 8888888$$
$$9 \times 9876543 + 1 = 88888888$$
$$9 \times 98765432 + 0 = 888888888$$

## OTHER NUMBERS

Here is an interesting stunt you can try on your friends: Ask them what number, between 1 and 9, they like to write best. And then, when they have given you that number, tell them to do a certain multiplication which, to their surprise, will give them a product consisting of that number repeated several times.

For example: Suppose they select 6 as their favorite number. Ask them to do the following multiplication:

```
   12345679
        ×54
   49382716
  61728395
  666666666
```

The same can be with any other figure between 1 and 9, as you will notice from the following table:

```
12345679× 9 =111 111 111
12345679×18 =222 222 222
12345679×27 =333 333 333
12345679×36 =444 444 444
12345679×45 =555 555 555
12345679×54 =666 666 666
12345679×63 =777 777 777
12345679×72 =888 888 888
12345679×81 =999 999 999
```

In the above table, note two important things:

1. In the multiplicand, the figure 8 is missing.

2. The multiplier consists of the digit that constitutes the product, times 9.

Notice the following neat arrangement of the figures from 9 to 1.

```
        1×8+1=9
       12×8+2=98
      123×8+3=987
     1234×8+4=9876
    12345×8+5=98765
   123456×8+6=987654
  1234567×8+7=9876543
 12345678×8+8=98765432
123456789×8+9=987654321
```

## THE MAGIC NUMBER 76923

One of the most curious numbers in the entire range of arithmetical calculation is 76923. Multiply this number by 1, 10, 9, 12, 3 and 4, and you will get the same sequence of digits when they are read from top to bottom or from left to right:

$$76923 \times 1 = 076923$$
$$76923 \times 10 = 769230$$
$$76923 \times 9 = 692307$$
$$76923 \times 12 = 923076$$
$$76923 \times 3 = 230769$$
$$76923 \times 4 = 307692$$

But this isn't all. The same number, 76923, when multiplied by 2, 7, 5, 11, 6 and 8, will give you another sequence of digits that will read the same from top to bottom and from left to right:

$$76923 \times 2 = 153846$$
$$76923 \times 7 = 538461$$
$$76923 \times 5 = 384615$$
$$76923 \times 11 = 846153$$
$$76923 \times 6 = 461538$$
$$76923 \times 8 = 615384$$

Note that in each of the above two tables all the answers consist of the same digits arranged in different groupings. Note also that the sum of the digits in all the answers is 27.

Just why this number has such strange peculiarities, nobody knows.

## THE NUMBER 37037

Another curious number is 37037, as you will note from the following table:

$$37037 \times 3 = 111111$$
$$37037 \times 6 = 222222$$
$$37037 \times 9 = 333333$$
$$37037 \times 12 = 444444$$
$$37037 \times 15 = 555555$$
$$37037 \times 18 = 666666$$
$$37037 \times 21 = 777777$$
$$37037 \times 24 = 888888$$
$$37037 \times 27 = 999999$$

## ODDITIES AND CURIOSITIES

### WHEN 1 = 24

Here is a strange example which apparently proves the impossible:

$$100 = 100$$
$$96+4 = 96+4$$

(Transposing): $4-4 = 96-96$
(Factoring): $2(2-2) = 48(2-2)$
(Dividing by $[2-2]$): $2 = 48$
(Dividing by 2): $1 = 24$

Question: Where is the mistake?
Answer: The mistake is in the factoring. $4-4=0$, and $96-96=0$; and 0 cannot be factored.

### HUGE FIGURES

Do you happen to know what is the largest number that can be expressed with three figures? No, it is not 999. The correct answer is the 9th power of the 9th power of 9. Arithmetically it is expressed as follows: $9^{9^9}$. Just what this number is, nobody has as yet been able to compute. The very task staggers the imagination. $9^2 = 81$; $9^4 = \$6,561$; $9^9 = 387,431,389$; and this number, raised to the 9th power, would take a whole library of books to figure out.

And now that we happen to be on the subject of huge figures, let us consider the following interesting facts:

Over small periods, there is very little difference between simple and compound interest. For example, the interest on $1000, invested at 6% at *simple interest*, amounts to $60 at the end of the first year. If the interest is *compounded* every second throughout the first year, it amounts to only $61.84. But over longer periods, the interest and the principal multiply with unbelievable rapidity. In 1922 there arose in California a lawsuit over a loan of $100, made in 1897, with interest at 10% compounded monthly. The Court rendered a judgment in favor of the lender. The amount of the judgment, which required a whole staff of accountants several days to compute, was the amazing sum of $304,840,332,912,685.16—all this sum accumulating out of a loan of $100 at compound interest over the comparatively short space of 25 years! It goes without saying, of course, that the judgment was never collected. If one dollar had been invested at *simple interest* at the time of the birth of Christ, it would now amount to $78.24. If the same dollar had been invested at the same time at *compound interest*, it would now amount to $600,000,000,000,000,000,000,000,-000,000!

## IS THAT SO?

And now let us relax from this welter of complicated figures. The following item will show you how you can spend the entire year in idle luxury without working:

| | |
|---|---:|
| Every year has............................................. | 365 days |
| If you sleep 8 hours a day, it equals...................... | 122 days |
| This leaves................................................ | 243 days |
| If you rest 8 hours a day, it equals....................... | 122 days |
| This leaves................................................ | 121 days |
| There are 52 Sundays..................................... | 52 days |
| This leaves................................................ | 69 days |
| If you take off a half-day on Saturdays................... | 26 days |
| This leaves................................................ | 43 days |
| If you take $1\frac{1}{2}$ hours for lunch.......................... | 28 days |
| This leaves................................................ | 15 days |
| Two weeks' vacation...................................... | 14 days |
| This leaves................................................ | 1 day |
| This one day is Labor Day, when nobody works.......... | 1 day |
| And so you have left for work............................ | 0 days |

And now that you know that you never work, don't you feel like a millionaire?

## CHAPTER XXXIV
# Tricks, Stunts and Puzzles

THE FOLLOWING TRICKS, stunts and puzzles, easy to learn and equally easy to perform, will give you a reputation as a clever mathemagician and will enable you to spend many a pleasant evening in the entertainment of your friends:

### GUESSING THE FAMILY SECRETS

Ask some one in the company to:

1. Put down, without your seeing it, the number of his living brothers.
2. Multiply the number by 2.
3. Add 3.
4. Multiply the result by 5.
5. Add to this product the number of his living sisters.
6. Multiply the result by 10.
7. Add to this the number of his dead brothers and dead sisters.

Then ask him for the answer and subtract 150 from it. The remainder will give you all the necessary information. The left-hand digit will give you the number of his living brothers; the middle digit will give you the number of his living sisters; and the right-hand digit will give you the number of his dead brothers and sisters.

Here is how it works out:

Suppose John has 3 living brothers, 4 living sisters, and 2 dead brothers and sisters.

$$3 \times 2 = 6$$
$$6 + 3 = 9$$
$$9 \times 5 = 45$$
$$45 + 4 = 49$$
$$49 \times 10 = 490$$
$$490 + 2 = 492$$
$$492 - 150 = 342$$

Answer: 3 living brothers; 4 living sisters; 2 dead brothers and sisters.

## FINDING THE DAY OF THE WEEK

The following simple calculation will enable you to tell the day of the week on which any date in the past has fallen:

Suppose a man born on January 15, 1868, wants to know the exact day on which he was born. In order to ascertain this, let him:

1. Divide 1868, the number representing the year, by 4.

Note: If there is any remainder, it is to be thrown out, as it does not enter into the calculation.

2. To the dividend and quotient add the number of days in the year 1868 up to and including January 15, the date of his birth.

Note: In this calculation, always reckon February as containing 28 days.

3. Divide the sum by 7, and the remainder will be the number of the day of the week, 0 indicating Saturday.

Here is the simple process:

```
4)1868
   467
    15
7)2350
   335—5
```

The remainder is 5. Hence January 15, 1868, fell on the 5th day of the week, which is Thursday.

## GUESSING YOUR GIRL'S AGE

If your best girl refuses to give you her exact age, you can find it out very easily, as follows:

Tell her:

1. To put down the number of the month in which she was born.
2. To multiply it by 2.
3. To add 5.
4. To multiply the result by 50.
5. To add her age.
6. To subtract 365.
7. To add 115.

The left-hand digit of the answer will give you the month in which she was born; and the other two digits will give you her age.

Illustration:

Suppose she was born in August (the 8th month) and she is 22 years old.

$$8 \times 2 = 16$$
$$16 + 5 = 21$$
$$21 \times 50 = 1050$$
$$1050 + 22 = 1072$$
$$1072 - 365 = 707$$
$$707 + 115 = 822$$

Answer: born in the month of August; 22 years old.

## AND THIS ISN'T THE WHOLE STORY

With just a little additional calculation, the foregoing trick will enable you to guess not only the exact age of your friend and the month in which she was born, but also the day of the month. Ask her to write down the date and the month of her birth. Suppose it is the 3rd of August. She will then write down 38. Tell her to multiply this by 2; to add 5; to multiply by 50; to add her age; and finally to add 365. Then ask her to give you the result. Subtract 615 from this result, and you have the whole story. The first digit on the left will give you the date of the month; the second digit, the month; and the last two digits, the age. Let us, for example, use the same age, 22, as in the foregoing trick and see how it works out:

$$38 \times 2 = 76$$
$$76 + 5 = 81$$
$$81 \times 50 = 4050$$
$$4050 + 22 = 4072$$
$$4072 + 365 = 4437$$
$$4437 - 615 = 3822$$

And there you have it! Your girl friend was born on the 3rd of August, and she is 22 years old.

## ANOTHER WAY TO GUESS ONE'S AGE

Ask your friend to tell you which of the following columns contains the number that represents his age. Then add the numbers at the top of the columns indicated, and the sum will give you his age.

| 1 | 2 | 4 | 8 | 16 | 32 |
|---|---|---|---|---|---|
| 3 | 3 | 5 | 9 | 17 | 33 |
| 5 | 6 | 6 | 10 | 18 | 34 |
| 7 | 7 | 7 | 11 | 19 | 35 |
| 9 | 10 | 12 | 12 | 20 | 36 |
| 11 | 11 | 13 | 13 | 21 | 37 |
| 13 | 14 | 14 | 14 | 22 | 38 |
| 15 | 15 | 15 | 15 | 23 | 39 |
| 17 | 18 | 20 | 24 | 24 | 40 |
| 19 | 19 | 21 | 25 | 25 | 41 |
| 21 | 22 | 22 | 26 | 26 | 42 |
| 23 | 23 | 23 | 27 | 27 | 43 |
| 25 | 26 | 28 | 28 | 28 | 44 |
| 27 | 27 | 29 | 29 | 29 | 45 |
| 29 | 30 | 30 | 30 | 30 | 46 |
| 31 | 31 | 31 | 31 | 31 | 47 |
| 33 | 34 | 36 | 40 | 48 | 48 |
| 35 | 35 | 37 | 41 | 49 | 49 |
| 37 | 38 | 38 | 42 | 50 | 50 |
| 39 | 39 | 39 | 43 | 51 | 51 |
| 41 | 42 | 44 | 44 | 52 | 52 |
| 43 | 43 | 45 | 45 | 53 | 53 |
| 45 | 46 | 46 | 46 | 54 | 54 |
| 47 | 47 | 47 | 47 | 55 | 55 |
| 49 | 50 | 52 | 56 | 56 | 56 |
| 51 | 51 | 53 | 57 | 57 | 57 |
| 53 | 54 | 54 | 58 | 58 | 58 |
| 55 | 55 | 55 | 59 | 59 | 59 |
| 57 | 58 | 60 | 60 | 60 | 60 |
| 59 | 59 | 61 | 61 | 61 | 61 |
| 61 | 62 | 62 | 62 | 62 | 62 |
| 63 | 63 | 63 | 63 | 63 | 63 |

Suppose, for example, your friend's age is 39. This number, as you will note, is contained in the first, second, third and sixth columns. The sum of the numbers at the top of these four columns is 39.

# TRICKS, STUNTS AND PUZZLES

## COUNTING UP TO FIFTY

Here is a mysterious little trick which you can play on your friends to their amusement and amazement:

You announce to them that you will have a counting race with any one of them who is willing to take up your challenge. Both of you will then try to count up to fifty. At first, one of you will name a number up to six. The other is then to add to it any number he pleases, but it must not be more than six. This adding of any number that is not more than six is to be continued alternately, and the one who first gets to fifty wins the race. Needless to say, that one will always be you.

Here is how you do it:

Remember, in your adding, the following figures—8, 15, 22, 29, 36, 43. For example: Suppose you give your opponent a start in this race. He will have to name any number up to six —let us say, 5. You add 3, to bring it up to 8. Your opponent will then add, let us say, 4, bringing the total up to 12. You immediately add 3, making it 15. This will continue until you bring the number up to 43. Your opponent, restricted by the rules of the game, can only add a number that is not higher than six. This will bring his total to 49 at the most, and so you add enough to make 50 and you win the game.

The result will be the same whether your opponent begins the game or you yourself do it. In order to mystify him all the more, let him begin the first game, and then you begin the second game with the very same number with which he began it. There's lots of fun in this. Try it.

## MAGICAL ADDITION

Here is one that will mystify your friends:

Tell your friends to select three lines of figures, and you will select two lines. But—and here is the mysterious part of it— the moment they write down the *first* line of figures, you will be able to write down the sum of all the five lines. For example, suppose they write down 6,742,573. You will know at once that the answer will be 26,742,571. The answer is obtained by subtracting 2 from the last digit on the right and placing it before the first digit on the left. Here is how the whole thing works out:

```
Your friends select   6,742,573
Your friends select   4,625,618
You select            5,374,381
Your friends select   2,564,573
You select            7,435,426
   Total             26,742,571
```

In this trick your friends make up the first, and the second lines; you make up the third line; your friends then make up the fourth line; and finally you make up the fifth line. All you need to do is to see to it that your third line and your fifth line consist of digits that will make nine when added up to the digits in the lines just above them. Thus, below the second line, 4,625,618, place 5,374,381. (4+5=9; 6+3=9; etc.) Likewise, below the fourth line, 2,564,573, place 7,435,426. The rest of the trick will take care of itself.

Here is another trick in addition that will amaze your friends:

What is the sum of all the odd numbers up to and including 29? Answer, at a glance, 225.

What is the sum of all the odd numbers up to and including 99? Answer, also at a glance, 2500.

How is it done? Easily enough. When you want to get the sum of all the consecutive *odd* numbers in a certain series, add 1 to the last number in the series, divide by 2, and multiply the quotient by itself.

For example:

Find the sum of all the odd numbers up to and including 59.
 59+1=60
 60÷2=30
 30×30=900            Answer, 900

This one is a little, but not much, harder:

What is the sum of *all* the numbers up to and including 29? Answer, at a somewhat longer glance, 435.

When you want to get the sum of *all* the consecutive numbers in a certain series, add 1 to the last number in the series, divide

# TRICKS, STUNTS AND PUZZLES

by 2, multiply the quotient by itself, double the product, and subtract the quotient. For example:

Find the sum of all the numbers up to and including 25.

$25 + 1 = 26$
$26 \div 2 = 13$
$13 \times 13 = 169$
$169 \times 2 = 338$
$338 - 13 = 325$    Answer, 325

## GUESSING ODD AND EVEN

Ask your friend to conceal an odd number of coins in one hand and an even number in the other. Tell him to multiply the number in the *right* hand by *2*, and the number in the *left* hand by *3*. Then ask him to add together the two products and to tell you their sum. If this sum is *odd*, the *left* hand has the *odd* number of coins. If this sum is *even*, the *left* hand has the *even* number of coins.

Here is an interesting variation of the same trick:

Tell your friend to conceal a dime in one hand and a penny in the other. Ask him to multiply the value of the coin in his right hand by 4 or 6 or 8, and the value of the coin in his left hand by 3 or 5 or 7. Then ask him to add the two products and to tell you the total. If the sum is *even*, he has the *penny* in his right hand; if it is *odd*, he has the *dime* in his right hand.

## MISCELLANEOUS TRICKS AND PUZZLES

1. Arrange the nine digits, in their proper order, in such a manner that they shall add up to 100.

*Answer:* $1+2+3+4+5+6+7+(8 \times 9) = 100$

2. Arrange five figures, all odd numbers, in such a manner as to add up even.

*Answer:* Ordinarily, this cannot be done, for how can any *odd* number of *odd* numbers add up so as to make an *even* number? But it can be done by the following trick arrangement:

```
  11
   1
   1
   1
  ――
  14
```

3. Arrange the number 8 eight times in such a way as to add up to 1000.

*Answer:*
```
      8
      8
      8
     88
    888
   ----
   1000
```

4. Subtract 69 from 55, and get a remainder of 6.

*Answer:*

SIX (6) plus IX (9)  plus XL (40) equals 55
 IX (9) plus  X (10) plus  L (50) equals 69

Subtracting:

```
  SIX      IX      XL
   IX       X       L
  ---      --      --
   S        I       X
```

And thus we get 6 as a remainder.

5. This one will show you that you've got to be careful when you ask your boss for a raise:

Two clerks start work in the same office and at the same salary. After a while, they both decide to ask for a raise. One of them gets an increase of $50 every six months, and the other gets an increase of $200 every year. The salaries are paid every half year. Which of the clerks fares the best?

*Answer:* Most people would say that the luckier fellow is the one who gets the increase of $200 each year. But they would be wrong. The clerk who gets the raise of $50 every six months keeps constantly ahead of the other. At the end of the first year the first clerk will have received $1050; and the other, $1000. At the end of the second year the first clerk will have received for his year's work $1250; the second clerk, $1200. Every year thereafter, the first clerk will be $50 ahead of the other.

6. Here's an interesting problem:

A shepherd is told to divide his flock into two unequal parts in such a way that the square of the smaller part added to the larger part is equal to the square of the larger part added to the smaller part. How does he do it?

*Answer:* With integral numbers, the solution to this problem is impossible. For example, suppose the shepherd has 64 sheep in his flock, and he divides them into groups of 24 and 40. Then
$24^2 + 40$ would have to equal $40^2 + 24$.
But $24^2 + 40 = 616$
And $40^2 + 24 = 1624$

Any other division of the flock into 2 groups would give you an equally absurd answer. But you can solve the problem very easily if you divide the groups of 24 and 40 into *fractional parts* of 64. The solution will then be as follows:

$$(\tfrac{3}{8})^2 + \tfrac{5}{8} = (\tfrac{5}{8})^2 + \tfrac{3}{8}$$
$$\tfrac{9}{64} + \tfrac{40}{64} = \tfrac{25}{64} + \tfrac{24}{64} = \tfrac{49}{64}$$

7. In a certain inn there were only six rooms. One night several travellers applied for lodging, and each one insisted on having a room for himself. The landlord put the first man in room No. 1 and asked one of the other men to stay there also for a few minutes. Then he put the third man in room No. 2, the fourth man in room No. 3, the fifth man in room No. 4, and the sixth man in room No. 5. Then returning to room No. 1, he took the seventh man and put him in room No. 6. Thus each man had his own room. Where is the catch?

*Answer:* The above arrangement takes care of every man with the exception of the *second* man. Read the problem carefully and you will see the point.

8. A wealthy farmer directed by his will that his 17 horses should be divided among his 3 sons as follows: one-half of them to the eldest, one-third to the second, and one-ninth to the youngest. When the administrator tried to divide the horses in accordance with the terms of the will, he found it a serious matter. Accordingly he went to the wise man of the village and asked him to help him out with the problem. Here is what the wise man did: He took one of his own horses and placed it among the seventeen belonging to the estate. He then divided the eighteen horses, giving nine to the eldest son, six to the second, and 2 to the youngest. And thus, since 9

plus 6 plus two are 17, the horses were distributed satisfactorily among the three sons. "And now," said the wise man, "since everybody is satisfied, I will take my own horse back to his stable."

9. A bottle and a stopper cost $1.10, and the bottle cost $1 more than the stopper. What did the stopper cost?

*Answer:* The stopper cost 5 cents, and the bottle cost $1.05.

10. When is 2 and 2 not equal to 4?

*Answer:* When it is 22.

11. Two drovers, A and B, meeting on the road, were talking about their sheep. Said B to A: "If you give me one of your sheep, I will have as many as you." Said A to B: "If you give me one of *your* sheep, I will have twice as many as you." How many sheep did each drover have?

*Answer:* A had 7 sheep; B had 5.

12. A woman carrying eggs to the market one day, sold some of them to three people. To the first she sold half the number she had, and half an egg more. To the second she sold half of what remained, and half an egg more. To the third she sold half of the remainder, and half an egg more. When she arrived home, she had 36 eggs left. How many eggs did she have at first?

*Answer:* If she had 36 eggs left, she must have had, before she sold her eggs to the third man, 73 eggs. For one-half of 73, plus half an egg more, equals 37 eggs; and 37 subtracted from 73 leaves 36. In like manner, before she sold her eggs to the second man, she had 147 eggs; and before she sold her eggs to the first man, she had 295 eggs.

13. If you had a pie and gave $\frac{1}{12}$ to A, $\frac{1}{6}$ to B, $\frac{1}{6}$ to C, $\frac{1}{4}$ to D, and $\frac{1}{3}$ to E, what would you have left?

*Answer:* The platter.

14. What is the difference between twenty four quart bottles and four and twenty quart bottles?

*Answer:* The difference is 56 quarts.

# TRICKS, STUNTS AND PUZZLES

15. What number multiplied by half of itself will produce $12\frac{1}{2}$?

*Answer:* 5.

16. What is the difference between six dozen dozen and half a dozen dozen?

*Answer:* 792

17. A man offered to sell his horse for $5000. When the buyer protested that this price was too exorbitant, the owner of the horse made him the following proposition:

"You can have the horse by paying me a certain sum per nail in his shoes. Pay me half a cent for the first nail, and double the amount for each succeeding nail. There are four shoes, and seven nails in each shoe."

The purchaser agreed to this proposition, since it sounded quite reasonable. When he went home, he sat down and figured out the price he would have to pay for the horse. What was that price?

*Answer:* $1,342,177.27$\frac{1}{2}$

18. Place three sixes together so as to make 7.

*Answer:* 6 6/6

19. What three figures multiplied by 4 will make 5?

*Answer:* $1\frac{1}{4}$

20. How can you take one from nineteen and leave twenty?

*Answer:* XIX − I = XX

21. How can you add five and six in such a way that the sum will be nine?

*Answer:* Make the following six strokes: I I I I I I. And then add to these the following five strokes: N I N E.

22. A snail, climbing up a post 30 feet high, ascended three feet every day and slipped down 2 feet every night. How long did it take him to reach the top?

*Answer:* 28 days. At the beginning of the 28th day he was 3 feet from the top, and at the end of that day he reached the top.

23. The Indian mathematician Sessa, the man who invented the game of chess, was told by the Shah of Persia that he could ask for a recompense whatever he might wish. Sessa modestly requested that he be given one grain of wheat for the first square of the chessboard, two for the second, four for the third, and so on, doubling the number of grains each time up to the sixty-fourth square. The wise men of Persia added up the numbers, 1, 2, 4, 8, 16, etc., and this is what they found: The number of grains to be given to Sessa amounted to 18,446,744,073,709,551,615. This meant more than 32,000,000,000,000 bushels, which is several times the annual wheat production of the whole world.

24. What number is that which, if divided by itself plus 1, equals $\frac{1}{4}$?

*Answer:* $\frac{1}{3}$.

25. A goose weighs one-half its own weight and ten pounds. How much does it weigh?

*Answer:* 20 pounds.

26. If the goose weighs five pounds plus a third of its own weight, how much does it weigh?

*Answer:* $7\frac{1}{2}$ pounds.

27. Adding the even digits, 2, 4, 6, 8 together, we get the sum of 20. Adding the odd digits, 1, 3, 5, 7, 9 together, we get the sum of 25. How can we rearrange the digits in each series in such a way that their respective sums shall be alike?

*Answer:*
$$1\frac{3}{8} \qquad 6\frac{4}{2}$$
$$\frac{5}{7} \qquad \frac{8}{16}$$
$$\overline{16} \qquad \overline{16}$$

28. Write the same figure four times so as to equal 100.

*Answer:* 99 9/9.

29. A man said he caught a fish whose head was 9 inches long —the tail being as long as the head and half the body, and the

# TRICKS, STUNTS AND PUZZLES

body being as long as the head and tail put together. How long was the fish?

*Answer:* Head, 9 inches; body, 36 inches; tail, 27 inches; total, 72 inches.

30. Here is an interesting bit of mathemagical guesswork:

Ask some person to put down, unknown to you, a number composed of three digits (say 864). Tell him to transpose or reverse the digits (making 468), and to subtract the lesser number from the greater. Then ask him to give you the first digit of the result, whereupon you will be able to give him the entire answer.

For example:

864 − 468 = 396

The only digit that is given to you is 3, which is the first digit of the remainder. All you have to do is to subtract 3 from 9, and you will get the last digit, 6. The middle digit is always 9. Hence the entire remainder is 396.

This is true in all cases where only three digits are used in the original number.

31. Prove that 7 is one-half of 12.

*Answer:* Write twelve in Roman numerals, and then draw a horizontal line through the middle, thus: XII. Thus you see that one-half of twelve, the upper half, is VII.

32. Asked what game he had bagged, the hunter replied: "I got 18 heads and 50 feet." What did he get?

*Answer:* 11 quail and 7 rabbits. 11 quail and 7 rabbits equal 18 heads (11+7), and 50 feet (22+28).

33. Here is one that is truly mystifying:
Select a number of three digits.
Reverse the digits.
Subtract the lesser number from the greater.
Reverse the digits of the remainder.
Add this to the remainder. What is the total?

*Answer:* 1089.

This will always be the answer—1089. Try it, for example, on the following figure, taken at random:

Original figure........................742<br>
Reverse it............................247<br>
Subtract the lesser from the greater......495<br>
Reverse this remainder..................594<br>
Add the remainder and its reverse......1089

34. The combined weight of a boy and a girl is 120 pounds. If the scales weigh no less than 100 pounds, how can you determine the weight of each?

*Answer:* This is an easy one. Weigh the two children together with their father. Then weigh the father and the girl together and subtract their weight from the weight of all three. This will give you the weight of the boy. Subtract this from 120, and you will have the weight of the girl.

35. A man goes to the spring with two pails, one of which holds 3 quarts and the other 5 quarts. He wants to fetch exactly 4 quarts. How does he do it?

*Answer:* He fills the 5 quart pail and empties 3 quarts into the smaller pail. This leaves two quarts in the larger pail. He spills out the contents of the small pail, and he pours into it the 2 quarts from the large pail. He then refills the large pail with 5 quarts and fills the small pail from it. Since the capacity of the small pail is 3 quarts, and since it already contains 2 quarts, 1 quart is all that is required to fill it. This leaves a remainder of 4 quarts in the large pail.

36. If a hen and a half lay an egg and a half in a day and a half, how many eggs will 21 hens lay in a week?

*Answer:* It will take a hen and a half to lay one egg in one day. It will take three hens to lay two eggs in one day. In a week three hens will lay fourteen eggs, and twenty-one hens will lay $7 \times 14$ eggs, or 98 eggs.

37. If five foxes, loose in a barnyard, can catch five geese in five minutes, how many foxes will it take to catch a hundred geese in a hundred minutes?

*Answer:* Don't jump to a hasty conclusion and say, as most people would say off-hand, "a hundred foxes." The correct answer is, five

# TRICKS, STUNTS AND PUZZLES 359

foxes. If five foxes can catch five geese in five minutes, the same five foxes can catch one goose in one minute, or a hundred geese in a hundred minutes.

38. A man owed another man $1.30. He gave his creditor a five-dollar bill, and asked for change. The latter gave him his change in five coins. What were the denominations of those coins?

*Answer:* $2.50 (in gold), 50 cents, 50 cents, 10 cents, 10 cents.

39. A man had $58 in six bills. He kept one of the bills for himself, and divided the rest of the money between two friends, so that each of the friends received the same amount. What were the denominations of the bills, and how were they divided?

*Answer:* The man who had the $58 dollars in six bills had one $50 bill, three $2 bills, and two $1 bills. He kept the $50 bill for himself. He was then able to divide the rest of the money, $8, equally between his two friends, by giving two $2 bills to one, and one $2 bill and two $1 bills to the other.

40. Here's an interesting fallacy:
    a. 2 cats have  8 legs
       3 cats have 12 legs
Adding, 5 cats have 20 legs.

    b. 1 cat has 4 legs
       0 cat has 2 legs
Adding, 1 cat has 6 legs.

41. Here is a trick that is calculated not only to mystify, but to stupefy your friends. Incidentally, it will give you a quite undeserved reputation for having one of the most powerful memories in the world.

In the following table, you will find 50 key numbers, each of which is followed by a larger number of 9 digits. Ask anyone to select any key number, and you will be able to give him, without any hesitation, the larger number that follows it.

This sounds like a prodigious feat of memory. But it isn't. Here is how it's done:

1. Add 11 to the key number selected.
2. Reverse the result.

3. Keep on adding the two previous numbers, leaving out the tens.

For example:
Suppose someone selects 26.
1. Add 11, and you get 37.
2. Reverse this, and you get 73, which are the first two digits of your answer.
3. Add the 7 and the 3, and you get 10. Subtract the 10; just put down the 0. This gives you 730.
4. Add the 3 and the 0, and you get 3. This gives you 7303.
5. Add the 0 and the 3 and you get 3. This gives you 73033.
6. Add the 3 and the 3, and you get 6. This gives you 730336.
7. Add the 3 and the 6, and you get 9. This gives you 7303369.
8. Add the 6 and the 9, and you get 15. Subtract the 10; just put down the 5. This gives you 73033695.
9. Add the 9 and the 5, and you get 14. Subtract the 10; just put down the 4. This gives you 730336954. You can keep this process up indefinitely.

Here is the table:

| | | | | | |
|---|---|---|---|---|---|
| 1; | 213471897 | 18; | 921347189 | 35; | 640448202 |
| 2; | 314594370 | 19; | 033695493 | 36; | 741561785 |
| 3; | 415617853 | 20; | 134718976 | 37; | 842684268 |
| 4; | 516730336 | 21; | 235831459 | 38; | 943707741 |
| 5; | 617853819 | 22; | 336954932 | 39; | 055055055 |
| 6; | 718976392 | 23; | 437077415 | 40; | 156178538 |
| 7; | 819099875 | 24; | 538190998 | 41; | 257291011 |
| 8; | 910112358 | 25; | 639213471 | 42; | 358314594 |
| 9; | 122460662 | 26; | 730336954 | 43; | 459437077 |
| 10; | 123583145 | 27; | 831459437 | 44; | 550550550 |
| 11; | 224606628 | 28; | 932572910 | 45; | 651673033 |
| 12; | 325729101 | 29; | 044820224 | 46; | 752796516 |
| 13; | 426842684 | 30; | 145943707 | 47; | 853819099 |
| 14; | 527965167 | 31; | 246066280 | 48; | 954932572 |
| 15; | 628088640 | 32; | 347189763 | 49; | 066280886 |
| 16; | 729101123 | 33; | 448202246 | 50; | 167303369 |
| 17; | 820224606 | 34; | 549325729 | | |

42. And here is a neat one with which to end up this section: Divide 100 into four parts so that, if one of the parts is increased by 4, one diminished by 4, one multiplied by 4, and one divided by 4, the result in every case will be the same.

*Answer:* The four parts are 12, 20, 4, and 64.
$$12+20+4+64=100$$
$$12+4=16$$
$$20-4=16$$
$$4\times 4=16$$
$$64\div 4=16$$

## THE MATHEMATICS OF CHANCE (GAMBLING)

Don't gamble. The dice of destiny are always loaded against you. Whether you are a skillful gambler, or just one of those who depend upon luck, your chances in either case are about the same—pretty slim. A recent computation of the chances in gambling shows the following interesting figures:

Sweepstakes—If you buy one of the 5,000,000 tickets in the Sweepstakes, your chance of winning the big prize is about one in 400,000. Your chance of winning any of the smaller prizes is about one in 3,000.

Poker—Your chance of getting a straight flush is about one in 62,000; four of a kind, about one in 4,000; a full house, about one in 600; three of a kind, about one in 50; two pairs, about one in 20.

Bridge—Your chance of getting thirteen cards of the same suit is about one in 153,000,000,000 (a hundred and fifty-three billion). Since there are only about two billion people in the world today, you can figure out your chance for yourself. The chance of your getting *twelve* cards of one suit, however, is about one in 300,000,000.

Roulette—The chance of your winning 36 times the amount wagered is about one in 36. The chance of your winning an amount equal to the amount wagered is about one in two.

Numbers Game—Not much luck in this sort of gambling. Your chance is just about one in a billion.

Dice—Your chances of winning on the first throw are four out of eighteen. The chance of getting a 7 on the first throw is one out of six; of getting an 11, one out of eighteen. This is a little better than the other forms of gambling   But then, who wants to play dice?

## CHAPTER XXXV
# Mathematical Superstitions

### WEDDING DAYS

AN OLD ALMANAC gives a list of the days best suited for marriage. "For on those days," writes the author, "women will be fond of loving." The days given in the Almanac are the following:

January 2, 4, 11, 19, 21.
February 1, 3, 10, 19, 21.
March 3, 5, 12, 20, 23.
April 2, 4, 12, 20, 22.
May 2, 4, 12, 20, 23.
June 1, 3, 11, 19, 21.
July 1, 3, 12, 19, 21, 31.
August 2, 11, 19, 20, 30.
September 1, 9, 16, 18, 28.
October 1, 8, 15, 17, 27, 29.
November 5, 11, 13, 22, 25.
December 1, 8, 10, 19, 23, 29.

Numerous other Almanacs, both ancient and modern, supply similar information. But all this information is useless because no two Almanacs agree. Any day of the year has the approval of at least half a dozen authorities, so that you are safe if you marry *any day in the year*.

On the other hand, do you remember the advice that Socrates gave as to the best time to marry? "When you are young," he said, "the best time to marry is later on. When you are older, the best time to marry is—never."

### UNLUCKY DAYS

The designation of certain days as being unlucky seems to have originated in Chaldea and Babylonia. But just why these superstitions came about, nobody knows. Perhaps certain days set aside for temple worship were violated, and the punishment for such violation consisted in tortures that might have led the victims to consider those days unlucky. Or perhaps prominent men began or ended unsuccessful ventures on certain days, and thus came to the belief that such days were unlucky.

At any rate, few nations are entirely free from this superstition. In some countries all the children who are born on unlucky days are put to death.

In ancient Greece, the 13th day of the month was considered unlucky for sowing, but lucky for reaping.

Friday was first considered as unlucky by the ancient worshipers of Saturn. For Friday was then regarded as the seventh or last day of the week,—a day wasted in idleness and in licentious practices.

Has Friday been an unlucky day for the United States? Well, look at the following record and judge for yourself:

Columbus set sail in search of a new land on Friday, August 3, 1492. He discovered it on Friday, October 12, 1492. He arrived here on his second voyage on Friday, November 22, 1493. King Henry VIII commissioned John Cabot to sail for the New World on Friday, March 5, 1496. Menendez founded St. Augustine on Friday, September 7, 1565. The Mayflower arrived at Provincetown on Friday, November 10, 1620; and the Pilgrims landed at Plymouth Rock on Friday, December 22, 1620. George Washington was born on Friday, February 22, 1732. General Burgoyne surrendered on Friday, October 17, 1777. Benedict Arnold's treason was discovered on Friday, September 22, 1780. Cornwallis surrendered on Friday, September 19, 1791. And John Adams moved that "these United States are and ought to be independent" on Friday, July 7, 1776.

Friday has been a lucky day indeed for the United States.

## THE NUMBER 13

For some strange and unjustified reason, the number 13 has long been regarded as the black sheep of the mathematical family. Do you know that many hotels and ships have no Room 13? Have you ever noticed that in skyscrapers no floor is numbered 13? Many hostesses refuse to seat 13 people at the same table or to leave 13 people in the same room. Automobile owners often beg the authorities not to issue to them license numbers that contain the number 13. Gamblers generally decline to sit in a game in which they must hold 13 cards (bridge, of course, is not a popular game for gamblers). People frequently refuse to start on a journey or to enter upon a new piece of work on the 13th day of the month. Many parents consider the thirteenth year as the most critical period in the lives of their children. Yet most of us are unaware of the fact that we keep on living through year after year of 13 lunar months.

Are *you* superstitious about the number 13? Then beware of our American quarter dollar. For it is covered all over with this number. There are 13 letters in the words "quarter dollar." On the scroll which the eagle holds in its beak you will find the motto, *E pluribus unum*. This motto contains 13 letters. Surrounding the coin on one side are 13 stars; and on the other side, there are 13 stars over the eagle's head. The marginal feathers on each of the eagle's wings are 13, and the feathers in the eagle's tail are also 13. The horizontal bars of the shield are 13 in number, and the vertical lines are 3 and 10. In its left claw (the right claw as you look at it), the eagle clutches 13 arrows. In its right claw it holds an olive branch of 13 leaves. And the number of feathers on the eagle's neck is 13.

The quarter an unlucky coin? Give lots and lots of them to every one of us!